RADIO ROOM, POLICE HEADQUARTERS, MANHATTAN, NEW YORK CITY

[PLATE I]

MODERN CRIMINAL INVESTIGATION

BY

HARRY SÖDERMAN, D.Sc.

Head of the Institute of Police Science, School of Law
University of Stockholm, Sweden

AND

JOHN J. O'CONNELL

Chief Inspector, New York City Police Department

DRAWINGS BY CHARLES A. HARROLD

REVISED EDITION

FUNK & WAGNALLS COMPANY
NEW YORK AND LONDON

INTRODUCTION

IN the story of progress, art always precedes science. Mankind meets its problem first by learning from experience. As an understanding of underlying forces becomes necessary, a science is developed. This is the history of every profession. This is the story of the development of police practise.

Experience has been and will continue to be the great teacher of police technique. In dealing with large populations living under every variety of condition, the value of a police officer is conditioned by the extent and character of his experience. Unless the best police experience we now possess is systematized and summarized it will be lost and the succeeding police officers will start without the lessons of their predecessors. Experience is an effective teacher but always a costly teacher. We must be saved from the sad waste of needless experience.

Police practise has long felt the inadequacy of mere experience and is now reaching out for all the help that can be obtained from all the growing sciences. Prevention of crime and the detection and apprehension of criminals are rapidly becoming technical processes.

The authors of this book have rendered police technique two distinct services: they have selected the most vital police experiences and have presented them very effectively; they have summarized the most significant lessons of the physical and biological sciences for police practise. In *Modern Criminal Investigation* the reader will find a lifetime of police experience and the lessons which the scientist has for the police officer. This is an epoch-making contribution to the art and science of police procedure.

LEWIS J. VALENTINE,
Police Commissioner,
City of New York.

▼

PREFACE TO THE PRESENT EDITION

THIS book was written primarily for policemen, detectives and other peace officers. However, it is gratifying that the volume has proven to be of great usefulness and interest to lawyers, students of criminology, sociologists and others interested in the detection and repression of crime. In its pages the authors have tried to include not only the fruits of their long experience in the field, but the most recent, up to date developments in police practise and the latest scientific technique employed in crime solution. It has been their purpose to present as wide a variety of problems as possible and to give, step by step, the procedures advocated in dealing with them. They have endeavored to steer clear of theory as such and to offer material that is strictly usable and practical.

This book has sprung out of the practise of a hard-working police department. It is our sincere wish that the book will continue to enhance the effectiveness of criminal investigation and be of permanent value as a reference.

THE AUTHORS.

ACKNOWLEDGMENTS

WE wish to tender our grateful acknowledgments to Lewis J. Valentine, Police Commissioner of the City of New York; John J. Seery, First Deputy Commissioner of the New York Police Department; John J. Sullivan, Assistant Chief Inspector commanding the Detective Division, New York Police Department; Inspector Joseph J. Donovan, Commanding Officer of the Statistical and Criminal Identification Bureau of the New York Police Department and specialists of that Bureau; Captain Edward J. Dillon, Automobile Squad, New York Police Department; Deputy Chief Inspector Daniel J. Curtayne, New York Police Department; Acting Captain Richard Fennelly, Safe and Loft Squad, New York Police Department; Lieutenant William J. McMahon, Police Academy, New York Police Department, for their expert assistance on various chapters of this work; and to Patrolman Charles A. Harrold of the New York Police Department for the drawings.

Acknowledgment for friendly assistance is also given to Major General John F. O'Ryan, former Police Commissioner of New York; Barron Collier, former Special Deputy Commissioner in Charge of Foreign Relations; Mr. Bruce Smith of the Institute of Public Administration, Columbia University; Dr. Edwin Zabriskie, noted psychiatrist and specialist on nervous disorders and Honorary Surgeon of the New York Police Department; Dr. J. Eastman Sheehan, eminent plastic surgeon and Honorary Surgeon of the New York Police Department; Dr. Bruno de Biasi, Hematologist of Columbus Hospital; Dr. Charles N. Norris, Chief Medical Examiner of New York City; Dr. Alexander O. Gettler, Toxicologist to the Medical Examiner's office, New York City; Dr. Erastus M. Hudson, Expert in Fingerprint Chemistry; Mr. Albert S. Osborn, noted handwriting expert; Thomas Francis Brophy, Chief Fire Marshal of the New York Fire Department; Dr. William Edward Grady, Associate Superintendent of Schools, Board of Education, City of New York; and to others.

Special acknowledgment is given to Dr. Paul Klapper, President of Queens College, New York City, for valuable criticism and help; also to Mr. J. V. Howe, author of *The Modern Gunsmith,* for expert advice and assistance.

THE AUTHORS.

New York City.

CONTENTS

ix

CONTENTS

ILLUSTRATIONS

MODERN CRIMINAL INVESTIGATION

I

ASPECTS OF DETECTIVE WORK

NATURAL science began to develop by leaps and bounds in the middle of the nineteenth century. This introduced exactness and widespread knowledge of things. The obscure mysticism which had prevailed concerning everything disappeared as the clear, cold light of science clarified matters, and the change quickly became apparent in criminal investigation. Justice, which had been trying for centuries to solve problems and search for the truth, turned to science. Bertillon, Gross, Galton, Henry, Vucetich, Dennstaedter, Locard, Jeserich, Reiss, Stockis, Heindl, Balthazard, Wentworth, van Ledden Hulsebosch, de Rechter, Kockel, Türkel, Kanger, Minovici, Metzger, Osborn, Mitchell, Bischoff, Lucas, Ribeiro, Schneickert, Schmelck and others built the foundation of police science and used the methods of natural and related sciences as aids in criminal detection.

Modern police science may be said to have three phases. The first phase embraces the identification of living and dead persons. The second embraces the field work carried out by specially trained detectives at the scene of the crime. The third embraces methods used in the police laboratory to examine and analyze clues and traces discovered in the course of the investigation. All these methods will be described in the following chapters.

Modern police science has had a striking influence on detective work, and will surely enhance its effectiveness in due time. There will, however, of course, always exist opportunity for the time-honored methods of practical detective work. Knowledge of the *modus operandi* of criminals and methods of their apprehension, skill, patience, tact, industry and thoroughness, together with a flair peculiar to the successful detective, will be everlasting primary assets in detective work.

Modern criminal investigation in a broader sense also has several phases. The first is the requirement of a thorough examination and inquiry into the method and technique used by the criminal in his approach to the commission of a crime. So it is absolutely vital that a policeman or detective, in order to investigate a crime, should visit the scene of it. This he must do in order to act intelligently, logically, and to avoid any preconceived notions or theories.

When a building has been entered, the place where the entrance was effected must be determined; likewise the means of entrance used by the criminal. If a jimmy, chisel, key, assistance of an accomplice, or bodily force has been used, this must be noted. The object of the crime must be determined. At or during what time, as exactly stated as possible, did the criminal transaction occur? Was it during some special occasion such as opening or closing time, on a holiday or over the week-end?

The investigating officer should also seek to ascertain if any representation was made by the criminal previous to the crime, or if an inquiry by any individual was made one or more days prior to its actual commission. This would include an approach by a canvasser, pedler, mechanic, bogus inspector, gas man or electrician. In many cases a criminal relies to a great extent on the tale he tells. It invariably indicates the calling or trade to which the criminal has been accustomed. It is likewise important to learn whether any individual has approached the victim or the premises ostensibly to locate a missing friend, to secure employment, to hire a room or apartment on the premises, or to make a purchase; and, if so, was opportunity afforded to make observations which would be helpful in planning the crime committed?

Some criminals work with confederates. It is essential for the investigating detective or police officer to be able to decide whether the crime has been planned by more than one individual. This conclusion can be arrived at after a thorough examination of the approach and the means used to enter and to attack the person or property.

The search for clues should not be confined to the premises

alone. The investigating officer should invariably seek for traces of vehicles—motor-power, horse-drawn or otherwise—in the neighborhood of the crime. The marks of vehicles that cannot always be accounted for by the ordinary traffic having business at the scene, if discovered, should be noted as having a possible connection with the crime. Many good cases of detection have been attributed to finding traces that indicated the way in which criminals moved in taking away property or in fleeing after committing a crime.

As criminals are frequently known to commit extraordinary acts not associated with the object of the crime, such as changing clothes on the premises, drinking liquors, smoking cigars or cigarets, eating food, committing nuisances, poisoning the dog, or preparing a particular get-away, the investigating officer should be careful to note any such peculiarities.

With the criminal's method and technique fathomed, progress in the premises is to be determined. This can be accomplished by keen observation and examination of the premises and their surroundings. Systematic search should be made for footprints, fingerprints, and any clue that might be of help to track the criminal. It is essential that a complete examination and record be made of the *corpus delicti,* which is the body of the crime or the subject-matter which has been the particular objective of the criminal. In simple language, *corpus delicti* means the essential, fundamental fact that a crime has been committed. In homicide cases, *corpus delicti* means the dead body or remains of the victim.

Important phases of criminal investigation are the techniques used by the policeman or the detective in establishing the fact that the crime reported is *bona fide;* in apprehending the criminal responsible; in recovering property stolen, if any, and in gathering and collating statements of facts, circumstances and clues necessary for the prosecution of the criminal.

Many a crime is simulated for the purpose of collecting insurance or covering up peculations, and so it is compulsory for the investigating officer to establish its authenticity. When this has been accomplished, clues available generally comprise the method of operation, the stolen property and the traces left by the criminal on the scene. When a criminal flees after the commission of a crime, his chance of escape will be greatly reduced if an accurate description is secured and immediately broadcast through a general alarm. The matter of descriptions of criminal fugitives is covered in detail in Chapter IV. Description of property sought to be recovered after having been stolen is covered in Chapter XIX. Emphasis must be laid upon the importance of both of these matters in helping in the solution of cases.

Corroboration of the criminal's identity should be obtained, if possible, from persons other than the victim. This corroboration may be secured from voluntary statements made by witnesses or in reply to questions asked by the investigating officer. When the necessary information has been obtained, pursuit of the criminal should be immediate.

It is well to bear in mind, when taking voluntary statements or questioning witnesses, that the scope of inquiry should cover matters known, seen, heard, tasted, discovered, smelled and felt, and that particular attention should be given to the motives of the criminal, both prior to the commission of the crime and subsequently, noting coincidences of presence, absence, and movements, as well as giving attention to the sequence of action of witnesses, and the connective accuracy of their account. Consideration must also be given to the results of their lines of conduct, suspicious discrepancies, omissions, false statements, unnatural reluctance, extreme prejudice, abnormal desire to volunteer evidence, and the general reliability of witnesses. After covering these aspects a definite conclusion can be reached on facts and statements substantiated, qualified or refuted.

QUESTIONS

1. Describe the phases of modern criminal investigation discussed so far.
2. Give four examples of *corpus delicti* in crimes other than homicide.
3. What do you understand a simulated crime to be? Describe one or more from experiences of yourself or of others.

II

PSYCHOLOGY IN DETECTIVE SERVICE

A. General Remarks About Questioning

THE interrogation should be conducted as soon as possible after the commission of the crime. Each person should be heard individually, and none of the suspects or witnesses should be allowed to hear the questioning of the others. If possible, the principal witnesses, especially the most trustworthy ones, should be heard before the suspect is interrogated—in order that the interrogator be sufficiently informed.

The method of questioning varies widely according to the mentality of the questioned person, his age and race, sex, religious and political views, social status and education. A good interrogator must therefore be highly experienced, with a keen comprehension of the psychology of the questioned person, being able to understand his mentality and behavior from moment to moment. Seriousness, kindness and patience also are necessary. To force a witness to give information or a suspect to admit his guilt by threatening him, frightening him, injuring him, or by giving him false information regarding the state of the investigation, is discreditable, unnecessary and unwise.

The questioning should be fair, legitimate and unprejudiced. All circumstances to the benefit of the suspect and apt to prove his innocence should be carefully investigated. It should never be forgotten that a suspect may be innocent even tho the adverse evidence momentarily seems to be strong and the interrogator is convinced of his guilt. The ability to be impartial and free from prejudice is a signal virtue of the superior interrogator.

Suggestive Questions—The questions should be clear and unambiguous. They should not be so formulated as to lead the questioned person to answer in a certain direction or suggest the answer to him. Such questions are called "suggestive questions" and should be avoided. For example, if the question is put in this way: "Did the man you met have on a black or a brown hat?" the person is led to think of a hat. The question should be: "What headgear did the man you met have on?" Such questions as: "It was so that ——, wasn't it?" should also be avoided.

B. The Denouncer—Who Is He?

The value of the denunciation has at first to be established and the facts or probabilities should be checked. The denunciation may be such that no investigation has to follow; thus it may be due to a monomaniacal idea of the denouncer; he may be insane or a crank. It may also be a mistake, as when, for example, a lost object is still in the possession of the owner without his knowledge.

The denunciation may also be false, as in cases where the denouncer is trying to harm an antagonist or to protect himself or to gain some advantage, as, for example, by simulated thefts, assaults and burglaries. When something of this kind is suspected, the statement of the denouncer must be checked up on the scene (see page 322), and all persons who may have information to give carefully questioned.

C. The Suspect

Before the suspect is questioned, the preliminary investigation should be finished, *i.e.,* the scene of the crime examined, evidence of a technical nature collected and examined, the residence and office—or workshop—of the suspect searched, and as much information as possible gathered. The interrogator must know all the facts thoroughly and possess the ability to keep them together. The latter is an art which is not acquired at once.

The interrogation should be made in such a manner that the road to admission (confession) is made easier for the suspect.

Such expressions as murder, rape, burglary, etc., should not be used, but more neutral words employed, especially when a young suspect or woman is questioned. People who have already served a penal term as a rule are not so sensitive.

The success of the interrogation often depends on where it takes place. The presence of parents, relatives or friends may prevent the suspect from speaking openly. The same applies if the questioning is conducted in the house, or in the place where the suspect works, or in the presence of employers or co-workers.

If the suspect confesses wholly or partly, or gives important information, the goal of questioning is achieved and the interrogation may then be concentrated on important parts of the events leading to the crime.

If, on the contrary, the suspect pleads innocence, the success of the interrogator depends upon the evidence gathered and the ability of the interrogator to plan and do the questioning. The suspect should never get any information regarding the investigation or the evidence at hand. In many cases he should not even know why he is being questioned. If little evidence is present, the interrogator has to complete the evidence through the suspect. It would be a fatal error to accuse him. He should be handled as a witness. No shadow of suspicion should be apparent.

The interrogation in such cases is founded on the experience that it is difficult to lie consecutively and logically. The interrogation should not consist only of questions from the interrogator and answers from the suspect. The latter should have an opportunity to give his own account of things. If the interrogator knows that the account is untrue he should not show it. The more the suspect lies the weaker his position becomes later on.

If several persons are suspected of the crime, they should, if possible, be questioned at the same time and in the same manner, but not together. In one case, for instance, a merchant had been robbed and killed. Several years afterwards the police got vague information that a waiter, T—, and his wife were probably the murderers. No motive was given. After a careful investigation, the pair were arrested and questioned along the same lines. To start with, they were compelled to give a thorough account of their common lives. The investigation brought to light the fact that T— had committed some small thefts. The suspects were next questioned about their economic condition and then about the thefts. Not a word was said about the murder. Several facts of importance bearing on the murder were in this manner unconsciously revealed. Finally there was enough evidence to open a murder trial.[1] There is no doubt that if the interrogation from the beginning had been directed towards the murder, the pair would have grown suspicious and never hinted a word which would have served as a guide.

It is a good practical rule that the more meager the evidence the later should it be brought to the knowledge of the suspect. In another case a girl was assaulted, robbed and killed. A young man was arrested on no other suspicion than that he had made several large purchases the same day, altho he was known to be absolutely without funds. When he was first questioned, the murder was not mentioned, but he told about his life, his means of earning a living, and so on. This did not arouse his suspicions, because he was an ex-convict and accustomed to being interrogated. Under this interrogation it was discovered that he was penniless the day the murder was committed.

If the interrogation had sought to establish where he had obtained the money for his purchases, his attention would have been directed to this point, thus putting him on his guard. By the method used he was prevented from answering, for instance, that he had won at cards, or from admitting some burglary to avoid the murder issue.

If a confession is obtained, the details of the crime must still be proven. For example, in burglary, the manner in which the burglar broke into the house and in which he left; what tools he used; in what room the goods were stolen; how stolen objects were kept and where they were hidden; whether he had accomplices or not, and so on. In important crimes, criminals should be taken to the scene of the crime, especially when there is suspicion that guilt will be denied before the courts. Such a recon-

[1] Related by Gennat, chief of the homicide squad of the Police Department, Berlin, Germany.

struction is a very effective method of proving the value of a confession.   Careful notes about the reconstruction and what the
suspect related should be kept.[2]

D. Methods of Detecting Deception

The Association Method—This is a method proposed to develop association of ideas by the suspect and in this way to get
knowledge of that part of his thoughts which he will not divulge.
Such association of ideas represents valuable information because
it is brought out against the desire of the individual.   An old
anecdote illustrates this: A young man asked a magician to teach
him how to manufacture gold.   The old magician told the young
man all about the ingredients and invocations, but warned him
never to think of a rhinoceros when making gold.   The young-
ster said that he had never thought of such an animal and it
would not be difficult for him to avoid thinking about it.   Shortly
after, however, he came back to the magician and told him that
he could not manufacture gold because his mind was constantly
on the rhinoceros.   Similarly the thoughts of the criminal are
circling around the crime.   He reacts unconsciously to his secret
thoughts when he hears something which is related to the crime.
Wertheimer, Klein, Wendt, Jung, Münsterburg and other research workers have made extensive researches in the use of the
association method for getting confessions from criminals who
deny guilt.   It has also been used when proving non-participa-
tion, or to pick out the guilty among several suspects.[3]   The practical use of the method is as follows:
One chooses a certain number of words that have relation to
the crime and puts them into a long list of irrelevant words.   The
words that have relation to the crime are called *critical* words and
the others *indifferent* words.   The words are read to the suspect in the order in which they appear on the list, and he answers

[2] See also Ernst Fontell, "The Technique of Interrogation," in *Handbok i kriminalteknik*, by Söderman and Fontell.
[3] Gross, *Handbuch für Untersuchungsrichter*, Seventh Edition; Freud, "Tatbestandsdiagnostik u. Psychoanalyse," in *Arch. für Krim. Anthrop.*, 1906; Gorphe,
La Critique de Témoignage; Münsterburg, *On the Witness Stand*.

with synonyms as rapidly as possible, giving the first word that comes to his mind. The answers are noted, as is also the time between questions and answers. The criminal will answer less rapidly to the critical words and still less rapidly to the *post-critical* words, which follow immediately after the critical words. This is a result of mental strain in trying to find innocent words. The experiment should be made several times in order to find which answers are altered. As a control for the experiment, non-suspected individuals should answer to the same words.

The value of the association method has been much discussed. It can only be used in special cases, and will prove of little or no value in dealing with professional criminals, gangsters and racketeers. It is related to other psychotechnical methods, as, for instance, the Pneumograph, the Psychogalvanometer and other apparatus that has been experimentally employed for detecting deception. The so-called Lie Detector, which is an adaptation of the above-mentioned methods, has attracted some attention.[4]

All these contrivances, however, give uncertain results. Facts brought out therefrom are not yet acceptable in court, even if they at times give some hints to the investigation. This is especially true of the much-written-about "truth serum," which seems too dangerous in its use and too adventurous in its claims even to merit discussion here.

E. Witnesses

The interrogation of a witness must also be formulated according to his mentality. Even if some witnesses must be handled with sternness, as a rule best results are obtained through kindness and patience. The difficulty lies in determining *when* a witness hides or gives false information; because witnesses often unconsciously give false information without any interest or desire to mislead the interrogator. Low intelligence, illness, lack of education, etc., may be sufficient causes for a witness, who tries to speak the truth, unconsciously to give false information or to

---

[4] See Inbau, F. E., "Scientific Evidence in Criminal Cases," in *Journ. of Crim. Law and Criminol.*, Vol. XXIV, No. 6, 1934.

recite things known only through hearsay as if they were parts of a personal experience.[5]

At times a person may be reluctant because he does not like to be involved in a trial. He may be a friend of the suspect or have business connections with him. He may be unwilling to go before the court and does not like publicity. He may have economic reasons, such as loss of salary for the time spent in court as a witness. He may dislike the police authorities. He may pity the suspect, or he may avoid speaking because of the annoyance it would cause him later. There may be many other reasons why he declares that he has no knowledge of the matter. Such occasions place great responsibility on the interrogator. He must not only attempt to understand the motive for the reluctance but create a new interest for the witness. Tactfulness, diplomacy and patience will help a good deal in such cases. Generally, very little will be achieved by threats and severity, altho if a real egoistical motive for the reluctance has been established, one should always proceed with sternness and determination. Here, as always when it is suspected that the witness is hiding something or giving false information, the motive for his acts must be established.

Unreliable persons or liars should always be allowed to talk as much as they like. If such a witness is allowed to give his own account of things related to the investigation, he will finally contradict himself and tell the truth. It is very difficult, not to say impossible, to lie consistently.

From shy and nervous persons one is compelled usually to drag information piece by piece. There is uncertainty about such testimony and it is difficult to get any real facts in such cases. The interrogator should be as gentle as possible. The interrogation should be held, if possible, in the milieu or environment of the person and in the form of casual questions and conversation rather than as a formal interrogation; i.e., the detective should act as a casual visitor having a chat about the case.

The garrulous person presents many difficulties. Altho patience may be strained to a high degree, it is necessary to let him give his own account. The interrogator through cautious questions keeps the witness on the right path. The risk of misunderstanding such witnesses is great if they are not allowed to use their own expressions. They are also apt to give exaggerated and false information. Leads and statements in such cases must be well sifted and controlled.

Children are generally good witnesses when handled with care. They are keen observers, especially boys of ten to fifteen years of age on questions regarding phenomena of nature, and girls of twelve to fifteen on personal and intimate occurrences in their environment.

On the other hand, children are very receptive to suggestive questions and sometimes will tell more than they know in order to hold interest. A fatherly and friendly tone is used in order to give them confidence, overcome their self-consciousness, and encourage them to talk. They should be told to tell only about their actual experiences and not what they have heard. Children easily confuse their own experiences with those of others. Interrogation of children should not be prolonged.

Persons in the early twenties are not looked upon as good witnesses because they are occupied with themselves and their own affairs and do not care for things which do not pertain to them personally.

In advanced age persons may have keen power of observation of details, especially in regard to things in their own sphere of activity.

In all interrogations of witnesses one should have a certain amount of suspicion, even if the witness seems to be truthful and serious. As a rule he should be allowed to give an account in his own way. When he has finished, through cautious questions, he should be made to relate details which the interrogator desires to know. The real interrogation then should begin. Details of importance should now be examined and eventual contradictions revealed to him if necessary. If memory fails him about the time of an occurrence, one may give him some associated idea, as, for instance, what he did on the day in question. In order to get precise facts about positions and other statements, the interrogation is simplified if it is made on the scene of the crime.[6]

F. Criticism of Human Testimony

In the preceding pages we have attempted to give some practical advice as to how to conduct the interrogation of suspects, criminals and witnesses. We have stressed how the interrogator should attempt to adjust himself to the individual in order to obtain the best possible results. By an ideal interrogation the questioner should be able to enter into the process of the criminal action as vividly as possible. There is, however, a link between the actual events and the witness. No matter how well the interrogator adjusts himself to the witness and how precisely he induces the witness to describe his observations, mistakes still can be made. The mistakes made by an experienced interrogator may be comparatively few, but as far as the witness is concerned his path is full of pitfalls. Modern witness psychology has shown that even the most honest and trustworthy witnesses are apt to make grave mistakes in good faith. It is, therefore, necessary that the interrogator have an idea of the weak links in the testimony in order to check up on them, in the event that something appears to be strange or not quite satisfactory.

Unfortunately, modern witness psychology does not yet offer means of directly testing the credibility of testimony. It lacks precision and method, in spite of worth-while attempts on the part of such learned men as Binet, Gross, Stein, Lipmann, Gorphe, Locard, and others. It does not, therefore, lead to definite ways of achieving certainty. At the same time, witness psychology has, through the gathering of many experiences concerning the weaknesses of human testimony, been of invaluable service to criminology. It shows clearly that only evidence of a technical nature has absolute value as proof.

Testimony presents three different aspects. The witness sees the occurrence, fixes it in his memory, and expresses it.

[6] There has been a tendency, of recent years, in cases of major crime, to make models of the house concerned or relief maps of the grounds concerned, in order to facilitate the interrogation of witnesses and the work of the court.

Fig. 1
Edmond Locard

In agreement with Locard the testimony may be separated into the following stages: (1) perception; (2) observation; (3) mind fixation of the observed occurrences, in which procedure fantasy, association of ideas and personal judgment participate; (4) expression in oral or written form, where the testimony is transferred from one witness to another, or to the interrogator.

Each of these stages offers innumerable possibilities of distorting testimony. In the following pages we will study these possibilities, following chiefly the ideas of Locard[7] and Gorphe,[8] who have examined the problem from a thoroughly practical angle.

Perception—This is a stage of testimony which may be verified readily. A witness states, for instance, that a certain occurrence took place in a mill at a certain definite time.

"How do you know the exact time?"

"I heard a clock strike the time."

An investigation at the scene of the crime shows that the noise coming from the mill completely drowns the sound of the clock, even to a very sensitive ear. The witness then remembers that he heard the clock strike only on leaving the mill.

Lacassagne, the famous French specialist of legal medicine, describes a case of this kind in which a man was accused of a

[7] Locard, *L'Enquête criminelle et les Méthodes scientifiques*, Paris, 1925. Edmond Locard was born in 1877 in Saint-Chamond, France. A Doctor of Medicine and a Master of Law, since 1910 he has been director of the scientific laboratory of the Police Department of Lyons, France. Locard is vice-president of the International Academy for Criminal Science and chief editor of the *Revue Internationale de Criminalistique*. He has created and developed numerous methods applied to police science and is regarded as one of the foremost criminologists in the world.

[8] Gorphe, *La Critique du Témoignage*, Paris, 1927.

number of sex offenses. Lacassagne proved that from where the accuser said he had witnessed the occurrence, it was impossible even to see the accused man. Many similar cases could be cited.

This example shows clearly that one must place oneself in an absolutely identical situation in order to verify the testimony. One must not forget, however, that certain deaf persons, when surrounded by noises, may hear sounds which are not perceptible to them under normal circumstances.

Observation—Bertillon has wisely said, "One can only see what one observes, and one observes only things which are already in the mind." Unfortunately, there are often many facts which are important for the investigation, but which were of no interest to the witness at the moment he experienced them. He simply did not pay attention to them, and as a rule does not know them, or at the utmost has only a meager knowledge of them. It is, indeed, very rarely that one realizes, during the time of perception, that he may be compelled to appear as a witness later on. The best witness is not the one who has seen a great deal, but rather the one who has a clear understanding of such facts as may prove to be of value to the investigation.

Feeling is one of the deceptive perceptions. In most persons it is very slightly developed unless controlled by eyesight. This naturally deceptive perception may lead to serious mistakes. If the witness, for instance, contends that he recognized an object in the dark merely by touching it, one must regard his testimony with the greatest suspicion. It is an entirely different matter when the witness is blind, for the touch perception may be so highly developed that his testimony must be regarded as having real value and application.

Olfactory experiences and *sense of taste* are also unreliable. In poisoning cases, for instance, the witness finds difficulty in determining the various sensations experienced. It is also difficult for him to express himself clearly in definite terminology. The objective sensation of smell or taste is easily replaced by the witness's conception of the good or bad taste which he experiences. It is well known that taste is individual, and as Locard pointed out, "It depends upon the taste of the individual whether the smell of a rotten pheasant makes him think of corpses and cadavers or places him in a condition of culinary happiness."

It is possible also to have a sensation of smell without the presence of any smell. Schneickert[9] reported a case in Berlin in 1905. A girl named Lucy Berlin, nine years old, had been murdered and mutilated in a house at No. 130 Ackerstrasse. On the 16th of June some boys, playing on the banks of Lake Plotzensee, found the head and the arms of the child, and on the 17th of June her legs and torso were discovered. On the 16th of June, however, before the discovery of the legs and torso, several persons reported to the police that they had sensed a strong odor of burnt flesh in the vicinity of the scene of the crime, and especially in the neighborhood of Nos. 125-130 Ackerstrasse. The thought prevailed that it must have been the murderer who had been burning the missing parts of the body. Their perception of the smell was, therefore, a mere suggestion, which may have had its origin in the fact that in 1904 a similar murder had been committed and the corpse had been burned.

A like occurrence took place some years ago at a resort in Northern Sweden. A maid had been arrested and accused of having murdered her new-born infant. The accusation was chiefly based on the reports of several neighbors, who on a certain day had detected a horrible odor of burnt flesh coming from the maid's room. The maid had been thought to be pregnant, but this condition was not noticeable after the day of the supposed crime. An analysis of the contents of the stove could not be made, as it had been cleaned out. Medical investigation, however, proved conclusively that the girl had never been pregnant. The girl herself had not noticed any peculiar odor and could not account for the rumor. Naturally, she was immediately released.

Aural experiences take an intermediary position between the above-described senses and the sense of sight, which is the most objective of all human senses. One must, however, make a careful distinction between mechanical noises and the human voice. The observation of a sound is often unclear and subjective. A

⁹ Schneickert, "Massensuggestion," in *Arch. f. Krim. Anthrop.*, XVIII, 1905.

loud noise may appear to have been produced near by, while a sound transmitted from some distance may appear weak. This difficulty of estimating distance from the site at which the sound is produced is increased considerably if the sound is of a nature unknown to the listener. The direction of the sound is a matter which the witness can never fully determine (see page 212). The sound which the witness perceives is unconsciously compared to a whole series of memories of sounds previously heard, and he attempts to coordinate them in his mind. Locard tells of a man who one night heard a peculiar sound and in an excellent altho absurd manner expressed this series of confused memories by exclaiming: "That dog is not a frog—it is a cartwheel!"

A witness is usually asked to recognize the voice of a person, to tell what language was used, to repeat as carefully as possible the exclamations heard, and finally to state at least the general trend of what he has heard. This places the witness at a great disadvantage. In order to recognize the voice, for instance, a highly intricate operation is necessary, including an analysis of the loudness of the voice, its intensity and tone, a comparison between these elements and former sound pictures, and then finally the actual identification. If the person is known to the witness, an identification of the voice is, however, rather certain.

In order to determine the language used in a conversation it is not necessary to possess a thorough knowledge of the language. The knowledge of certain characteristic phrases is sufficient. It is, however, not advisable to accept such perceptions without verification.

When we ask a witness to state the content of a conversation, we are confronted with one of the most dangerous parts of testimony. We do not listen to all sounds which form a spoken sentence, and those which we hear we compare unconsciously with sound pictures which we already possess, or else we undertake the more complicated work of forming visions which correspond to them. When we listen to a conversation, therefore, we are not registering a long series of sounds, but rather are reconstructing the talk from separate aural fragments and filling up the gaps with the aid of our power of combination. When a witness repeats a conversation which has taken place, he does not describe what he has heard, but what he has reconstructed in his own mind. If he has had a mistaken conception of the conversation from the very beginning, he reconstructs it accordingly, and his testimony is utterly false.

The theory of fragmentary observations is also applied to *visual observations*. The mere survey of an object does not represent a detailed analysis of the shape and color of it. We observe only a few characteristic points and unconsciously complete the picture. The witness, for instance, who sees a well-known face or a nose of unusual shape, does not hesitate afterwards to fill the gaps as to the identity of the individual. Yet, in spite of all these possibilities of error, visual observation is still looked upon as the most accurate. It has also been the most studied from the viewpoint of witness psychology.

Colors are observed and described in an indefinite manner, and many cases illustrating this fact could be related. In a case, for example, where a man had been assaulted, he had seen his assailant only for a moment in the moonlight. He was under the impression that the man wore a vest and a black hat. It was proved later that the man had been wearing light blue overalls and a white Panama hat. (See also Sodium Light, page 33.)

Many experiments along these lines have been carried out by research workers. Altho these experiments have generally been made from a purely scientific viewpoint in circumstances having slight relation to reality, some have produced very interesting results. In 1913, Dauber[10] showed to 369 school children a picture of a small boy with brown hair, blue trousers, brown coat and brown shoes, and asked them shortly afterwards to describe the colors of the different parts in the picture.

The blue trousers were described:

> By the boys:
> 15 times as blue
> 20 times as brown
> 5 times as yellow
> 4 times as gray

[10] Dauber, "Die Gleichförmigkeit des psychischen Geschehens und die Zeugenaussagen," in *Fortschr. d. Psychologie*, 1913.

By the girls:

    8 times as green
    19 times as brown
    3 times as yellow
    7 times as gray
    3 times as red
    3 times as black

The brown coat was described:

By the boys:

    28 times as blue
    18 times as green
    13 times as gray
    20 times as red
    2 times as yellow

By the girls:

    21 times as blue
    12 times as green
    19 times as gray
    9 times as red

The brown hair was described:

By the boys:

    35 times as black
    2 times as light

By the girls:

    12 times as black
    2 times as light

Eighteen children described the brown shoes as black, and many claimed that the boy in the picture was barefooted.

Such experiments serve to illustrate the many pitfalls met in criminal investigations when a suspect is identified through an untrained witness.

Even trained observers may make mistakes. The authors performed some interesting experiments along these lines. In a training course in Police Science for prosecuting attorneys given by the Swedish Department of the Interior, about seventy of the students, among whom there were many experienced policemen, were submitted to the following experiment: While they were listening to a lecture, a young lady entered the hall and remained for about five minutes. She then arose and explained that she had come into the wrong room and walked out. The eyes of the men were naturally fixed on the good-looking young lady for five minutes. The next day they were asked to give a description of the lady, and only one of the seventy was able to give an accurate description. Many other such tests made here and abroad could be cited.

In describing the position of persons and objects, errors made by a witness are also very common. The witness may change his position without orienting himself, and when one asks him if an individual was on this or on the other side, or whether a vehicle was traveling to the left or right, he may easily make mistakes and confuse the correct position. Such mistakes are especially common when the witness has no fixed points to use as guides. Locard tells of a case in which a young girl was killed, during a concert, by a man in the audience. He was immediately arrested and he confessed. During the trial six witnesses stated that the young girl and her mother had been sitting in the fourth row. The blood, however, was found in the fifth row. Two witnesses claimed that the murderer had taken his weapon from the left inner pocket of his coat, but the murderer himself —and he surely should have known—said he had had it in the right outside pocket of his coat.

In many visual observations there is some movement of the object or person, and this also is observed only fragmentarily. The total picture of a moving object is composed of a series of pictures of each successive movement. We seldom observe all the movements in the series, but fill the gaps with imagination or reasoning. Hans Gross [11] tells of a case, for instance, where a man was prosecuted because he had struck the head of another person with a glass. The witnesses did not agree as to whether the defendant had thrown the glass at the victim or had used it to strike him. Each one reconstructed the scene according to

[11] Hans Gross was born in 1847 and died in 1915. He was professor of penal law at the University of Graz, Austria. Gross is regarded as one of the founders of police science, and his famous book, *Handbuch für Untersuchungsrichter* (*Criminal Investigation*), is regarded as a classic.

his own idea of the brawl, and his imagination filled the gaps in the memory picture of the movements. This phenomenon may well be explained by describing the successive positions of the glass as A, B, C, D, etc. Each witness had seen only some of the successive movements, thereby forming a picture of the entire occurrence. One, for instance, saw only A, C, D, H, another only C, E, G, I, etc.

Fig. 2
Hans Gross

Mind Fixation of Observed Occurrences—The memory picture is not subject to many alterations if it can rest in a portion of the mind which is sparingly used. On the contrary, if the memory picture is subject to much thought, and especially if it is expressed in oral or written form, it alters each time, so that it finally will have very little resemblance to the original impression. With time it will alter and gradually become faint even if it remains latent.

Expression—This is the part of the testimony which is most important from the viewpoint of the interrogator, and it is generally here that we find many sources of error.

The most common sources of error are inaccuracies of fact, exaggerations, and inaccurate expressions.

The tendency of the witness to relate only what he thinks is important gives rise to many inaccuracies. It would not be so bad if the witness excluded only unimportant details, but he often omits things of value to the investigation.

Exaggerations are, as Locard points out, still more common than understatements. The witness will often multiply numbers and evaluate facts excessively. If he has taken part in a riot he will exaggerate the number of persons present. If he has been assaulted by one or two persons, these will readily become a gang of men; if he has seen an accused person getting drunk, the glasses will become as many bottles; if he knows that a person has a mistress, she will be multiplied into many women. By exaggerating, the witness magnifies not only the value of his observations, but the importance of his own person. Race characteristics and the individuality of the witness here play an important rôle.

Unanimous Statements—A witness does not generally remain alone from the moment he makes his observations until he is questioned by the interrogator. The longer the period of time elapsing between observation and interrogation, the greater the possibility of his being influenced by others. By discussing the matter with other persons he inevitably enriches his tale with fabrications of his own. If several witnesses of the occurrence are by chance brought together, they may by the exchange of actual and imagined details reconstruct a body of testimony which may be regarded as an average of their collected true and imaginary experiences. The collective testimony concocted by this unconscious and seemingly harmless conspiracy may differ widely from the original experience. The danger of this peculiar state of mind lies in the fact that the unanimous testimony will be looked upon as absolute proof.

When the witness happens to be a member of a group at the time of observation he falls unconsciously under the spell of mass-suggestion (see page 30). In such a case his testimony will probably agree with those of the other members of the crowd. The crowd, says Dupré,[12] observes and interprets the occurrences and reacts differently from the individual. Dupré should have added, says Locard, that the witness in the crowd regularly observes, interprets and reacts as the most mentally-inferior member of the crowd.

Related tendencies, which to a certain degree are found in all individuals, even if very different, may give rise to collective mistakes even if the witnesses are independent of one another. The

[12] Dupré: "Le Témoignage: Etude psychologique et medico-légale," in *Revue des Deux Mondes,* 1910.

value of testimony is then not proportionate to the number of witnesses.

The following illustration will make this point clear.[12] Professor X had black hair and Professor Z blond hair. During their absence from class, 153 students, who knew them very well, were asked to record the color of the hair of the two professors. The hair of Professor X was indicated by 125 students as black, by 16 as brown, by 9 as blond, and by 3 as gray. The hair of Professor Z was indicated by 77 students as blond, by 16 as red, by 5 as yellow, by 3 as white, by 2 as gray, *by 18 as black,* by 21 as brown, by 8 as light brown, and 3 could not recollect the color. The surprizing result of the questionnaire may be explained by the fact that most of the students had black hair, a common characteristic in that part of the country. They had testified as they had been in the habit of perceiving.

The interrogator may especially have to deal with false testimony given unconsciously in the identification of dead bodies as well as of living persons. Mass-suggestion does not sufficiently explain such phenomena, but a careful analysis of specific cases will show that habit and autosuggestion play a large rôle.

The Description—One of the most difficult tasks confronting the witness is to describe the fugitive criminal. Mistakes are commonly made. If the witness has seen a person of average height, for instance, accompanied by two or three short ones, the person in question will be described as being tall. Concerning colors, testimony is often very positive and very false.

Heindl has especially studied some parts of personal description (height, age, color of hair and shape of the face). In two series of tests there were collected 20,000 answers containing 80,000 parts of the description. In the first series an individual was described whom the tested persons viewed for four minutes. In the second series the tested persons described a well-known person who was not present; school children described their teacher, soldiers their officers, etc. The height was generally overestimated by about 5 inches and the age by 8.2 years. The descrip-

[12] Arvid Wachtmeister: "Vittnespsykologi," in *Svenska Dagbladet*, July 30, 1929.

tion of the shape of the face gave very erroneous results. Men had a better conception of form than women, and children better than adults. The color of the hair was as a rule missed, as 83 per cent of the tested persons erred. Adults had a better conception of the color of the hair than children, and women better than men.

Experiments of this nature may tend to awaken a belief that most descriptions of fugitive criminals are false and misleading. It is, however, a fact that every day persons are arrested by the police with the aid of descriptions given by witnesses. Gorphe says in respect to this, and rightly, that the question is more complicated than the psychologists believe. The psychologists have made up averages of errors occurring in their experiences. An investigator, however, has no great aid, because 20 per cent of the tested persons will err in one case and 40 per cent in another. This does not prove, however, that Mr. Smith is wrong when he says on the witness stand that the burglar had brown hair, a tooth-brush mustache, and wore a gray peak cap. No logician could arrive at such a conclusion from general circumstances in a specific case.

The above-mentioned experiments will, if nothing else, teach the detective or policeman not to accept descriptions without due consideration, especially when the color of the hair, the height of the person, the shape of the face and the wearing apparel are concerned. Much depends on how close the witness was, the light, etc.

Identification of Living Persons Through Witnesses—Mistakes made by confrontations are innumerable. The following circumstances, especially, tend to promote mistakes: *similarity to others, bad light, witness excited, witness not sufficiently alert, suggestions,* and *great lapse of time since day of occurrence.*

It is customary in confrontations to have the witness brought into a room where several persons are found lined up with the suspect. The witness is asked to pick out the culprit. Photographs or descriptions of the suspect should naturally not be supplied to the witness.

Some psychologists claim that identification of an individual by witnesses *normally* gives false or negative results. Such an opinion may be exaggerated, but it is nevertheless true that the individual to be identified should, if possible, be placed in the same circumstances as when seen by the witness, *i.e.,* the same position, the same movements, the same light, etc. The best method is to attempt the identification at the scene of the crime at approximately the hour the crime was committed.

Identification of Dead Bodies—It is not always easy to recognize a dead body, especially if it has been subjected to putrefaction or mutilation. Errors in this respect occur. Hellwig [14] reports an interesting case, which shows that even relatives may be mistaken under the most favorable circumstances. A German railroad man named Kirstein quarreled one evening with his wife. The wife left the room. Soon afterwards Kirstein was informed that a woman had thrown herself in the neighboring river and been drowned. He rushed there, certain that his wife had committed suicide, thought he recognized the body with the aid of a lamp, wept and was greatly grieved. His brother and sister, who had accompanied him, confirmed his recognition. The body was carried home and artificial respiration was applied for some time. After the excitement had waned, suddenly Kirstein remembered that his wife had had more money on her and had worn different clothes. He rushed upstairs to see if she had changed her clothing, saying, "I wonder what clothes she had on today?" One can imagine the shock when he heard the voice of his wife answer, "The clothes which I had on today are hanging here." Kirstein ran down terrified, crying, "Now I believe in God. The ghost of Emma is in the bedroom!" No one dared to enter the room until Mrs. Kirstein herself came out. It became at once apparent that there was not the slightest resemblance between her and the drowned person. The case can only be explained by the supposition that Kirstein had been the victim of powerful autosuggestion. It is peculiar that the husband, who had been at work applying artificial respiration to the dead body, had not

[14] Hellwig, "Einige merkwürdige Fälle von Irrtum über die Identität von Sachen und Personen," *Arch. f. Krim. Anthrop.,* 1907.

been able to perceive the difference existing between this woman and his wife. His agitation and preoccupation obscured all other observation.

In Chapter IV methods of reconstructing dead bodies are described. Such methods will without doubt diminish possibilities of mistakes in the identification.

Identification by Photographs—A witness should never be shown a photograph and asked if he recognizes the person. On the contrary, the photograph should be put among several others and the witness asked to pick out the person in question. Such a procedure does not, however, eliminate mistakes, as the witness may previously have seen a picture of the person suspected of being the criminal in newspapers or elsewhere. The identification by photographs involves another danger: if the witness's mind-picture of the criminal is vague and unclear, he may complete the mental picture erroneously by looking at a photograph of a person having some slight resemblance to the suspect. When this mind-picture becomes fixed, the witness in later confrontations may identify the wrong person from the photograph.

G. Mental Abnormalities

Every good detective should have a general knowledge of mental illnesses and constitutional abnormalities of the mind. In the course of his investigations he will often meet persons whose actions and motives may seem puzzling to him if he is not equipped with some knowledge of psychiatry. He should, in fact, be somewhat familiar with the common mental illnesses and abnormalities to enable him to make a tentative preliminary diagnosis for his own information. This fact has also been recognized by several police and medico-legal institutions in which the subject is taken up not only in theory—in didactic lectures, etc.—but also in practise by giving students the opportunity to make observations in insane asylums and psychopathic wards.

A knowledge of signs and symptoms tending to prove mental

illnesses is, of course, necessary. Familiarity with the personality make-up of neurotic persons, of epileptics and hysterics, should be of particular interest to the interrogator, as these conditions often affect suspects as well as witnesses.

An individual who is not insane in the true sense of the word, but who nevertheless shows great divergences in character and emotional reactions from those of a normal person, may be classified as a psychopathological person. The intelligence of such a person is often quite satisfactory and at times highly developed. It exercises, however, entirely too little control over his actions, which, instead, are generally influenced by compulsive emotional reactions or more rarely by previously acquired mental diseases in which delusions play a prominent part. Among these persons we encounter many criminals.

In this group are found sexual perversions, which play a rôle, directly or indirectly, in both the planning and the commission of many major crimes. Space forbids us to enter into this question, which, however, deserves a careful study.[15]

The so-called moral insanities also should be considered here. This term covers a group of abnormal individuals, in which students of psychiatry usually include many criminals; but for practical reasons it is customary to regard these all as one group. To the psychic abnormals belong also persons suffering from feeble-mindedness, pathological liars and swindlers, and highly emotional (explosive) persons.

A general knowledge of all these illnesses and abnormalities will be of enormous aid to the interrogator.[16] Here we will only deal, very briefly, with epilepsy and hysteria, which, on account of their frequency and the extreme danger they represent to the interrogation, are especially important.

Epilepsy—Epilepsy is characterized not merely by attacks of

---

[15] See Kahn's *Psychopathic Personalities*, New York, and Healy's *Mental Conflicts and Misconduct*, Boston, 1928.

[16] See William and Mary Healy, *Pathological Lying, Accusation and Swindling*, Boston, 1926; M. Hamblin Smith, *The Psychology of the Criminal*; A. G. Rosanoff, *Manual of Psychiatry*.

convulsions. Many epileptics are inveterate liars, who readily simulate, and who are easily irritated.

Epileptics are highly unreliable witnesses. Besides being often habitual liars, they frequently show signs of impaired memory. In the latter case they no doubt often give false testimony. Furthermore, they are highly susceptible to suggestion, particularly after an attack of the malady. They are, also, subject to visual or auditory hallucinations which may give an entirely erroneous account of what they have actually witnessed. Furthermore, they are subject to states of partially clouded consciousness in which their observations are wholly unreliable. This serves as an additional reason why it is of importance to have the witness examined by a psychiatrist, particularly when he is to be used in cases of major importance.

Hysteria—There is no neurosis that causes the interrogator as great and as many difficulties as those due to hysteria. This illness exists more generally than one might suspect. It is not easily recognizable in its milder forms, and sometimes it is quite difficult to recognize even in its advanced stages, because of its multiform symptomatology. All kinds of mistakes, misjudged actions and formal injustices may well be ascribed to it.

Hysteria occurs both in women and in men. It may be characterized by paralysis, emotional outbreaks or convulsive attacks. The hysterical convulsion differs from the epileptic in that the unconsciousness is not so profound, nor does it usually display the real elements of a true convulsion.

Hysterical persons have oftentimes many characteristic traits, which cause them to be highly dangerous both as accusers and as witnesses; they lack deeper ethical feelings, are extremely egocentric, mendacious, and malicious; they have ability to simulate and lust for intrigues. Hysterical women sometimes accuse men with whom they have had only a casual acquaintance of personal attacks of a sexual nature. Young physicians are cautioned against being alone in a room with an hysterical woman. Similar advice may also be given to the interrogator. It is always advisable to have a third person present during an interrogation.

As hysteria is an illness which is difficult to recognize, the following signs, which are given by Gross, are of importance: the ill person believes himself disdained, thinks himself a martyr, has sudden changes of moods, has exaggerated sensitivity, and is abnormally receptive of external influences. If these symptoms are not marked, one may attempt to ascertain, through cautious questions, whether the person under examination has severe headaches, a sensation of choking, stomach-ache, or uncontrollable laughter. If these symptoms present themselves, it is necessary to obtain the advice of a physician, because if the person afflicted by hysteria is called as a witness his testimony should be regarded with a great deal of suspicion.

False accusations by hysterical persons may depend on their lack of ability of perception, and also on their suggestibility.

H. Suggestion and Hypnotism

Suggestion and hypnotism are both of importance to criminology in so far as they may serve to influence or utilize individuals for criminal purposes.

Suggestion—Suggestion is a term covering all those mental influences, good or evil, which exercise a certain degree of compulsion upon our thoughts and actions. The suggestive influence is in direct opposition to any influence resulting from reasoning. In order to understand the phenomena of suggestion, we must bear in mind that human beings have a natural tendency to believe or—to be more accurate—to assume everything as true that does not awaken conflicting ideas or emotions; everything is then assumed to be true and real, provided there is no reason to doubt it. One may, through suggestion, cause the performance of actions and arouse emotions and feelings, as well as changes in a person's bodily and mental functions—even within fields which are otherwise not under the control of the human will.

Hysterical and nervous persons are particularly susceptible to suggestion, and morally defective persons of this type are easily influenced by suggestion in an evil direction. They have no ethical promptings to prevent the suggestion from exercising its full power.

Other types of influence similar to suggestion are *habit* and *example*. One does as one is in the habit of doing, without paying any attention to it, and often one does just as other people do without being aware of it. As regards *example,* mass suggestion seems to play a certain rôle.

Mass Suggestion—While sporadic suggestion usually plays only a minor part in the life of a normal person, even the most intelligent often cannot escape the influence of mass suggestion. Human beings influence each other through mutual suggestion when they are gathered in dense crowds. The power of independent thought is then weakened. In its stead there is formed what may be called a collective mass soul, which is not the sum total of the mental wealth of the members of the group, but a new and independent phenomenon. This mass soul lies on a far lower plane than do the mental powers of each individual. This explains the savage acts, the lack of thoughtfulness and the incredulousness which characterize the mass.

Hypnotism—Hypnotic conditions are caused by suggestion, and the person who is under the influence of hypnotism is to a very high degree susceptible to suggestive commands from the hypnotist. In cases of deep hypnotic trance only those things which the hypnotist permits can be observed and thought about by the person under his influence, and this person follows and obeys almost every command. Furthermore, the subject may preserve the impressions of the hypnotic influence even after he has awakened (post-hypnotic influence). So it is easily understandable that it is within the realm of possibility to make use of hypnotism for criminal purposes.

Altho sensational news items dealing with hypnotic influence are common, cases of this kind really are rather rare. Most of those in the newspapers are cases of simulated hypnotism, in which the culprit is trying to escape the consequences of his act by claiming to have been under hypnotic influence. Insane persons also frequently insist that they have been under the influence of hypnotism.

Crimes in which hypnotism plays a rôle may be divided into two categories: (1) Cases where attempts are made to utilize a person for criminal acts while he is under hypnotic influence; (2) crimes in which the culprit has made use of the fact that a person is in a state of hypnotic coma in order to commit a crime against him. If the culprit in the first case should utilize the hypnotic condition of the other person, he would have to make use of so-called post-hypnotism, as, *e.g.,* to command the hypnotized man to shoot a particular person the first time he meets him. Here, of course, the same rule as mentioned before prevails: that one cannot easily be suggested to perform acts for which one has a definite distaste. In spite of the power of suggestion, we find in most persons of high moral standard several "hampering" factors which spring from the ethical personality of the individual and which counteract and prevent the suggestion from being transformed into action. Very few crimes of this kind are known.

Crimes of the other category are also very rare. They are, however, particularly dangerous, as the victim can be made to forget what has taken place. An incident is related in which two young men hypnotized a young girl, raped her, and then through suggestion compelled her to forget what had happened. Cases have also been reported in which a person has been robbed and then compelled by suggestion to forget his own personality and his entire previous life.

If one suspects that a person has been subject to hypnotism or suggestion, it is, of course, necessary to obtain the advice of a psychiatrist. Regarding the manner in which hypnotism may be applied, it is of importance to the interrogator to know that it can be done in several ways, as, *e.g.,* by making the subject gaze into a crystal for some time or into the eyes of the hypnotist, or by massaging the forehead of the victim. Hypnotic influence achieved by a quick look or a short command cannot, with few exceptions, be easily brought about, except with persons who have on several previous occasions been under the influence of the same hypnotist.

I. Sleep and Dreams

Criminal attacks are sometimes committed while the culprit is in a state of somnolence. The observation has been made that as a rule such attacks have been committed by young persons who before retiring to sleep have been through severe physical or mental exertions. Often the attack is directed against the first person they encounter, as, *e.g.*, against a roommate. During these attacks the culprit develops tremendous power—usually far above his normal physical strength.

From a psychiatric viewpoint this condition is regarded as an abnormal transition stage between being asleep and awake. It is characterized by a slower awakening of the intellectual faculties as compared to the faculties of motion. It is, of course, most pronounced when it occurs after a deep sleep. According to investigations made by Pick, Michelson and others, a person's sleep is deepest after the first hour, and becomes lighter and lighter until a minimum is reached in the sixth and seventh hour, whereupon it grows once more deeper as the morning approaches. It is quite natural that somnolence should exert an influence upon a person's capacity for perception, so that one must regard observations made by persons who have just awakened after profound sleep with a certain degree of caution.

Dreams may often be so intensive that one believes them to be real experiences or, in other words, true. It is known that epileptics are subject to such particularly vivid dreams.

The modern science of psychoanalysis attempts to interpret dreams. It is most uncertain, however, whether such analysis of a person's dreams can be of any practical value to the criminologist, as dreams can be related only very incoherently. It may also happen that important matters are added to the continuity of the dream through sheer imagination on the part of the narrator. In such a case there exists no possibility of testing the accuracy of the information.

Listening to a person talking during his sleep is an entirely different matter. Some persons have a habit of revealing what they wish to keep secret when, during sleep, they lose control

over their actions. Often such talks are incoherent and difficult
to understand. Criminal history shows, however, that some people have disclosed their secrets while sleeping.

J. Effects of Sodium Light on Colors

In all localities where sodium light is used, investigating officers
must give careful consideration to statements made by victims
and witnesses as to the color of materials and objects. The apparent colors of objects under sodium lighting will, in the main,
bear no resemblance to the actual colors in daylight. This applies, among other things, to descriptions of complexions of individuals, colors of clothing, colors of automobiles and other motor
vehicles and road equipment. However, if an object is yellow in
daylight, it will, as a rule, appear yellow when viewed in sodium
light. Tests and experiments should be made, as occasion permits, in order that first-hand knowledge may be had in this field.
A simple process for observation tests may be arranged by placing
color cards, such as are issued by paint manufacturers, under
sodium light.

QUESTIONS

1. How should the interrogation of witnesses be conducted?
2. What is meant by a suggestive question?
3. Why is it essential to visit the scene before questioning a suspect?
4. Enumerate methods for detecting deception.
5. Describe some different types of witnesses.
6. What are the stages of testimony?
7. What is your opinion of aural experiences in testimony?
8. Describe some case out of your own or others' experience where witnesses were mistaken in good faith.
9. What circumstances tend to promote mistakes in the identification of
   persons through witnesses?
10. Describe briefly the influences of epilepsy and hysteria on testimony.
11. What is meant by mass suggestion?

III

TRACING THE FUGITIVE

ABILITY to secure information about a fugitive criminal has always been and will lastingly be an asset for success in the work of a policeman or detective. This ability can be attained and developed by tact in the performance of one's duty; by becoming acquainted with residents, owners, managers and employees of business concerns, storekeepers, proprietors of licensed premises, hotel managers, chauffeurs, clerks, porters, taxicab starters, taxicab drivers, truckmen and other persons following divers vocations in the territory in which the officer is working. This knowledge should be enhanced at every opportunity throughout the municipality.

Aptitude for receiving information can be stimulated by friendly intercourse and cooperation with other officers working in the same or other districts. The habit of jotting down and keeping permanent notes regarding aliases, places of residence, hangouts, habits, and police records of potential and professional criminals will be found invaluable. For this purpose, a small card 3 x 5 inches in size may be kept, on which can be written memoranda. In all but the smallest police departments there is a central office in which a file of criminal records is kept and displayed for official inspection. Sometimes detectives do not avail themselves as fully as they should of this service, resorting to it only when a crime occurs in the territory to which they have been assigned. In some metropolitan police departments nowadays "refresher" courses in training are given to the personnel in service. Such courses include visits to local bureaus of criminal information and identification at headquarters so that observations can be made and knowledge secured of the *modus operandi* file, photograph gallery, criminal record and fingerprint classification files. Here police officers and detectives can have recourse to the index of crimes and criminals. Information is obtainable as to the identity, history and methods of criminals, all of which is of practical use in solving problems of crime.

With the identity of the fugitive criminal established, the first step to be taken in the pursuit is transmission of an alarm. A complete description of the individual should be given in the alarm. Likely places in which the fugitive may be found should be visited, kept under surveillance and searched if circumstances demand it. These include his residence, former residences, places or hangouts frequented, residences of relatives, close friends or associates and places of employment. Inquiries under suitable pretexts can be made of members of the family, relatives, friends, and shopkeepers who would be likely to know of the whereabouts and movements of the person wanted or with whom he would probably communicate.

The habits of the fugitive should also be considered. Many criminals of the so-called accidental type, as well as of the potential and professional types, frequent gambling places, night clubs, pool parlors, dance halls, burlesque and motion picture theaters, saloons and restaurants and hotels of the bizarre type. Frequently residence is located or sought in a neighborhood which has undergone a transition in type from the better-class private home to a furnished-room type of dwelling.

The Motive—Motive causing the commission of the crime is ofttimes helpful in tracking the fugitive. Motive may be said to include the elements of gain, sex, revenge, anger, homicidal mania, and sex perversion. "Cherchez la femme"—"Seek the woman"—is an axiom that has been followed successfully in tracking criminals in many cases. Many acts of criminals before and after the commission of a crime, as well as in supplying the motive for a crime, have been done at the urge of or on account of a woman. Often the woman is innocent of the criminal transaction. The present era, however, has brought to public notice repeatedly the participation by females in bold and daring crimes, including murder, kidnaping, robbery, extortion, and other felonies.

Aiding Agencies and Identification Through Photographs—Of
the many aids in tracking and identifying the fugitive criminal,
one of the most valuable is found in the records of the Criminal
Record Office or Bureau of Criminal Identification maintained
by municipal and State police departments and by national gov-
ernments. Here also application should be made for search to
be instituted of the *modus operandi* or crime index. If the offender can be identified, arrangements should be made for the
victim and witnesses to attend and inspect photographs of suspects or persons likely to have committed such a crime. There
are two aims to be achieved in this respect—(a) to establish
identity, (b) to trace the perpetrator.

Photographs of suspected persons should not be shown to a
witness if the criminal himself can be arrested and placed on
view for identification, nor in cases where it is intended to arrest the person at once for having committed a crime. But if
the criminal cannot be found, or if it is still a matter merely of
suspicion that he might have committed the crime, there should
be no objection to placing his photograph among a dozen others
and showing them to a victim or witness, with the object of selection. Care should be exercised to see that no assistance is
given, that no consultation is permitted with other victims or
witnesses, and that names, aliases, or other indices to identity are
kept out of view.

When a felony is under investigation, it often becomes essential to locate the fugitive or a suspect, or to find stolen property
under conditions which necessitate a search beyond the territorial
jurisdiction of the precinct, district or zone in which the crime
occurred. Inquiries in adjacent or remote precincts, districts or
zones are desirable. Places are usually specified, such as pawnshops, second-hand jewelry stores, furnished-room houses, garages, warehouses, or others. It is of the utmost importance that
these inquiries be made promptly, intelligently, tactfully, and con-
scientiously, because the solution of a major crime and the arrest
of its perpetrator often depend on the speed with which inquiry is
made. Cooperation is essential to success. It must be given will-
ingly and thoroughly.

If the fugitive sought is a member of a mob or gang and has a criminal record, it is reasonable to expect that records on file at the Central Information or Identification Bureau will show with whom he was arrested previously. Check should be made to determine if these persons are at liberty. By locating them, the fugitive, whether he has or has not a criminal or police record, may be found. Should they be in prison, it is possible that letters may be written to the fugitive you are seeking. Such addresses are a matter of record. Parole and Probation Boards cooperate with police departments in taking into custody parolees who have returned to the field of criminal operations. Contact should be made with the appropriate boards or officers thereof immediately when it is found that the fugitive is on parole or probation.

It is possible that a fugitive may attempt to leave the country on a steamship either as an employee or passenger. Information regarding passengers who apply for passports may be obtained from the Passport Bureau maintained in some cities by the Federal Government, or through the Passport Bureau, State Department, Washington, D. C. The United States Shipping Board maintains a record of persons going to sea on American boats in various jobs. Steamship companies also print, post and distribute sailing lists of passengers and crews.

Alien Fugitives—If the fugitive is or was an alien, information on his personal history, destination and friends may be obtained from the Immigration Bureau of the Department of Labor. Knowing the port of entry into this country is an aid to making a rapid search. Every steamship from foreign ports files with the Immigration Department a list of passengers and crews.

Aliens seeking first or second papers of citizenship are required to produce witnesses who have known them for a number of years. The names of these witnesses are on file at Naturalization Bureaus. If the fugitive is an alien it is possible to locate him through such witnesses.

Tickets and Checks—When a railroad ticket for any distant point is purchased at a station, including perhaps a Pullman chair or berth, a sales ticket filled out by the agent gives the number of the ticket, the car and berth. Tickets collected are returned to the office of the railroad company. Punch marks on the tickets identify the conductor in charge of the train. Locating the conductor will lead to locating the trainman and the Pullman porter. These are means by which identification of fugitive criminals using railroad transportation can be made. There is also the possibility that travel insurance was purchased from the ticket agent by the fugitive.

Helpful information regarding fugitive criminals who have been depositors may at times be secured at banking institutions. Canceled checks supply information and leads. Entry to safe deposit boxes generally is secured through a court order. In many jurisdictions an order from the Supreme Court is required before examination of the contents of the box can be made. Subsequent to such an examination, if anything found is wanted to be taken therefrom, an order of replevin generally issues.

A fugitive criminal whose identity is known may carry insurance or may have been rejected as a risk. Aid in locating him may be secured from information given at the time of applying for insurance.

Crime Index—The important work of assisting in the detection of criminals through a crime index or *modus operandi,* that is, by method of crime committed, and by description, is carried out in practically all metropolitan police departments, and in Central Bureaus of Criminal Information and Statistics located in a number of States. In Canada, a Central Repository along these lines is maintained at Ottawa. In European, South American and other countries Central Bureaus are likewise maintained. Most police departments as well as most sheriffs, prisons and jails have their fingerprint records of criminals cleared through the Federal Bureau of Investigation, United States Department of Justice, Washington, D. C. Therefore, it is important to report fully on the identity and aliases of persons wanted, and to have inquiry made through official channels of the Division at Washington for the purpose of determining whether any information is already recorded. In the event of the individual wanted being taken into custody elsewhere, there will be on file a record showing that he is wanted locally. It is also advisable to consult police reports of aided and accident cases and to consult hospital records.

Various techniques are used in different sections of the country in tracing fugitives on information secured from spoken or written communications. These channels will be discussed in subsequent chapters. When cases of sufficient notoriety or importance occur, investigating officers should consult with their supervisory heads to see that such channels of intelligence, including the mail, telegraph, telephone, dictaphone, various license and permit bureaus, water, gas and electric lighting corporations, tax and assessment bureaus, school systems, election board records, divers mailing lists and directories, fraternal, veteran and labor organizations, laundry and dry-cleaning establishments, bonding and loan corporations, auto rental agencies, bus, aeroplane and other transportation agencies, social service and welfare organizations, are approached and the facilities thereof used to the fullest measure.

To the laundry industry has come an invisible, indelible identification system. A mark that cannot be seen under ordinary conditions is placed in the fabric at the laundry. The mark is visible only when exposed to the ultra-violet rays. Police officers and detectives should see to it that fabrics, including tablecloths, napkins, handkerchiefs, doilies, towels, wash cloths, bath towels, knit underwear, etc., found under circumstances having or suspected of having a relationship to a criminal operation, or to investigations of missing persons or other police cases, are examined by means of ultra-violet light to determine whether an invisible laundry mark has been placed in the fabric and what aid may be obtained therefrom.

QUESTIONS

1. What is meant by the crime index?
2. Describe briefly the different registers and indices which are at your disposal in your department.
3. Describe briefly the steps to be taken in order to obtain information about an alien.
4. Enumerate the channels of intelligence at your disposal for the tracing of a fugitive.

IV

IDENTIFICATION OF INDIVIDUALS

A. Short Historical Survey

Positive identification of individuals has at all times been a problem of vital importance for the maintenance of law and order. In prehistoric times criminals were punished by mutilation and branding. This may well be looked upon as the first attempt toward subsequent identification, as the limb which had sinned was frequently the one subjected to mutilation; thus the hand of the thief would be amputated or the tongue of the slanderer would be cut off.

Branding disappeared less than a century ago—in Russia, for example, not until 1860 or thereabouts. Lifetimers sent to Siberia were branded on the forehead and on each cheek. By the time this barbaric method of identification finally disappeared from the Russian scene, it had already disappeared from the rest of Europe. In France, branding was abolished at the end of the Revolution, reintroduced later, and finally abolished in 1832. It had already disappeared in Germany, but Holland continued to employ it until 1854 and China until 1905.

Descriptions of wanted criminals were used even in Egypt of the Ptolemys and the Romans; and the system used had a surprizing similarity to the *portrait parlé* of today. The German criminologist Heindl, after studying these Egyptian descriptions, came to the interesting conclusion that centuries before the birth of Christ a very complicated method of description similar to the original *portrait parlé* was used, and that the Egyptians later gradually simplified it to embrace only the most important signs. This fact is in complete accord with the modern police, who now use only a very simplified *portrait parlé*.

In medieval days and until the middle of the nineteenth century the descriptions used were in no way better than those of the Egyptians. They were planless, unmethodical, and gave rise to serious mistakes. Contemporary accounts from the beginning of the nineteenth century of the "identification parades" in London give a good picture of the conditions which existed in olden times. Owing to the heavy penalties dealt to second offenders, criminals made every possible effort to appear as first offenders. In order to check up on these persons, certain days of the week were designated for a parade of the newly arrested criminals. They were lined up in the prison yard, and experienced policemen from the different districts of the city scrutinized them carefully to discover whether criminals were posing under assumed names.

Anthropometry—About 1840, the Belgian statistician Quetelet [1] stated that there are no two human beings in the world of exactly the same size. This theory is said to have been used for the first time for criminological purposes by Stevens, the warden of the prison in Louvain, who in 1860 proceeded to measure heads, ears, feet, breasts and lengths of the bodies of criminals.

Stevens then should be credited with having been the first man to identify criminals scientifically. However, his measurements had only the character of a trial and were soon discontinued. The invention of a system of identification founded on the thesis of Quetelet and the then existing knowledge of anthropology was left to another. This man was Alphonse Bertillon,[2] a young clerk in the Police Department of Paris who had many opportunities to convince himself of the unreliability of the old meth-

[1] *Quetelet, Lambert Adolphe Jacques,* statistician, astronomer and mathematician, was born in Ghent 1796 and died in Brussels in 1874 while director of the Observatory in Brussels. Quetelet is looked upon as the father of modern statistics.

[2] *Bertillon, Alphonse,* born 1853 and died 1914, was founder and leader of the Bureau of Criminal Identification of the Paris Police Department. He invented anthropometry, the *portrait parlé,* the photography of criminals, and metrical photography. Accounts of the priority of Stevens regarding anthropometry were given by Heindl, who, however, in his work, *System und Praxis der Daktyloskopie,* has not done Bertillon full justice. Heindl regards anthropometry as a detriment to the development of dactyloscopy. It is true that Bertillon was against dactyloscopy, but anthropometry had, however, been used for decades before dactyloscopy had won recognition worth mentioning. No one can deprive Bertillon of the honor of having been a pioneer in the technique of identification.

Fig. 3
Alphonse Bertillon

ods of description. Bertillon originated a new method of classifying criminals according to bodily measurements. At first he met with strong opposition from the chief of the Paris Detective Division, Macé, but finally the Bureau of Identification was established in 1882 with Bertillon as its director. The new method of identification, which was called anthropometry or *bertillonage,* gave very good results, and on the 15th of February, 1889, the famous *Service d'identité judiciaire* was founded and soon became known the world over.

The method of anthropometry was based on the following principles:

1. The human skeleton is unchangeable after the twentieth year. The thigh bones continue to grow somewhat after this period, but this is compensated by the curving of the spine which takes place at about the same age.

2. It is impossible to find two human beings having bones alike.

3. The necessary measurements can easily be taken with the aid of simple instruments.

The anthropometrical measurements may be divided into three categories:

1. Bodily measurements: height, width of outstretched arms, and sitting height.

2. Measurements of the head: length of head, breadth of head, bizygomatical diameter, and length of the right ear.

3. Measurements of the limbs: length of left foot, length of left middle and left little finger, length of left arm and hand from the elbow to the top of the stretched middle finger.

Each of these eleven measurements is classified in three groups, small, medium and large. The subclassification begins with the length and breadth of the head and is subdivided into nine groups. Each of these nine groups is again divided into three new groups according to the length of the left middle finger, and these twenty-seven groups are divided into three new groups according to the length of the left foot. The division continues with the elbow measurements (three groups), the height of the body (three groups), the length of the small finger (two groups), the color of the eyes (five groups), the length of the ears (three groups), etc. With this sixty-fifth division, 65,610 subclassifications are had.

Boys and young men, in whom the measurements of the bones are not constant, were classified by Bertillon according to the color of the eyes and details of the ear. The classification of women was very superficial; the measurements of the head, the left foot and the elbow were excluded.

The anthropometrical system gave immediate good results. During the first year of its application, in 1882, 49 individuals giving false names were identified. During the following year, 241 were identified, and in 1892 as many as 680. The system had, however, serious drawbacks. It was limited to adults, and there was often a marked difference in the measurements of a person who had been measured in different Police Departments, or even when measured for a second time in the same department. A table of measurement allowances was introduced, but serious mistakes still could not be avoided. Persons having the same anthropometrical measurements as others already registered occasionally were arrested. The anthropometrical description has now been replaced almost everywhere by the fingerprint description or simply exists as an additional aid, as in France, where an old law compels the recording of anthropometrical measurements in the identification books issued to Gipsies, vagrants, etc.

Bertillon invented also the *portrait parlé,* a clear and precise method of describing a person, as well as the photography of criminals as practised today.

Fig. 4
Rudolph Archibald Reiss

Beginning of Criminal Photography—Before the English physician Maddox invented the photographic dry-plate which made photography inexpensive and simple in its application, others had already succeeded in photographing criminals with Daguerre's method, the first photographic method, using wet plates with the exposure lasting several minutes and each "print" requiring a new sitting. Reiss [3] showed that this method was already in use in Switzerland in 1854, and that by 1860 important scenes of crimes had already been photographed. Paris was the first city in the world to establish a special photographic studio for the police. To Léon Renault, the Commissioner of Police, belongs the credit for adopting it.

The first photographs of criminals were taken front-view and the scale was very arbitrary. Bertillon made them uniform and introduced a fixed scale, so that bodily measurements could be calculated from the photographs. He finally photographed the criminals in both front view and profile, simplifying identification enormously.

B. Description of "Wanted" Persons

A knowledge of how to obtain a description of a wanted person from statements of witnesses, how to identify a wanted

---

[3] *Reiss, Rudolph Archibald,* was born in 1874 in Baden, Germany, and died in 1929 in Belgrade, Yugoslavia. Reiss was Professor of Police Science at the University of Lausanne, Switzerland, until 1915. From 1920 on he directed the laboratory of the Yugoslavian National Bank in Belgrade. Reiss is the author of numerous works on police science and especially on photography.

man from a photograph, and how to give a description of a prisoner for future use, is necessary for the detective. In spite of all progress in police science one cannot get along without a knowledge of personal description.

The first accurate description of prisoners, also called *portrait parlé* (spoken picture), was invented by Bertillon. In its original form the *portrait parlé* was divided into four categories:

(a) Determination of color (left eye, hair, beard and skin).
(b) Morphological determinations (shape, direction and size of every part of the head).
(c) General determinations (grade of stoutness, carriage, voice and language, dress, social standing, etc.).
(d) Description of indelible marks (scars, tattooings, etc.).

The *portrait parlé*, with its hundreds of exact definitions and details, was, however, altogether too complicated for detectives.

Fig. 5

Three principal forms of baldness. From left to right: *frontal, occipital* and *covering the whole top of the head*

Some parts are still used, but the great bulk of it has been discarded. It is, however, regarded as one of the classic subjects of police science, and at least the members of the Identification Bureaus ought to be familiar with it.[4]

The following description of wanted persons will cover the items necessary to note in most cases:

[4] Bertillon's classic book, *Photographie judiciaire*, is recommended.

Name ....

Sex ....

Color ....

Nationality ....

Occupation ....

Age ....

Height ....

Weight ....

Build—Large; stout or very stout; medium; slim; stooped or square-shouldered; stocky.

Complexion—Florid; sallow; pale; fair; dark.

Hair—Color; thick or thin; bald or partly bald; curly; kinky; wavy; how cut or parted; style of hairdress.

Eyes—Color of the iris; eyes bulgy or small; any peculiarities.

Eyebrows—Slanting, up or down; bushy or meeting; arched, wavy, horizontal; as to texture, strong; thin; short or long-haired; penciled.

Nose—Small or large; pug, hooked, straight, flat.

Whiskers—Color; Vandyke; straight; rounded; chin whiskers; goatee; side whiskers.

Mustache—Color; short; stubby; long; pointed ends; turned-up ends; Kaiser style.

Chin—Small; large; square; dimpled; double; flat; arched.

Face—Long; round; square; peg-top; fat; thin.

Neck—Long; short; thick; thin; folds in back of neck; puffed neck; prominent Adam's apple.

Lips—Thick; thin; puffy; drooping lower; upturned upper.

Mouth—Large; small; drooping or upturned at corners; open; crooked; distorted during speech or laughter; contorted.

Head—Posture of—bent forward; turned sideways; to left or right; inclined backwards, or to left or right.

Ears—Small; large; close to or projecting out from head; pierced.

Forehead—High; low; sloping; bulging; straight; receding.

Distinctive marks—Scars; moles; missing fingers or teeth; gold teeth; tattoo marks; lameness; bow legs; pigeon toes; knock-knees; cauliflower ears; pockmarked; flat feet; nicotine fingers; freckles; birthmarks.

Peculiarities—Twitching of features; rapid or slow gait; long or short steps; wearing of eye-glasses; carrying a cane; stuttering; gruff or effeminate voice.

Clothes—Hat and shoes—color and style; suit—color; cut; maker's name; shirt and collar—style and color: tie—style and color; dressed neatly or carelessly.

Jewelry—Kind of: where worn.

Where likely to be found—Residence; former residences; places frequented or hangouts; where employed; residences of relatives, etc.

The wanted person may at times be afflicted with some chronic disease. It is a good plan to obtain information from his family physician and neighborhood druggist concerning the disease, also the address or addresses given to them by the patient, from time to time, during a period of years.

Personal Associates—Friends who would be most likely to know of the movements or whereabouts of the person wanted, or with whom he would be most likely to communicate.

Habits—Heavy drinker or smoker; drug addiction;[5] gambler; frequenter of pool parlors; dance halls; cabarets; baseball games; resorts, etc.

How he left scene of crime—Running; walking; by vehicle; direction taken.

Regarding the details of the above list the following should be noted:

Height—When questioning a witness about the height of a wanted person one should ask the witness to compare the

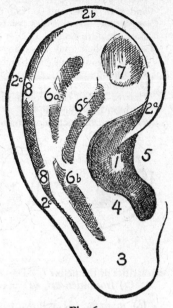

Fig. 6

The principal parts of the ear: (1) concha, (2a) beginning helix, (2b) upper helix, (2c) rear helix, (3) lobule, (4) antitragus, (5) tragus, (6a) upper antihelix, (6b) lower antihelix, (6c) lower branch of upper antihelix, (7) fossa digitalis, (8) fossa navicularis

height of the person with the height of another person familiar to the witness. It cannot be expected that the witness will be able to

[5] It is worth while to remark that cocaine addicts generally are recognized at first glance by the experienced detective, especially after they have had the "dope." Their bright, shiny eyes, air of self-confidence, and loud, self-assertive speech betray them immediately. Without the "dope" the drug addict is extremely nervous and shaky.

tell more than the average height of the body, *i.e.,* distinguish between small, medium and tall persons. A "small person" is between 5 ft. and 5 ft. 3 in., a "medium person" between 5 ft. 4 in. and 5 ft. 7 in., and a "tall person" 5 ft. 8 in. to 6 ft. and over.

Complexion—Peculiarities such as freckles, pockmarks, pustulous skin, etc., are noted.

Hair—The hair may have any of the colors—(a) light blond, (b) blond, (c) dark blond, (d) brown, (e) black, (f) red, (g) white, (h) mixed gray, (i) gray. Baldness should be specified, *i.e.,* it may be *frontal, occipital, cover the whole top of the head* or be *total.* Hair of buried corpses sometimes turns red owing to the action of the humus in the soil.

Eyes—Seven distinct colors may be seen in the iris: (a) blue, (b) gray,

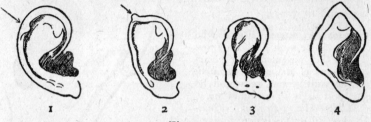

Fig. 7

Peculiarities of the helix: (1) Darwinian extension, (2) Darwinian tubercle, (3) frostbitten ear, (4) upper helix in acute angle at the top

(c) maroon, (d) yellow, (e) light brown, (f) brown, (g) dark brown. Peculiarities such as *pronounced bloodshotness, different colors in the two eyes* (multicolored iris), *white spots on the iris, albinos* (blue eyes with red pupils), *arcus senilis* (a glossy ring surrounding the iris), *squinting, large, pear-shaped* or *eccentric pupils, amputations, artificial eyes,* and *watery eyes,* are noted. Peculiarities of the eyelids, such as *skin folds by the greater canthus* (inner eye corner), one or both eyelids *hanging, long* or *sparse lashes* and *pronounced sacks under the eyes,* also should be noted.

Eyebrows—The color should be especially noted when it differs from the hair.

Nose—The nose is without doubt one of the most important parts of the face from the viewpoint of recognition, altho its form may undergo changes due to accidents, disease or plastic surgery. Some peculiarities are: *The root of the nose,* or the nose saddle, which may be *very narrow* or *very wide; the bridge of the nose,* which may be *broken, flat, very wide* or *deviating to the left* or *to the right: the point of the nose,* which may be *blunt* or *split; the nos-*

THE "LINE-UP" OR "SHOW-UP"

Detective Bureau, Philadelphia Police Department

MODUS OPERANDI FILE OF CRIMINALS

[PLATE 2]

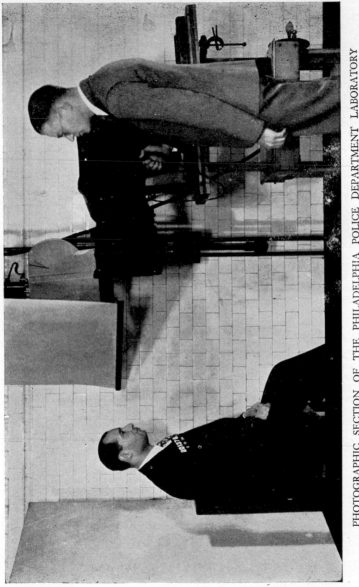

PHOTOGRAPHIC SECTION OF THE PHILADELPHIA POLICE DEPARTMENT LABORATORY

[Plate 3]

trils, which may be *very thick* or *very thin, flat to the left* or *to the right, higher to the left* or *to the right,* or *strongly revealed.*

Whiskers and mustaches—This part of the description has generally little value because of the facility with which it may be changed.

Ears—The ears constitute the most characteristic part of the body next to the patterns of the friction ridges. They remain unaltered from birth until death. In cases where an arrested person has to be identified by photograph they play a deciding rôle.[6]

The principal parts of the ear are the *helix,* the *lobule,* the *tragus,* the *antitragus,* the *antihelix* and the *concha* (see Figs. 7, 8, 9).

The *helix,* which is generally divided into *beginning helix, upper helix* and *rear helix,* may be *flat* (when the fold is missing), form different *angles,* or the rear helix may be *fused* with the antihelix. Among peculi-

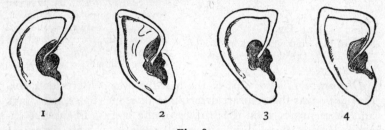

I	2	3	4

Fig. 8

Peculiarities of the helix: (1) upper helix with acute angle in front, (2) upper helix with acute angle in rear, (3) upper helix with right angle in front, (4) upper helix with right angle in rear.

arities we find the *Darwinian extension,* the *Darwinian tubercle, frostbitten ears,* and *cut helix.*

The *lobule* may or may not be adhering to the cheek. The border furrow of the ear may or may not be continuous with the lobule. Some peculiarities are the *pierced, split* or *twisted* lobule.

The tragus and antitragus. The antitragus is examined as to *sloping, profile, prominence* and *peculiarities.* Among peculiarities there may be

---

[6] An interesting case in which the ears were used for identification purposes was that of the false Grand Duchess Anastasia of Russia. Some years after the World War a woman, after an attempt at suicide in Berlin, Germany, declared herself to be a daughter of the murdered Czar Nicholas. She said she had escaped the execution of the Czar's family in Ekaterinburg, Siberia, lost her memory as the result of a blow on the head, and after many adventures had finally come to Berlin. She had a superficial similarity to the real Anastasia, but Professor Marc Bischoff, the head of the Scientific Police Institute of Lausanne, Switzerland, established her non-identity by means of the ears—by comparing profile photographs of the impostor and of the real Anastasia.

noted *tragus with one or two protrusions, tragus* and *antitragus* **hairy;**
tragus missing, ridge separating antitragus from the rest of the ear, *very
small concha, fossa navicularis with pit* (a round cavity instead of the
sharp angle in which the fossa navicularis generally ends).

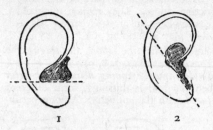

I   2

Fig. 9

Slant of the antitragus: (1) horizontal,
(2) oblique

The *antihelix* is examined as
to its *prominence.* It may be
markedly *flat* or very *prominent*
and broad. Peculiarities are:
*upper antihelix in several
branches, upper antihelix fused
with upper helix* and *upper
helix with some growth.*

It goes without saying that
the *general form* of the ear
(oval, rectangular, triangular
and round), as well as the *pro-
trusion from the head* and the
position on the head (vertical or
oblique), should be noted.

Distinctive Marks—One of the best features of Bertillon's *portrait parlé* was the accurate description of scars, moles, tattooings
and other marks upon the surface of the body. They were examined as to shape, dimensions and positions. This system of
description, however, was invented in the 1880s when fingerprints were not yet used. Today tattooings, except on the hands,
neck and face,[7] have very little importance for identification.

Almost all distinctive marks can nowadays be removed by
plastic surgery or other cosmetic methods. If surgery has not
been used, however, there is always a possibility of at least locating the place where a tattoo mark has been removed. This
is done by rubbing the suspected part of the skin until it red-
dens. The scar of the tattooing will then blanch in contradis-
tinction to the surrounding red skin.

C. Photographing Prisoners

A prisoner is always photographed in the anterior view and in
profile. The anterior position causes a ready recognition of the

[7] French criminals or persons associating with *apaches* have quite often one or
several blue points tattooed at the outer corner of the eye.

individual, but the profile photograph is necessary for certain identification. We are so accustomed to viewing our fellow citizens from the front, that it is quite possible, at first sight, not to recognize some one if a profile photograph is shown. Experience shows that the public will easily recognize front-view photographs in the Rogues' Gallery, but the trained observer will prefer the profile photograph when attempting to identify an individual.

Front-view photography shows very little of the most important details of the description, *i.e.,* the profile of the nose and the details of the ear, but gives a good survey of the general appearance of the person, and in some cases peculiarities which are not shown in profile.

Some place a mirror alongside the head of the criminal when he is being photographed, so that the front view and the profile are photographed simultaneously. This method, however, is to be rejected, chiefly because the profile is reversed, so that, for instance, a mole on the right cheek will appear on the left cheek in the photograph. This may give rise to serious mistakes.

Bertillon's method of photographing the front view and profile is now universally used. The best reduction—the relation between the size of the individual in reality and the photograph—was determined to be 1:7 by Bertillon. This size gives a picture large enough to allow the identification of all peculiarities of the face. On account of the constant ratio of reduction such a photograph can be regarded as a metrical picture, where all the

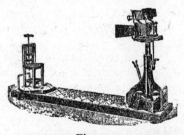

Fig. 10

Special camera with chair for photographing prisoners

measurements of the face may be ascertained quite accurately. In some places a reduction of 1:5 is used.

Through the reduction of 1:7 a head is 1.2 to 1.4 inches high on the photograph. Over the head there should be a free space of about .4 inch. In this manner two pictures may be taken on a plate 3.25 by 5.50 inches, so that 3.25 by 2.75 inches is reckoned for the front view and the same for the profile.

For this type of photography, some police forces use a special camera and a special chair mounted on a jointed platform. The camera has two lenses mounted over one another, the upper lens being for the ground glass. By means of this arrangement, the man to be photographed may be observed during the exposure. The seat of the chair is as small as possible and is framed with wooden slabs surrounding the sides and dividing evenly. In order to sit more comfortably with this arrangement, the sitter instinctively tries to sit erect. The chair is supplied with a head support to give the head the correct position. It also serves to keep in place the numbers to be photographed with the subject. The chair revolves upon itself, so that the person to be photographed does not find it necessary to move when changing position from the anterior to the side view. A lever attached to the camera may serve the purpose of revolving the chair.

Some departments use only a studio camera equipped with a portrait lens, with 3¼ x 5½ ground glass, and a special adapter (mentioned later). The camera is placed 7 feet from the subject and is moved 6 inches forward when the profile is photographed.

In order to take two pictures on the same plate, the camera is equipped with a special adapter causing only one-half of the plate to be exposed at a time. To get a sharp photograph without using too small a diaphragm, the focusing is made upon the outer corner of the eye.

The correct position of the head is of importance. In order to obtain this position, two lines crossing each other at an angle of 75 degrees may be drawn on the ground-glass with a pencil. The head in the profile photograph should then come to occupy such a position that the intersection of the lines is at the outer corner of the eye and the horizontal line passes through the center of the ear.

The negative of a criminal's photograph should not be retouched. Scars and other marks must show sharply and clearly.

A black or dark maroon background is used for white people and a gray background for colored people; the light should if possible be uniform for all photographs. This can only be obtained by artificial light, which should be allowed to come chiefly from above, and the rest from the front and side. The light should play on the ear so as to bring out its details very sharply.

At times additional photographs are taken, front view with hat on or the whole figure, or both. If several persons have been arrested in the same case, they are photographed together in a group with a 7-foot stake marked off in inches to show the relative height of each prisoner.

The number of the photograph and the date marked on the strip are photographed with the prisoner to make it unnecessary for the operator to make any marks on the negative. This may be important in court to offset any charge of altering the picture.

If no special apparatus is at hand, good pictures may be taken in the following manner:

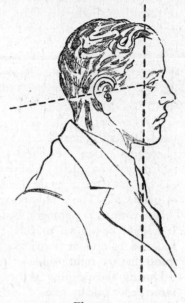

Fig. 11

The correct position of the head while photographing a prisoner. The line passing through the tragus of the ear is at an angle of 75° with the vertical line

Instead of the special chair, a common wooden chair with a straight back is used. The camera is placed on its tripod facing the chair, with the lens approximately on a level with the eyes of the person to be photographed. To obtain the correct distance between the chair and the camera (the photograph should be one-seventh of the natural size of the head), a person is made to sit in the chair, holding a straight strip of cardboard, vertically, in the vicinity of the outer corner of the eye. The strip should be 14 inches long. A rectangle 3.25 by 2.75 inches is marked with a pencil in the center of the ground-glass. After having made certain that all the details of the head show up sharply on the ground-glass, the size of the cardboard strip viewed on the ground-glass is measured. The camera should be placed at such a distance that the 14-inch cardboard strip measures 2 inches on the ground-glass. The reduction is then 1:7. The positions of the camera and the chair should be marked with white chalk or small wooden blocks nailed to the floor.

If no special plate-holder is available,[8] one can photograph on two different plates of 2.50 by 3.50 inches. The person is first photographed in the anterior view. The chair is then given half a turn to the left. The position of the person should remain exactly the same after the turn, the markings on the floor being of great aid. The profile photograph is then taken.

If a woman is photographed, her ear should receive attention. It should be shown in full. If necessary, her hair should be fastened behind or above the ear. It is important to keep in mind that the right profile of a criminal should be photographed!

During the printing process, the two plates are put on the same paper side by side.

D. Identification of the Individual by Means of Fingerprints

The greater portion of the human body is covered with hairs. Most of these are very rudimentary, while the fully developed occur on a few parts only. Some parts of the body are devoid of hairs—namely, the palm of the hand and the palmar surface of the fingers, as well as the soles of the feet. On these parts we find friction ridges which form different patterns. Such friction ridges, more or less developed, will be found on corresponding parts of the body in all mammals.

[8] American view cameras generally are made with a divider which exposes only one side of a negative at a time; this can be used in place of an adapter.

The skin consists of two principal layers, the epidermis and the corium. In the upper portions of the corium are the so-called corium papillæ, forming the pattern of the friction ridges. The nerves of sensation terminate in the furrows between the ridges.

If a friction ridge is examined through a magnifying glass, one finds that on each ridge there is a row of pores, the mouths of the sweat glands. They are equally distant from each other.

One sweat pore with the surrounding part of the friction ridge is called an *island*. There is reason to believe that the friction ridges are formed by the fusion of such islands. The number of sweat pores therefore represents the number of islands fused into a ridge.

From the viewpoint of identification, the portions of the friction ridges are divided into three groups: *fingerprints,* meaning the patterns on the tips of the fingers, *palmar prints,* or prints of the palm of the hand, and *sole prints,* or prints of the sole of the foot.

Of these, the fingerprints are the most important. Nowhere are the patterns so intricate and complicated as on the fingerprints; the friction ridges on the two lower joints of the finger and the palm of the hand are comparatively monotonous. The chance impressions found at scenes of crimes in most cases originate from the fingertips. This fact adds to the importance of their patterns.

Early History—The history of the use of fingerprints is fairly meager, altho there are some early accounts of interest about them. These, curiously enough, come from the Far East; so far as the records show, there were only a few occasions in which our ancestors in Europe or America showed interest in fingerprints.

A prehistoric tomb was discovered in 1839 on the island of Gavr'Inis, Brittany, France. Peculiar patterns in the form of arrows, rings and snakes were found on its stone walls. It is now believed that these represented stylized designs of patterns of friction ridges. Another early record, probably aboriginal, is an Indian pictograph showing representations of the finger patterns carved on a rock at Kejemkoojic Lake, Nova Scotia.

We also know that in the first century after Christ, a Roman lawyer, Quintilian, was the defending attorney for a blind man who was prosecuted for having killed his father. At the scene of the crime there were bloody palm prints on the walls, which were thought to have been made by the blind man after the murder. The defense attempted to show that the real murderer was the stepmother of the defendant, and that she had made

Fig. 12
Robert Heindl

those palm prints on the wall in order to cast suspicion on her blind stepson. The Roman lictors must have been very near to a discovery of the palmar patterns as evidence, but no attempt at identification was made.

When the famous Italian anatomist, Marcello Malpighi (1628-1694), examined different parts of the human body with the then recently invented microscope, he also "discovered" the patterns of the friction ridges; but neither Malpighi nor Purkinje, a professor of physiology at the University of Breslau, Germany, who in 1832 wrote a book in which he also dealt with the patterns on the skin, had any thought whatsoever of using those patterns for the purpose of identification.

The credit for having adopted fingerprints for commercial purposes belongs to the Far East. Fingerprints were found on Babylonic clay plates. The Babylonians, in order to protect themselves against forgeries, pressed a fingerprint into the soft clay when they wrote receipts and other important documents. It appears that even before Christ the Chinese used fingerprints as seals for personal identification.[9]

[9] In China and Japan, seals are used by all classes of people from the Mandarin to the laborer, and seals are necessary for all kinds of signatures. The laws regu-

The German criminologist, Robert Heindl,[10] has thoroughly studied the history of fingerprints in the Far East and found that they were already commonly used for identification purposes during the Tang dynasty (618 to 906 A.D.). Later the Chinese developed a classification of fingerprints based upon loops and whorls for the identification of criminals. This Chinese system of classification was described by a Dr. McCarthy in an American journal in 1886, and Galton learned of this. Heindl is convinced that Galton derived his classification system from the Chinese. The Galton-Henry system, the one most widely used, is therefore said to be derived from China.

Discovery of Modern Dactyloscopy [11]—Dactyloscopy was invented at the same time, but independently, by two Englishmen living in Asia. They were Sir William J. Herschel, Administrator of the Hooghly district in Bengal, India, and Dr. Henry Faulds, on the staff of the Tsukiji Hospital, Tokyo, Japan. Both inventors denied that they had had previous knowledge of Asiatic fingerprints, but it seems to be more than a coincidence that dactyloscopy was born in Asia, the classical continent of fingerprinting.

Herschel's first attempt to use fingerprints was made when he compelled two natives who wrote their names on a contract to press an inked finger on the paper after the signature. This mystical procedure is alleged to have been carried out in order to frighten them against later denials of their signatures. At this time, 1858, Herschel had no thought of the individuality of fingerprints. Very soon, however, he realized their importance as a medium of identification, and used them in his district to prevent pensions from being paid out to impostors, a common

lating the use of seals are very elaborate, and the seals must be registered by the police in order to be valid. It is still very common in China that a signature is made valid by putting a fingerprint in Chinese ink on the paper. These fingerprints generally are so blurred that their use for identification is impossible.

[10] Dr. Robert Heindl, former Chief of the Criminal Investigation Department of Saxony, and now Privy Councilor at the German Foreign Office, is the author of *System und Praxis der Daktyloskopie,* which is unique in the literature of identification. Through his initiative, fingerprint classifications were introduced in Germany at the beginning of our century and he has made extensive researches on fingerprints and their history.

[11] Dactyloscopy = Technique of fingerprinting.

crime in India, where the registration of the people is very defective.

Herschel, in 1877, sent a semi-official report on fingerprints to the Inspector General of Indian Prisons, requesting him to introduce fingerprinting in the prisons of India. This gentleman, however, did not accept Herschel's offer, and the latter continued to work without publishing the results achieved. We can imagine his astonishment, when in 1880 he read in *Nature*, a journal of popular science, an article signed by Henry Faulds, describing fingerprints and pointing out their usefulness for tracing criminals by chance impressions left at scenes of crimes. Dr. Faulds had commenced to study fingerprints of living persons after having become interested in fingerprints found on prehistoric Japanese pottery. It is interesting to note that Faulds' studies led him to the discovery of chance impressions, while Herschel, on the contrary, looked upon fingerprints as a dependable means of identification. Herschel answered immediately, in the next issue of *Nature,* and while making no claims of priority, stated that he had used fingerprints for more than twenty years and had introduced them for practical purposes in India.

If we compare Herschel's work of twenty years, during which he established the usefulness of fingerprints as a means of identification, and Faulds' brief work resulting only in general speculation, we must certainly regard Herschel as the pioneer of modern fingerprinting.

The ideas of Herschel and Faulds were adopted by a scientist who gave fingerprinting its scientific foundation. Sir Francis Galton (born 1822 in Birmingham and died 1911 in London) was a famous English anthropologist. He worked out the foundation of the Galton-Henry system of classification, the final touch being added by Sir Edward Richard Henry, who had studied with Herschel in India and later became the Police Commissioner of the metropolitan district of London. The Galton-Henry system was first introduced in India, and later—in 1901— was adopted by Scotland Yard. This latter step definitely put an end to the anthropometrical system of Bertillon.

Bertillon's enthusiasm for fingerprinting was lukewarm, be-

cause he looked upon it as a rival of anthropometry. A fingerprint system, in the modern sense of the word, was therefore not
introduced in Paris until after the death of Bertillon in 1914.
In view of these facts, it is odd that Bertillon is sometimes
credited with having been the inventor of the fingerprint system.

A contemporary of Galton, the Argentinian Juan Vucetich,
had also invented a system of fingerprint classification. In 1898,
he introduced in Argentina a system very similar to Galton's
original system. Later he accepted Galton's subclassification with
ridge tracing and ridge counting. The system of Vucetich has
found widespread use, especially in Latin countries, and is used
in the original or modified form in all South America; in Lyons,
France; Geneva, Switzerland; Oslo, Norway, and other places.

*First Rule of Dactyloscopy: There Are No Two Identical Fin-
gerprints.*

At the very beginning of fingerprinting, defending attorneys
would sometimes object to fingerprint identification, claiming
the possibility that identical fingerprints could be found. Galton, in his book, *Fingerprints,* showed mathematically that there
could not be two identical fingerprints; but opponents raised the
objection that these calculations were purely theoretical and that
a sufficient number of fingerprints had not yet been examined.

Today, however, after the fingerprinting of millions and millions of individuals through thirty-five years, one can offer a convincing demonstration that two identical fingerprints do not exist.
Fingerprints, like other physical objects, obey Quetelet's rule:
Every nature-made thing shows unlimited and infinite variations
of forms. Nature never repeats the same work. We may, for
instance, search in vain for two identical leaves. If we found
two which seemed alike to the eye, a microscopic examination
would immediately show a formidable unlikeness. Galton calculated that 64,000,000,000 different patterns were possible, *i.e.,*
about four times the number of fingers existing in the world on
the basis of a total population of 1,500,000,000.

A South American scientist calculated that if only twenty
characteristic points in each pattern are recorded and these are
compared with the present population of the earth, there will be

the possibility of getting the same pattern only once every 4,660,-337th century. There is a saying that one should not force biological facts into a mathematical straitjacket, and this is certainly true about such calculations. Much more important is the fact that two identical fingerprints amongst the millions registered have never been found.

The Heredity of Fingerprints—At times the daily newspapers print articles concerning the inheritance of fingerprints, giving the impression that fingerprints may be inherited in all their details, and that they may even be used to determine paternity. Such opinions conflict with one of the fundamental principles upon which dactyloscopy rests, namely, the absolute individuality of fingerprints.

Galton's researches on the inheritance of fingerprints conclusively showed that they were *not* inherited. After Galton, several scientists studied the same problem. For instance, in 1892 Forgeot's studies down to the third generation in different families where intermarriages had occurred demonstrated that the patterns were not inherited. Senet came to the same conclusion after having examined several families down to the fifth generation. In 1908 Cevidalli found that there existed a certain tendency to heredity. After Cevidalli, several research workers —Helweg, Harster, Sommer and others—have expressed the opinion that fingerprints are not inherited.

These dissimilar opinions may lead one to regard the question as perplexing, but it is necessary merely to note that it has been looked upon from different viewpoints. Anthropologists have been satisfied with a mere similarity in the general arrangement of the patterns, thereby drawing their conclusion that inheritance plays a part. On the contrary, criminologists who have dealt with the problem have sought an absolute identity, and this has never been found.

All researchers unanimously state that identity, from the dactyloscopic viewpoint, has never been found between parents and their children or between brothers and sisters.

During the past few years, the question of the heredity of fingerprints has been extensively debated, and several scientists, such as Ethel M. Elderton, K. Bonnevie, Poll and others, have found that there is a tendency to heredity in certain patterns. However, the question of proving paternity is a different matter. Nevertheless, tho researches in a very large number of cases may give interesting results for the science of heredity, it is unlikely that it will prove possible to determine fatherhood from fingerprints.

Second Rule of Dactyloscopy: Fingerprints Are Not Changeable—Fingerprints are already formed in the fourth month of pregnancy, between the one-hundredth and one-hundred-and-twentieth day of the development of the fetus. A three-months-old fetus has absolutely smooth fingers. From this stage on, the friction ridges begin to grow on the fingertips and finally cover the whole finger. During further intrauterine growth, as well as after birth, the patterns enlarge, but no changes take place in the number or arrangement of the friction ridges. The same relation exists between a fingerprint of an infant and the fingerprint of the same individual when an adult, as between a photograph and an enlargement of the same.

The best proof of the unchangeability of fingerprints is found in those taken of the same person at different ages. The oldest known print of a friction-ridge pattern was made in 1856 by the German anthropologist, Welker, in Giessen, Germany. At thirty-four he recorded a print of his palm. In 1897, at the age of seventy-five, he made a similar print. There is an absolute identity between the prints. Herschel also made prints of his own hands at an interval of twenty-eight years, and these likewise show an absolute identity. All bureaus of identification tell the same story.

The pattern is not influenced by illnesses—except by leprosy (see Ribera). Fingerprints of infantile-paralysis patients, rachitic and acromegalic persons (an illness which enlarges the face, hands and feet) have established the fact that altho the distances between the friction ridges can be changed, the patterns as a whole will not show any alteration. If the skin on the fingertips is wounded or burned, the whole pattern, with all its details, will reappear when the wound heals. Locard and Witkowski, of

Lyons, who performed rather painful experiments on themselves by burning their fingertips with boiling water, hot oil and hot metals, showed that after the healing of the epidermis the original patterns reappeared.

If the wound is too deep, the resulting scars constitute no obstacle for identification. On the contrary, the scars are characteristic clues of high value. It has been observed that scars on a fingerprint will make a much deeper impression on the judge and jury than the entire pattern.

Recent attempts of criminals to alter or destroy the skin on the fingers by plastic operations have also proved unsuccessful.

The friction ridges disappear only after death, by the decomposition of the body. It can truthfully be said of them that they are an indelible signature which we carry with us from the cradle to the grave.

Equipment for Taking Fingerprints—In order to make impressions of fingerprints for registration or comparison, the following materials are needed: paper, printer's ink, rubber roller and plate.

All smooth white paper can be used except blotting paper. The best paper for fingerprinting purposes should be of an absolutely white color, as glossed as good writing paper, and perfectly smooth. Paper with a rough surface, with watermarks or with printing on the back should be avoided. The ink should be of the best type used for mimeograph or neostyle, in tubes.

The plate can be a glass plate or a polished metal plate about 6 x 10 inches. It should be covered when not in use, and should be cleaned daily with gasoline or turpentine. The regular mimeograph rolls are the best, but the hard rubber rollers employed in photography can also be used.

The taking of good fingerprints requires a certain amount of experience, altho the actual process is in itself very simple. The fingerprints should be rolled, so as to show the whole pattern, from one side of the finger to the other, to bring out all deltas.[12] The determination of the delta is of great importance for the

---

[12] The Greek letter Δ, which looks like a triangle and signifies the meeting place of three ridges.

classification and for the identification of many chance impressions, when only one side of the pattern is had.

The ink is spread in a thin layer on the plate with the aid of

Plain Arch   Tented Arch   Exceptional Arch

Plain Loop   Whorl   Central Pocket
                                       Loop

Twin Loop   Lateral Pocket   Accidental
                   Loop

Fig. 13
The fingerprint patterns

the roller. The person to be fingerprinted must have clean fingers. Perspiring hands are cleansed with ether, benzol or soap and hot water to avoid spotty prints. The person is told to relax both the fingers and the hand, and under no circumstances should he be allowed to exercise any pressure on the paper himself. The fingers are now printed in order, generally from the right thumb to the right little finger, and from the left thumb to the left little finger. The tip of the finger to be printed is placed on the plate with the right edge of the nail downward, and rolled slowly with a light pressure to the left edge of the nail. The finger is then rolled on the paper from the right to the left. The finger should never be rolled back again.

If a finger is mutilated or curved, it is inked directly with the roller, and the paper is then pressed against it. Persons who resist fingerprinting may be fingerprinted in this manner.

Fingerprinting Persons Without Their Knowledge—In cases where the person is to be fingerprinted unknowingly, it may be arranged that he touches a clean bottle or a glass, altho a special trap will give the best results. Such a trap may consist of two heavy thick glass plates, about 6 x 10 inches in size, whose corners are held together by screws. There should be no frame, and the plates should hang on a chain fastened to two of the screws. A photograph is sandwiched. The suspect is asked if he has seen the photograph before. At the same time the plates are carelessly swung toward him. He is then forced to grasp the plates with both hands leaving prints of all the ten fingers on the glass. These fingerprints are powdered and photographed.

Registration of Fingerprints—The registration of fingerprints may be divided into *principal registration* and *single-fingerprint registration*. In the principal registration, the fingerprints are classified in such a manner that only with the aid of the ten patterns is it possible to look up a certain registration card in order to establish the identity of the fingerprints. The principal registration is then intended to identify a second offender with the aid of *all ten fingerprints*. The single fingerprint registration (see page 118) is intended to identify chance impressions left at the scene of a crime, something which is almost impossible to accomplish by means of the principal register. The average detective is not supposed to be familiar with the registration of

IN THE FINGERPRINTING DIVISION OF THE PHILADELPHIA
POLICE DEPARTMENT

[PLATE 4]

IDENTIFYING FINGERPRINTS IN THE PHILADELPHIA POLICE
DEPARTMENT

[PLATE 5]

fingerprints, altho, in our opinion, a rudimentary knowledge of this subject is absolutely necessary in order to understand the fingerprints and their identification.[13]

Delta and Loops—The delta is a triangular-shaped detail of the pattern which is found in all fingerprints. It is not found in the arches. A delta is formed by the bifurcation of a ridge, or through the wide separation of two ridges which have, up to this point, run side by side. For the subclassification, the determination of the "point of the delta" or "outer terminus" is very important. For this there are the following rules:

If the delta is formed by the bifurcation of a ridge, the point of the delta is the place where the line becomes divided. If there is more than one point of division, the one nearest the core is the point of the delta. If the delta is formed by the separation of two parallel ridges, the point nearest the place where the lines separate is the point of the delta. In this latter case, the point of the delta may be an isolated island or a point on the outermost loop in a loop pattern.

The core is the center of the pattern. It may consist of a loop or a rod, or be composed of whorls of concentric figures, circles or ellipses. The "point of the core" or "inner terminus" is of importance for the subclassification. If the core consists of a single loop, the point of the core is on the part of the loop farthest from the delta and where the curving begins. If the core is a rod, the tip of the rod is the point of the core, and if there are an uneven number of rods, the point of the core is the tip of the middle rod. If the rods have an even number, the two inner rods are thought to make a loop and the point of the core is determined as above described. In whorls, the point of the core is the middle of the innermost circle or the innermost part of the spiral.

There are five principal patterns:

1. *Arches* in which the ridges go from one side of the pattern to another, never turning back to make a loop. In the arches, as a rule, there are no deltas.

---

[13] Henry's standard book, *Classification and Uses of Finger Prints*, is recommended for this purpose.

2. *Tented arches* are modifications of the simple arches, and they are also devoid of real deltas. In the tented arches, one line goes more or less straight upwards in the center of the pattern, and the other lines are grouped in pointed angles around this axis.

3 and 4. *Radial loops and ulnar loops* are characterized by the fact that one or more ridges turn and make a loop. There is only one delta in the loop. If the opening of the loop is directed toward the ulnar side of the hand, the loop is called an ulnar loop. (The ulna is one of the two bones of the forearm—

Fig. 14

Determination of inner and outer terminus and the ridge counting

the one located on the same side as the little finger.) If the loop opens toward the opposite direction it is called a radial loop (named from the radius, the bone of the forearm on the same side as the thumb). It is impossible to determine if the loop is ulnar or radial from a single fingerprint without knowing which of the two hands you are dealing with. The following rule should then be followed: On right-hand prints, ulnar loops have the delta to the left and radial loops have the delta to the right. On left-hand prints, ulnar loops have the delta to the right and the radial loops have the delta to the left.

5. *Whorls.* To this group belong all patterns with two deltas, and patterns too irregular in form to classify. The following patterns belong to the whorl group:

(a) Simple whorls which have two deltas, with the core consisting of circles, ellipses or spirals turning to the right or left.

(b) The central pocket-loop, which looks like a simple loop; in the core, however, we find at least one ridge which forms a convex curve toward the opening of the loop. This can be looked upon as a tendency to whorl formation with a second delta. In order to separate loops and central pocket-loops, the following rule should be applied: If a straight line is drawn through the axis of the loop, at least one ridge which is convex to the side of the opening, should cut the line at a right angle.

(c) Lateral pocket-loops, in which there are at least two loops opening at the same side.

(d) Twinned loops, in which there are two loops opening at different sides.

(e) Accidentals. For these patterns, no rules can be made. They are very rare and often have more than two deltas.

Ridge Counting—By this procedure, an imaginary line is drawn from the point of the delta to the point of the core, whereupon all ridges which cut this line are considered.

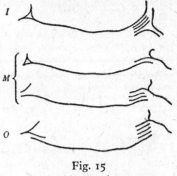

Fig. 15
Ridge tracing

When this procedure is carried out, the two points should not be included in the counting. Lines close to the imaginary line are not included if they do not touch it, but very small fragments of ridges which cut it are included.

An amateur may possibly need to draw the line between the point of the delta and the point of the core with a lead pencil, but the experienced person will not find this necessary. For counting, a magnifying glass and a needle should be used.

Ridge Tracing—Through ridge tracing, the whorl patterns are divided into three groups. One begins at the lowest line running from the left delta and follows it to the right delta. If the ridge bifurcates or ends, the line underneath is followed. If the ridge actually meets the right point of the delta, the pattern is called a "meeting whorl." If the ridge which is traced passes inside the right point of the delta, the pattern is called an "inside whorl." If the ridge which is traced passes outside the right turn of the delta, the pattern is called an "outside whorl." At least *three ridges* must separate the traced ridge and the right point of the delta in order to classify the pattern as "outside whorl" or "inside whorl." If there are only two ridges between them, the pattern is known as a "meeting whorl."

E. Identification and Reconstruction of Dead Bodies

When an unknown body is found, the following items should be noted:

1. Place where the body is found.
2. Time when found.
3. Cause of death.[14]
4. Time when death occurred.[14]
5. Supposed age.
6. Supposed profession.
7. Description of body (see page 44).
8. Description of clothing (with special attention to laundry and dry-cleaning marks).
9. Jewelry and other objects.

Hands and nails may give important information as to the profession of the person. Cobblers, blacksmiths, musicians, seamstresses, etc., have characteristic callosities on the hands. The appearance of the nails may give information. We should note their shape, length and cut, and whether or not they are torn, bitten, manicured or well kept. Bleeding under the nails caused by blows or clamping persists for a long time and extends forward to the tip of the nail. Fingernails will grow about one-twenty-fifth of an inch in a week, and the toenails about one-fourth as fast. A characteristic appearance of the nails will be seen in laundrymen on the thumb and index finger of the left hand; in cobblers on the left thumb; in engravers and jewelers on the right thumb, and in lacemakers on the right index finger. Dyers, photographers and pharmacists usually have brittle nails.

All unknown dead should be photographed in the same manner as a criminal is, *i.e.,* front view and profile.

For photographic purposes it becomes necessary to have the face of the dead appear natural and with as lifelike an expres-

[14] These questions should be answered by the medical examiner or coroner.

sion as possible, because of the difficulty encountered by most persons in recognizing a dead relative or friend from a post-mortem photograph. The eyes are in most cases shut, or if open, they are sunken and covered with a gray film. There is no contrast between the color of the skin and the lips, and finally the rigid, unnatural appearance of the face gives the impression of something unreal. In order to make the face more lifelike, one should improve on the appearance of the eyes and the lips. Numerous methods have been proposed for this purpose. Generally, a mixture of equal parts of glycerin and water is inserted in the eye-sockets with the aid of a syringe with a fine tip. The eye-lids are then raised. The lips are covered with a mixture of carmine in alcohol, which is applied with a small brush. If the body has been submerged in water for a long time and the skin is already partly gone, one can give the face a more natural appearance by powdering it with talcum, which is gently massaged over the flesh and the remaining skin. Rubber gloves should be used for this purpose.

If putrefaction is so far advanced that large portions of skin and flesh have disappeared, one may be able to reconstruct the face even in seemingly impossible cases. The putrefaction ceases when corrosive sublimate solution is used as an external wash. Plastelina, clay, or cotton fixed with collodion and covered with the proper shade of wax, replaces the lost flesh. As the eye-sockets are generally empty, glass eyes are inserted. The missing hair is replaced by a wig and the face is made to assume its natural color with make-up.

Dead bodies, or parts of them, that have become mummified as a result of being buried in dry places, may be returned to their natural shape by putting them in a 3 per cent potassium hydroxid solution. They should be allowed to stay in the solution until they have resumed their natural contour. They should be soaked for a short time in water and then preserved in a weak solution of alcohol or formalin.

Attention should be drawn to the possibility of making lifelike casts of the faces of dead bodies through the moulage process (see page 435). In certain Continental police laboratories, as, for instance, in Vienna, casts are made of the heads of practically all unknown dead bodies. The casts are painted in natural color and placed in a gallery for future identification. A cast is superior to a photograph for identification purposes, and should if possible be made in cases where a major crime is suspected. Continental police records show that such casts have aided in solving certain crimes. The assistance of a sculptor is employed when reconstructions or repairs are needed. The results obtained through casts sometimes are quite remarkable.

In cases where teeth have been treated by a dentist, there is a possibility of identification if the dentist can be located. Fillings, crowns, bridges and other items of dental work are mainly individual, and may sometimes be traced to a certain dentist through his records and teeth charts.

The teeth are the hardest and most lasting of tissues. Heat and chemicals have little influence on them.

When a skull is found, the possibilities of identification are indeed small if the teeth are missing. However, a method invented by the German anatomist, Wilhelm His, may be of aid in such cases.[15] When the supposed skull of the famous composer Johann Sebastian Bach was found, Professor His modeled a head, in clay, over the skull of Bach, in order to bring out the similarity with contemporary portraits. To determine the average thickness of the layers of flesh on the face, measurements were made on dead bodies in a normal state of nourishment. The measurements were made by introducing a needle deep into various parts of the face. The thickness of the fleshy portion was thus obtained. With the aid of the average measurements determined, a table was computed which was utilized by the sculptor. The same method has been advantageously used for the reconstruction of other faces.

The method, tho, has its weak points. By modeling the ears, no clue to their original shape can be obtained. If the individual who is to be reconstructed was unusually stout or unusually

[15] For more comprehensive information, see Wilder and Wentworth, *Personal Identification*, Boston, 1918.

thin, the similarity would not be very striking. It is also quite difficult to reproduce the lips and the contour of the mouth, both of which give the face its characteristic countenance. The reproduction of the nose appears difficult, but the results are good, because of the distinctive length of the nasal bone.

The La Rosa murder, which occurred in New York in 1916, is a good example of resourceful reconstruction.

On September 12, 1916, a skeleton of a human being was found in a house on Hegeman Avenue at Powell Street, Brooklyn. It appeared to belong to a man about 25 years of age, and 5 feet 6 inches tall. He had a small amount of brown hair on the scalp, and the lower jaw contained two gold teeth. The body was dressed in trousers and coat of blue fabric, with a black belt surrounding the waist. The only article found in his pockets was a briar pipe. The wisdom teeth had not yet grown. Some dark brown hair was also found on the neck. The autopsy showed that the skull had been fractured in four places. Since the investigations as to the identity of the man proved fruitless, it was decided to attempt a reconstruction of the face.

A sculptor remodeled the face with plastelina. Dark brown hair was obtained from a barber, and two brown glass eyes were bought, on the assumption that the man was Italian. Rolled newspapers covered with plastelina formed the neck. The eyes were put in place, the eyebrows were made of brown hairs, and a quantity of hair was put on the top of the head and down along the neck. This reconstructed piece of work was photographed.

A few days later, a new skeleton was found in the same vicinity, together with a check payable to a certain Rosario P. The Bureau of Missing Persons reported that a man of that name had been missing. The skeleton was identified by a sister, together with the clothing and the contents of the pockets. When friends of P. were questioned, they were also shown the reconstructed head of the first skeleton, and one of them quickly cried: "This is Domenico La Rosa," whereupon he tried to open the lips of the head saying: "Domenico had two gold teeth besides being inclined to baldness." Another witness testified that he had known La Rosa for many years and that the reconstruction was similar, altho La Rosa's face had been stouter. When this omission was corrected with plastelina, the witness declared that the reconstruction was now absolutely similar to La Rosa's facial appearance.

Naturally, a skull, with teeth, is the most valuable part of a skeleton for identification purposes, but most of the bones will give some information.

The height of the person, relative size, relative age, and very often the sex, may be determined from the bones. Diseases of the bones, their shape and fractures may also give information.

For the determination of sex, the skull, the hip bones and the sacrum are most important. Each may, in most cases, reveal the sex; but if all three are missing, the determination is uncertain. In such cases the size and proportions of the other bones may, however, be of help.

The age of a skeleton, during the first eight to ten years of life, can be determined within approximately one year; and under one year of age examination of the skull may determine the age within approximately one month. The older the individual, the less precise must be the determination of age. During growth, and until 25 years of age, various changes in the bones and teeth are still going on. This fact may give good clues to the age of the person. In the adult stage no such changes take place. In the aged, slight and very approximate changes may be noticed.

In order to determine the height of the person from various portions of the skeleton, there are numerous tables and calculations worked out by anthropologists. The length of the thigh bone, for instance, multiplied by 3.7 (in women 3.6) is equal to the height of the body; the length of the whole skeleton plus 1 to 1½ inches is equal to the height of the person, etc.

Determination of the race can only be made from the skull, and even here the conclusions are far from certain if the racial characteristics are not distinct. Examinations of this kind should be made only by experienced anthropologists.

F. Fingerprinting Dead Bodies

Fingerprinting dead bodies is necessary in murder cases and should always be done. Experience shows that some dead bodies found in water are those of tramps or criminals previously finger-printed. Identification from their fingerprint records is then quite easy.

On a fresh dead body the fingers are unclenched and each one is inked individually with the aid of a small rubber roller.

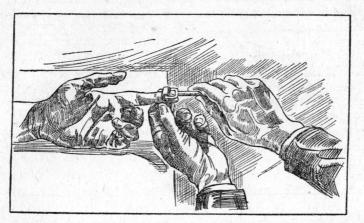

Fig. 16

Fingerprinting a fresh dead body. The ink is applied directly on the finger with the aid of a small roller

A piece of paper is put in a spoon-shaped piece of wood and slowly and evenly rolled over the pattern. If the fist should be too tightly clenched, a small incision may be made at the base of the fingers. The contraction may also be overcome by dipping the hands in hot water.

On "floaters" that have been in the water for only a short time—and if the so-called washerwoman's skin is not too marked —the finger is dried off with a soft towel and glycerin is in-jected with a syringe under the skin of the fingertips in order to smooth the surface. The fingerprints are then taken as described above.

If the "floater" has been in the water a longer time and the friction ridges have disappeared, the skin of the fingertip is cut away (an area corresponding to the part of the pattern necessary for the classification). This area of skin from each finger is placed in small labeled test-tubes containing formaldehyde solution. These tubes are kept in a small box made for the pur-

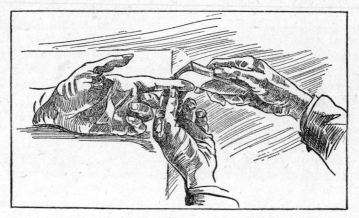

Fig. 17

Fingerprinting a fresh dead body. A piece of paper, attached to a semi-lunar-shaped piece of wood, is rolled over the inked finger

pose. If the papillary ridges are still preserved on the outer surface, the person taking the prints places the portion of the skin on his right index finger, protected by a rubber glove, and takes the prints. That is to say, he first rolls the finger on the inking plate and then on the fingerprint record form. If the papillary ridges on the outer surface have been destroyed, as often happens, one fastens the portion of skin carefully on a cardboard, inner surface out, and photographs it. As is well known, the entire papillary pattern may be found on the inner portion, and it remains until the skin is totally destroyed. One should photograph with oblique light to get the relief.

In cases of putrefied or burned bodies, one should use the above-described techniques, applying them according to the circumstances.

G. Plastic Surgery and Criminal Identification

The desire to change the appearance of the face in order to escape recognition by the police has since time immemorial tempted criminals. In most cases these alterations have been confined to the dyeing of the hair, growing or cutting off of mustaches and beard, wearing of spectacles, etc. Before the World War, however, a few cases were known in which criminals endeavored to alter the appearance of the face by means of more or less crude operations. A certain member of the gang of the ill-famed Bonnot, the French automobile *apache,* for instance, made slits along the inner corners of the eyes in order to make the eyes appear longer. This operation changed his appearance very little. Since the war, several cases have been reported in the newspapers. The notorious John Dillinger is alleged to have had surgical operations performed on his face. Figure 18 gives two views of Dillinger's face before the operations were performed, and two after his death. It will be noticed that the changes are very slight.

There is no doubt that a good plastic surgeon may be able to work wonders by altering the facial appearance; it must be pointed out, however, that such changes will prove to be of little value if the criminal cannot cut off all his connections with his old surroundings and start anew.[16]

There are two reasons why attempts to conceal identity by resort to plastic surgery are likely to be unsuccessful. One is that in a normal face it is difficult to make changes that will really deceive, and if they are made the surgical traces are not obliterated for a longer time than a hunted criminal can count upon. The other is that he finds it difficult to locate in a place where he is a stranger and to stay there unobserved long enough to allow the healing influence of time to be of aid. He must do

16 See J. Eastman Sheehan, M.D., F.A.C.S., *Plastic Surgery*, New York. Also Maliniak, *Sculpture in the Living*, New York.

Fig. 18

Front and side views of Dillinger before and after attempting to change his
facial appearance by plastic surgery

more than alter his face. His posture, his manner of walking, may expose him to scrutiny. Short-sighted people recognize their friends not by their features but by some familiar movement when they walk. Time is therefore an essential, and time the hunted criminal cannot command. When he is found, the evidence of what has been done is readily detected. Where there has been surgical incision there is some scar or trace of scar for skilled eyes to see.

The situation is somewhat different when the person sought is known to have had some definite deformity. The photographs of him may show a broken nose, or peculiar eyebrows, or protruding ears, a burn scar, a birth-mark, the scar from a knife wound, a harelip, an injured eyelid, any one of a score of disfigurements to which attention is immediately attracted, and whose absence will divert attention. In his lecture to the New York Police Academy recently Dr. J. Eastman Sheehan demonstrated from actual cases how significant may be the changes resulting from correction of these disfigurements. Moreover, the effort is made, and properly so, to leave no visible trace of the surgery that has effected the improvement. But there are traces to be found when sought for, if an opportunity to seek them is afforded.

The framework of the nose may be reconstructed with no surface incision, but there will be the mark of an incision within the nose. A protruding ear may be laid back against the head, but the skin had to be incised to get at the cartilage whose removal made this possible. The scar may be looked for behind the ear. The sunken lip that goes with harelip may be well out in place, but the means of holding it there can be quickly discovered. Even a protruding jaw may be shortened, but not without leaving evidence within the mouth of how it has been done. Perhaps the only exception to the rule is in the case of an absent finger-nail. It can be replaced from another finger-nail, but that donor nail must have time to grow. If it does, no trace is left of what was done.

It is true, also, that these betterments produce changes that influence not only the appearance of the whole face but even the general bearing of the person.   Back of these, however, are the personality, the individuality, the history, the movements from place to place, by which identity may primarily be disclosed. Surgery cannot disguise these.   It may be necessary first to catch your hare, but once caught the recipe for treating it is at hand. Like all camouflage, surgery may for the moment deceive, and so constitute a measure of defense, but it is not in itself a perfect defense.   It may be, if there is time for it to become so, an obstacle to criminal investigation; but it is an obstacle that intelligent observation can overcome.

QUESTIONS

1. Describe briefly the history of criminal identification.
2. Why was the anthropometrical system abolished?
3. Describe the most important details of the human ear.
4. What are the most important elements of the description of a wanted person?
5. What is the relation between the size of a person and the size of his criminal photography?
6. What precautions should be taken in photographing a woman prisoner?
7. On what parts of the body do the friction ridges appear?
8. Describe briefly the history of fingerprinting.
9. Give reasons for the first rule of dactyloscopy: there are no two identical fingerprints.
10. Are fingerprint patterns inherited?
11. Give reasons for the second rule of dactyloscopy: fingerprints are not changeable.
12. What is the difference between a principal registration and a single-fingerprint registration?
13. What do the terms "inner" and "outer terminus" mean?
14. What is meant by ridge tracing?
15. Describe some methods of making a dead body look more natural.
16. What information is to be gained from a human skull?
17. How is a body found in water fingerprinted?
18. Does modern plastic surgery represent a danger to criminal identification?

V

SKETCHING THE SCENE OF A CRIME

OFTEN the scene of a crime plays an important part in gathering evidence necessary for the prosecution. It serves also to outline evidential facts and circumstances to court and jury. The appearance of the scene should be presented and recorded in such manner that witnesses, prosecutors, attorneys, jury and judges can get a clear perception of it. The history of criminal investigation shows some cases which have been unsuccessfully prosecuted because an accurate description of the scene of the crime was not made immediately. It is therefore essential that an accurate objective description be made before anything can be altered, removed or destroyed.

There was a time when long and intricate descriptions of scenes of crimes were written. Such descriptions, being too complicated, fail to give the imagination enough substance to form an accurate picture of the scene. A good sketch will provide this substance.

After the discovery of the daguerreotype, eighty-odd years ago, photography began to be used on rare occasions to record scenes of crime. Twenty years later, with the creation of the dry plate, this method came into common use by the metropolitan and national police forces. Today sketching and photography, individually or combined, are used to describe the scene of a crime. They are related in such a way that one might compare the sketch to the skeleton and the photograph to the flesh and blood of the description. The sketch furnishes information about distances; the photograph presents the details.

Sketching and photography combined should as a rule be used in describing the scenes of homicides and felonious assaults, fatal and critical vehicular traffic accidents, arson, major burglaries and other notorious felonies.

A. General Rules for Sketching

All measurements should be taken with equal accuracy in order to prevent distortion. One, for instance, should not judge one distance by footsteps and another by mensuration. A common error is to measure a distance by pacing and expressing the result on the sketch in feet and inches. Another frequent mistake is to draw the outlines of a room from accurate measurements and then put furniture into the sketch by mere visual estimate when the placement of the furniture is the major factor.

Decide what is to be sketched before the work of sketching is started. This is especially true when sketching an outdoor site. Sketching cannot begin before one is sufficiently familiar with the scene, but on the other hand it may be of great help if at least the first rough sketch is ready before the victim or witnesses are interrogated. Time and considerable explanation can be saved if the victim and witnesses can explain their respective positions and observations with the aid of the sketch.

The following rules for sketching, which were given by Hans Gross, are still valid:

1. Never forget to determine the direction of the compass. Draw it on the sketch.
2. Control measurements. Don't rely on others to give them.
3. Do not draw things which are clearly irrelevant to the case. The advantage of sketching over photography is that the sketch only contains the essentials, whereas the photograph often is overcrowded.
4. Never rely on memory to make corrections at station-house, at home or at a place removed from the scene.
5. The scale must be drawn on the sketch. If camera has been used, mark its position on the sketch.

B. Different Types of Sketches and Scales

Sketching for police use falls into three types, the sketch of locality, the sketch of grounds, and the sketch of details.

1. *The Sketch of Locality*—The sketch of locality gives a pic-

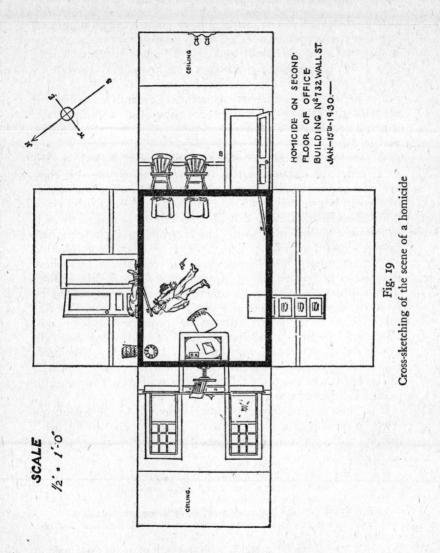

SCALE
½" = 1'-0"

HOMICIDE ON SECOND
FLOOR OF OFFICE
BUILDING Nº 732 WALL ST.
JAN.-15ᵀᴴ-1930.——

Fig. 19
Cross-sketching of the scene of a homicide

ture of the scene of the crime and its environs, including such items as neighboring buildings, roads leading to the location or house, etc. In arson cases the sketch of locality is of great value as an aid in determining whether the fire was dangerous by being contiguous to inflammable property.

2. *Sketch of Grounds*—The sketch of grounds describes the scene of the crime with its nearest physical surroundings, *i.e.,* a house with garden, the plan of one or more floors in a house, and so forth.

3. *The Sketch of Details*—The sketch of details describes the scene only; for instance, a room in which the crime was committed and the details thereof. Nowadays the sketch of details of a room is generally carried out by what is known as a cross-projection. In this method walls and ceiling are pictured as if in the same plane as the floor. The accompanying picture shows how a cross-projection is made (Fig. 19). The cross-projection gives an especially clear impression of the scene in all cases where bloodstains or bullet holes are found on walls or on the ceiling. This method of describing a room was further augmented by Kennyeres, who developed the plastic cross-projection. In this case the cross-projection is drawn on cardboard and cut out. Light cuts are made along the junctions of walls, floor, and ceiling, so that the cardboard may be bent. The folding of the cardboard walls in proper relation to one another reproduces a model of the interior of the room. One of the walls is left hanging to permit looking into the room.

It is important to determine a scale suitable to the locality or scene to be sketched, and also to the size of paper being used. Suitable scales for use in police work are:

½ inch = 1 foot—for small rooms.
¼ inch = 1 foot—for large rooms.
⅛ inch = 1 foot—for large rooms and small buildings.
½ inch = 10 feet—for large buildings.
½ inch = 10 feet—for buildings with surrounding gardens.
⅛ inch = 10 feet—for large areas with several buildings; for instance, a village.
⅛ inch = 100 feet—for a region with a length of at least one mile in each direction.

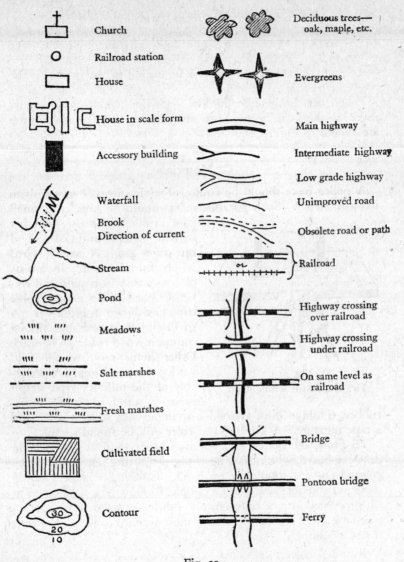

Fig. 20
Common "conventional signs"

The work of sketching is made easier by using cross-section or graph paper. The scale, together with the title, date, time, and the sketcher's name, must always be drawn in the corner of the paper in traditional fashion.

When sketching large outdoor sites the "conventional signs" used on maps can be used advantageously. The most common are shown in Figure 20.

C. Materials

A police force should be equipped with adequate materials to make sketches. Such paraphernalia should be kept in a small

Fig. 21
Drawing-board with alidade

case available for use, together with a general outfit described on page 429. A sketch-board will be found useful.[1] It consists of a square of soft pine and can be attached to a photographic tripod as shown in Figure 21. A small alidade is desirable, altho a common wood ruler can be used. Other items required for field work are a good compass, preferably of the military type, graph paper, a soft lead pencil, india-rubber, common pins, a wooden triangle with scale, a scale, and a tape measure. A flexible steel ruler will be found useful.

To finish the sketch at a location other than at the scene, a drawing-board, white drawing-paper, a drafting outfit and multi-colored crayons should be on hand. Coloring a sketch should serve to make it clearer. For example, to show how a motor vehicle proceeded after a collision, use a different color of crayon before and after. Be careful not to use too many colors. A sketch is not a painting.

---

[1] The military type of traverse-table, with its attachments, is convenient for this purpose.

D. Surveying Methods

Sketching must be done in a logical and methodical manner. Some draftsmen without previous technical training develop individual methods which are quite accurate. When comparing the self-taught methods of old policemen with standard surveying methods used in modern police and detective service, one is struck by the resemblance. However, it takes time before this state of self-development is attained.

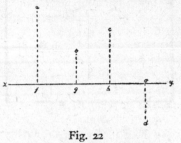
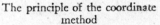

Fig. 22

The principle of the coordinate method

Sketching consists of determining the position of one point in relation to another point. The method most commonly used for this purpose is the *coordinate method* [2] (Fig. 22). It consists of locating points by perpendicular distances from a common base line.

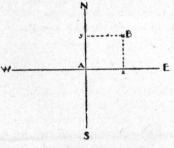

Fig. 23

Determination of the position of point B in relation to point A by the coordinate method

Let us suppose that the position of the point A in relation to the point B is to be determined (Fig. 23). Through the point A two lines are drawn at right angles to each other. Let one of these lines represent north-south, the other east-west. From B draw two straight lines perpendicular respectively to north-south and east-west. These lines, By and Bx, are termed coordinates of the point B in relation to A. $AxBy$ is a rectangle, therefore By equals Ax and Bx equals Ay. In order to determine the position of the point B in relation

[2] For further details on the coordinate system see Griffin, *Mathematical Analysis*, New York.

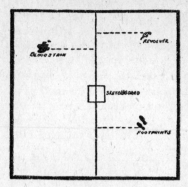

Fig. 24

Sketching the interior of a room
by the coordinate method

to *A*, measure the distance *Ax* on the line *AE* and the distance *xB* at right angles from *x*.

When performing this operation, measure eastward from *A* to a point directly opposite *B*, then determine the distance from this point to *B*. The point *B* may then be plotted. When buildings, rectangular fields, crossroads or right-angled ditches are in the area to be sketched, it frequently simplifies matters to use them as coordinates instead of north-south and east-west.

To sketch the interior of a room, a tape-measure is stretched across the room as a coordinate, and the ordinates to pieces of furniture, footprints, bloodstains, and so on, are determined (Fig. 24).

Figure 25 shows how a road *AB* is sketched by the coordinate method. The sketching table is set up by *A*. A stick is set at *B*. An additional stick is set at each point where the road crosses *AB*. Care must be exercised to set the most distant sticks first in order not to obstruct the line of sight as each stick is located. Measure

Fig. 25

Sketching a road by the coordinate method

ordinates from the different parts of the curve to the base line.

A method related to the coordinate method is the *polar coordinate method* (Fig. 26). In order to determine the position of a point *B* in relation to the point *A*, at which the sketching table is set, one draws a line of known direction, for instance, east-west (use the compass), through the point *A*. *A* is then connected with *B* by a straight line, following which the angle *BAE* is measured. The distance *AB* and the angle *BAE* are termed the polar coordinates of *B* in relation to *A*. The whole is called a polar coordinate system. When using this method, point *A* is marked on the sketch-board with a pin, around which the alidade is swung and aimed at *B*. Distances are measured with the tape-measure.

Sometimes the coordinate method takes too long. Sometimes it cannot be used. In such cases the *traverse method* is used (Fig. 27. To sketch a road by this method, proceed thus: The base line *AB* is marked and measured, and the sketch-board is set up on point *A* and oriented with the compass. The table must be hori-

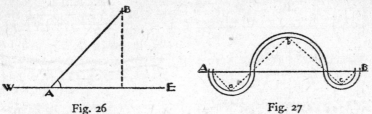

Fig. 26	Fig. 27
The polar coordinate method	The traverse method

zontal. The point *A* at which the sketch-board is located is marked with a pin, whereupon one aims with the alidade at the point *a*, where the road makes its first turn. A fine lead-pencil line (traverse line) is drawn to mark the direction of *a* from *A*. This direction is now fixed. The distance *Aa* is measured. The sketch-board is now set up at *a* and the place marked with a pin. The board is then oriented in the same compass direction as in *A*. This orientation is accomplished by aiming back from *a* to *A*. A sight is then taken from *a* to the next point *b* and the distance *ab* is measured. This procedure is continued until all points have been located.

It should be noted that an error in the traverse method carries on to all succeeding points on the traverse.

Broken lines—for example, the edge of a forest—may advantageously be drawn by the *polar or radial method,* provided there is an open field between the sketcher and the broken line. If, for instance, the forest edge *AG* is to be drawn, the drawing table is put up at the point *P* and oriented with the compass

(Fig. 28.) The point *P* is marked on the paper with a pin. With the aid of the alidade, rays are drawn to the more important points of the edge, namely, *PA, PB, PD, PF,* and *PG.* The distances are measured and recorded in a suitable scale on the paper. If the ends of the rays are connected, a projection of the edge of the forest results.

When the positions of two points are known, a third point may be determined by *triangulation.* This method is used most advantageously when the sketcher is separated from the third

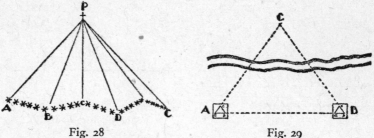

Fig. 28
The polar or radial method

Fig. 29
Triangulation

point by a great distance or an obstacle such as a river. In Figure 29 the points *A* and *B* are accessible to the sketcher. The position of the point *C* is to be determined. The sketch-board is set up horizontally at *A.* This point is marked on the paper with a pin as *a.* Point *B* is then aimed at with the alidade and the line *ab* measured and drawn, and the direction of the compass marked on the paper. One aims now at point *C* and draws the aiming line *ac* on the paper. The sketch-board is next set up at point *B.* The alidade is set on the line *ab* and the board rotated until point *A* is in the line of sight. Then the aiming line *bc* is drawn with the aid of the alidade. The point where the lines *ac* and *bc* cross each other is *C.*

By this method the position of several unknown points may be determined from two known points without direct distance measurement. Care must be taken that the angles in which the lines are crossing each other never are smaller than 35 degrees or larger than 145 degrees; otherwise the possible margin of error will be greatly increased. If several lines are drawn from one point the aiming lines should not be drawn on the paper but only the part where the crossing point is supposed to come.

Measurement of Height—Sometimes it is necessary to measure heights. Appliances required are a sketching table and two straight sticks, one of which is graded. A simple graded stick can be made by fastening a tape-measure to a stick by means of thumbtacks. When measuring, the sketching table is set up before the object to be measured. The graded stick is put about

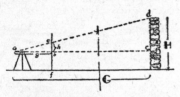

Fig. 30

Measurement of height when the ground at the drawing-board is at the same elevation as the ground at the object

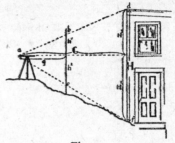

Fig. 31

Measurement of height when the drawing-board is on sloping ground

two yards in front of the table. Aim on a slant from the near edge of the table to the top of the object and read the measurement on the point of the graded stick that is cut by the aiming line. The distance between the table and the object is also measured. This gives us two triangles, *acd* and *abe*. We know *abe*, and the ground line respectively distance *G*. The two triangles are similar because their three angles are equal. The sides are therefore in proportion to each other according to the formula:

$$\frac{h}{g} = \frac{dc}{G}; \; dc = \frac{hG}{g}$$

If the ground is horizontal, add the height of the sketching table *bf* to get the real height.

If the ground is sloping, take two aiming lines and measure the distance h_1 and h_2. The side h_1 in the small triangle corresponds to the side H_1 in the large triangle. This is also the case with h_2 and H_2. It is also possible to compare directly the triangles *abc* and *adf*, as they are similar. The real height H equals H_1 plus H_2.

$$\frac{h_1 + h_2}{g} = \frac{H}{G}; H = \frac{(h_1 + h_2)G}{g}$$

By this latter method it is not necessary to know the height of the sketching table.

Two examples will illustrate this method: (1) The height of a flagstaff on horizontal ground is to be measured. The sketch-board is set up 30 yards from the flagstaff and is 1.5 yards high. The vertical graded stick is 2 yards from the table and the aiming line is cutting the graded stick at a height of 1.5 yards.

$$\frac{1.5}{2} = \frac{X}{30}; X = \frac{30 \times 1.5}{2} = 22.5 \text{ yards}; H = X + 1.5 = 22.5 +$$
$$1.5 = 24 \text{ yards} = 72 \text{ feet}$$

(2) The height of a tree which grows on a hillside is to be measured. The sketch-board is 72 yards distant horizontally from the tree and is 1.5 yards high. The upper and lower aiming lines intercept an interval (h_1 and h_2) of 40 inches on the graded stick, which is 2 yards away from the table.

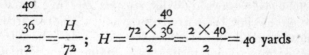

$$\frac{\frac{40}{36}}{2} = \frac{H}{72}; H = \frac{72 \times \frac{40}{36}}{2} = \frac{2 \times 40}{2} = 40 \text{ yards}$$

QUESTIONS

1. Enumerate the different kinds of sketches used in police work.
2. What is meant by a coordinate system?
3. What is meant by triangulation?
4. Describe how heights are measured from the sketch-board.

VI

PHOTOGRAPHING THE SCENE OF A CRIME

PHOTOGRAPHY represents one of the most important aids to criminal investigation, whether it concerns the exact reproduction of the scene of a crime or the numerous laboratory methods in which it plays an important rôle. This chapter deals only with the photographing of the scene of the crime; the use of scientific photography in laboratory work will be dealt with elsewhere. Space forbids us to enter into problems of elementary photography. We refer the reader to the publications mentioned in the footnote.[1]

The usefulness of photography at the scene of the crime is obvious. The photograph is a sort of artificial memory, often very sorely needed by the policeman. Many small details may escape the investigator at the first examination of the scene. These may later prove to have great importance. In most cases it is impossible to examine certain details repeatedly because the scene of the crime has been altered, furniture has been moved, floors have been washed, etc. As an illustration, let us suppose that a dead man is found in his bed, shot through the forehead. A pistol is still clasped in his hand. The investigator makes the usual examination, sees no traces of violence and draws the conclusion that he is confronted with a case of suicide. The body is buried. After some time, doubts about the suicide arise and the person is believed to have been the victim of a clever murderer. It is no longer possible to examine the hand that held the pistol to determine if the position of the fingers was natural or un-

[1] Books on the subject are: Mees, *The Fundamentals of Photography*, Rochester, 1934, and Blumann, *The Photographic Workroom Handbook*, Camera Craft, San Francisco, Cal.

91

natural. It is no longer possible to determine whether there were suggestive traces of violence on the bed or on the carpet. A good photograph of the scene of the crime and of the body will help enormously in such a case.

There are cases in which remote developments compel the investigator to reconstruct, for instance, a room in detail, as it was arranged at the time of the crime. One can say that a good photograph of the scene is a permanent reconstruction which is always at one's disposal. The possibility of reversing the photograph may be of great aid if the plate is printed on both sides so that two prints are obtained—the natural, and the other turned with the right side to the left and left side to the right. When the two pictures are compared quite another impression of the room will be had.[2] In many cases the reversed picture is quite unrecognizable, but in many other cases our attention will be focused on details and objects we have seen at the examination in the normal position without having paid any attention to them.

The photograph is also necessary as a court exhibit. The persons playing a leading rôle in court proceedings, as, for example, the judge and the defense attorney, and perhaps even the prosecutor, have generally never visited the scene of the crime. The photograph facilitates to a high degree their work.

Paul[3] illustrates the immediate influence which photography may have on the trial. A farmer, in building a barn, used old materials in order to economize. The beams and boards were quite decayed, and later, when a farmhand ascended to the second floor, a board gave way and the unfortunate man fell through the floor and was killed. The farmer was prosecuted for manslaughter in the third degree, but, in order to avoid judgments and expenses, soon after the accident he substituted new boards for the defective ones. However, the police had photographed the scene immediately after the accident. The photograph clearly showed that the death of the farmhand was caused by the old building material used. Furthermore, it brought out the fact

[2] Reiss—*La photographie judiciaire*, Paris, 1903.
[3] Paul—*Handbuch der kriminalistichen Photographie*, Berlin, 1900.

that the farmer had replaced the boards after the photographs had been taken.

In another case, reported by Balthazard, the Paris police had photographed the interior of a room which was suspected to have been the scene of a homicide. No bloodstains were found during the search. When the photograph was developed, however, a large washed stain on the carpet, invisible to the eye, was revealed. Here, as in many other cases, the photographic lens saw more than the human eye.

In Vienna, some years ago, a young woman sitting on a bench in a public park was found dead. She had apparently shot herself through the head with a pistol which was lying in a natural position where it had presumably slipped from her hand. The scene was immediately photographed—in the early morning before sunrise. Later in the day, after developing the plate, the police photographer discovered that a person had been sitting close to the woman. This was shown by the marks in the dew which had collected on the bench. The marks were very faint, but the photographic lens had caught them before evaporation had taken place. Investigation brought out the fact that a homicide had been committed.

It goes without saying that the photograph also has a psychological influence on the defendant and the jury as well as on the court. No description can as forcefully tell the horrors of homicide as a photograph can.

The Outfit—The most important item in photography is a first-class camera. The photographic outfit should be as adequate as the allowance permits. It may be had for a relatively small sum. The following suggestions are given:

1. A camera, 5 x 7 inches, with holder for cut film.
2. A good lens of about 8 inches focus and a speed of F. 4.5, mounted with a Compur shutter.
3. A wide-angle lens of about 5 inches focus and a speed of F. 9.
4. A collapsible tripod.
5. A flashlight lamp and photo-flash bulbs.
6. One tilting tripod head.
7. An exposure meter.

The camera should have bellows and ground glass, and be of sturdy and reliable make. The front and rear parts should be movable in all directions. Altho such a camera may be more expensive, it has the advantage of serving all purposes. It may be used in the small police laboratory for reproduction purposes, for photographing fingerprints, photographing with ultra-violet rays, and making simple photomicrographs.

Special cameras for various purposes are advisable for larger police laboratories.

During the last few years the miniature camera has come to play an important rôle in field work as well as in the laboratories. The research laboratory of the New York Police Department uses a miniature camera for photographing all sorts of traces. Moving-picture film, positive or negative, is used. Owing to the fact that the negatives must be enormously enlarged, a film used for criminological purposes must have a very fine grain. The process of development should be thoroughly uniform, accurate, carried out in a tank, and an electrically operated agitator should be used. The attachment for photographing with a fixed focus has proven to be especially valuable for the photographing of footprints, fingerprints, traces of burglars' tools, etc. If the miniature camera is used in conjunction with an accurate modern exposure meter, there is no possibility of making mistakes.

This type of photography has the added advantage of being very cheap, as a foot of panchromatic film, sufficient for ten pictures, costs only seven cents.

The choice of lenses is very important. The lens should have no distortion; i.e., straight lines on the object should not be reproduced as curved on the optical picture. There should also be no dispersion of colors and no astigmatisms. A picture angle of from 80 to 90 degrees is generally sufficient. If the picture angle is larger than 90 degrees the perspective is exaggerated, and if the angle is too small the camera must be placed at a longer distance from the object, because of the relation between the angle and the focus of the lens. The focus should not be too small or too large; a focus of about 8 inches is the best. Most anastig matic lenses manufactured by well-known and reliable lens manufacturers will do very well for this type of photography.

It often happens, in criminological investigations, that very small rooms, narrow passages, etc., must be photographed. The lens with a normal angle in such cases will reproduce inadequate pictures, showing only parts of the space. In order to get as much space as possible on the plate the wide-angle lens should be used. The time of exposure is much longer than when the ordinary lenses are employed, because the wide-angle lens must be diaphragmed to obtain a picture with a sharp border. The angle, however, which is generally 110 degrees, permits the photographing of a large surface from a near-by distance. One should be very careful in drawing conclusions of distances from photographs made with a wide-angle lens, because the perspective is often grossly exaggerated.

The tripod should enable the setting of the camera in a horizontal as well as a vertical position, so that a footprint, as well as a dead body on the ground, may be photographed. Tilting tripod heads, with the aid of which the camera can be placed in all positions, from the horizontal to the vertical, may be obtained.

In homicide cases a detail photograph of head and trunk, as well as a photograph covering the whole body taken from the side, is generally sufficient.

Very often artificial light must be used. The modern photoflash bulbs are superior owing to the safety factor and the absence of smoke. They have, however, some drawbacks, being fairly expensive and often giving insufficient light. In the latter case several of them can be used simultaneously. It should be noted that several photo bulbs may be made to light by merely allowing them to touch the first bulb lighted by a battery. The heat from the electrically lighted bulb penetrates the glass casings, causing the others to light. For interior photography many police departments now use the photo flood lamps which, under various names, are on the market. They are attached by long cables to the electric current. Such lamps give a very uniform and satisfactory light. They may also be used advantageously for examining a house at night.

A modern exposure meter of the actinic type is essential to obtain good results. It gives immediate readings, from 1/100 second up to several minutes, is independent of the judgment of the human eye, and lasts indefinitely.

A very important problem in all criminal photography is the depth of focus. Various diaphragms are available for this purpose, and no one who does not feel absolutely sure about his judgment in this matter should hesitate to use them.

Very often the necessity will arise to mark details, as, for instance, the hole of a bullet, small bloodstains, etc., with a ring of white chalk in order to facilitate their recognition on the photograph. A piece of white chalk should be part of the outfit. It must, however, be pointed out that such chalk markings may be objected to by resourceful defense attorneys who do not accept marked photographs as representing true pictures. In such cases one has to be prepared by taking two pictures, the first without any markings whatsoever, and the second with the markings.[4]

The Actual Photographing—Police photographers should be systematic in planning their work. The main purpose should be to give a thorough and true account of the occurrence so that all important events of the crime are registered and told by the photographs. The first photograph to be made on the scene of a homicide, suicide, burglary, etc., is a general view of the scene. Many times photographs of general views must be taken repeatedly.

Let us assume that a homicide has been committed in a one-family house standing isolated on open ground. The route of the perpetrator is first examined and the general view photographed from the outside, showing how he may have approached the house. Such a photograph can be taken from the roof or window of a neighboring house and should include a part of the

---

[4] The prosecutor, Muhl, in Danzig, who is also the chief of the criminal investigation department of the Free State, has invented a practical device to mark important spots on photographs. Small arrows of iron plate, black or white, with corresponding black or white ciphers, are used for this purpose. The arrows are fastened to a thin steel rod, which may either be inserted in the soil or placed in a stand. In using this device it is recommended that photographs without the arrows be taken first in order to get a "true picture."

street, the gateway in the hedge through which the perpetrator passed, and the distance covered before he reached the house. The next step is to take a photograph of that side of the house by which he gained entrance. The next photograph is a close-up, for instance, of the window which the assassin opened, and to this are added detail photographs of the traces of his tools on the window frame. Other photographs are now taken showing the interior of the house, the rooms through which he walked, the room where the victim was murdered, followed by detailed photographs of the body and of all traces of importance.

Such a series of photographs will enable all parties concerned in the legal trial to get a clear and vivid picture of what took place. In other words, the photograph should reenact the story of the crime from beginning to end. The general views should at least be photographed from two different angles—for instance, one in the center and one from the left or right side.

Negative Material—Today panchromatic cut film predominates in criminal photography owing to the necessity of reproducing colors as faithfully as possible. Because of the danger of fire they should be of the safety type. Such safety films can be stored in large quantities without danger.

Moving-picture Cameras in Police Work—Sometimes moving-picture cameras are used, especially when photographing scenes of riots. It has often been proposed that moving-picture cameras be used regularly in all riotings in order to pick out the ringleaders and persons who resist arrest. For such purposes the modern miniature moving-picture cameras may be used to advantage. It should, however, be pointed out that the position of the photographer is a dangerous one, as he may in many cases be the target of the rioters. He should then be at a safe distance, using a telephoto-lens.

Metric Photography—There is no possibility of determining distance on a photographic print, especially if it has been made under unfavorable circumstances, as, for instance, when a wide-angle lens is used. The perspective is then often highly distorted. The need for photographs from which distances could be calculated was felt keenly for years until Bertillon adopted metric photography. Special cameras render possible the direct reading of all measurements from the prints without added calculations. It is, however, strange that this invention has not gained wide use. This is probably due to the weight of the camera and to the complicated method of photography.

In metric photography a series of wide-angle lenses is used, the focal distances of which are in "decimals," *i.e.*, exact multiples of 10. Each lens is mounted on the front board with a screw having a pitch, each full turn of which corresponds to one-tenth of the focal length. This arrangement allows sharp focusing for all plans of reduction at intervals of 1/10th.

The camera is a simple square box without bellows, cogwheel or rack. The plates are 30 x 30 centimeters in size (about 12 x 12 inches).[5] The box has a depth of 30 cm. and is provided with five grooves to receive the plate-holders. The distance from one groove to another is 5 cm. The lenses are placed 5 cm. in front of the first groove. Owing to the decimal focal distances and the regularly increasing intervals of the plate-holders, all kinds of combinations to meet the varying needs of photography may be had.

When photographing, the camera must be placed absolutely horizontally and generally at a height of ½, 1, or 1.5 meters. A special tripod is used for this purpose.

All measurements may be read by a simple geometrical method on the finished prints. In order to simplify matters Bertillon mapped out on a special cardboard printed scales which varied according to the height of the camera and the focus of the lens. All distances can be measured on the mounted print with the aid of a ruler.

Simplified Metric Photography—Bertillon also produced a method of simplified metric photography which may be used with advantage in many cases. For this purpose a number of strips of white paper, one meter long and 10 cm. wide, are used. Each tenth part of a meter, on each strip, is marked with China ink. The strips are hung in the room at important points. On

[5] A meter is 39.37 inches, a centimeter .3937 inch, a millimeter .03937 inch.

the print the strip nearest to the camera is measured in millimeters. The second strip is then measured similarly. The number 1000 is then divided by each measurement respectively. The difference between both measurements is then multiplied by the length of the focus in millimeters. The distance between the two strips is then expressed. If the first strip measures 80 mm. and the second measures 25 mm., then $1000 \div 80 = 12.5$ mm. and $1000 \div 25 = 40$ mm., $40 - 12.5 = 27.5$ mm., $\times 100$ mm. (focus) $= 2750$ mm. or 2.75 meters. The measurement of the focus may naturally vary according to the lens used. In order to obtain the distance between the first strip and the lens 12.5 is multiplied by the focal distance (10 cm.). If one knows the measurement of a strip one can also calculate the measurement of all objects in the same plane. The camera should be placed horizontally if the calculations are to be exact.

What was said above, regarding possible objections to the introduction of markings on the photograph, applies here also. The room must first be photographed without the strips.

It may be mentioned that in many places in the United States measurements and sketches made by a registered architect or draftsman furnish this information.

QUESTIONS

1. Give some examples out of your own or others' experience when a photograph of the scene of a crime has been of immediate importance.
2. Can you mark important spots on the scene with white chalk or otherwise?
3. Enumerate the necessary photographs to be taken in case of an ordinary homicide in an apartment house.
4. What is meant by metric photography?

VII

FINGERPRINTS AT THE SCENE OF THE CRIME

A. Different Types of Chance Impressions

IDENTIFICATION of individuals from their fingerprints and the fundamentals of dactyloscopy have been dealt with in Chapter IV. It should be pointed out that the identification of chance impressions is founded on quite other grounds from the viewpoint of evidence, and that chance impressions require a totally different technique.

In most cases the impressions of friction ridges may be found at the scene of a crime. They are usually made by the palmar surface of the fingertips and very seldom from the two lower joints of the finger or from the palm itself.

Theoretically, it is also possible that some part of the body devoid of friction ridges—for instance, the arm—may leave impressions of the pores on an absolutely smooth surface. This, however, has only been produced experimentally, and so far as we know, has not been encountered in actual criminal investigations.

There are three different types of chance impressions:

Plastic prints, which may be formed on plastic objects, such as melted paraffin from a burning candle, plastelina, putty, resin, pitch, tar, paste on envelops and stamps, fat, butter, pomade and soap.

Visible prints, which are left by a finger smeared with some colored substance, generally blood or dirt. They are seldom clear and often resemble common stains. However, the visible fingerprints will more often attract the attention of amateurs and untrained policemen than the latent fingerprints, which give the best results.

Latent fingerprints are generally invisible, but can sometimes be seen on smooth surfaces with the aid of indirect light. Where the surface is smooth and non-absorbent, they may be revealed or "developed" by the use of very fine-grained powders. They have been found on such objects as glass window panes, glass plates, mirrors, glasses, bottles and other objects of glass; [1] also on glazed earthenware, crockery, porcelain, furniture of veneered or polished wood; smooth surfaces on weapons and all smooth metal surfaces; bodies of motor cars and other vehicles; glossy, smooth leather, harnesses, celluloid and tortoise shell. Where the surface is somewhat rough and absorbent, latent fingerprints are invisible. Altho they may be developed by powders in rare instances on such surfaces, the best results are obtained through the use of silver nitrate, iodin, and other chemical reagents. Latent fingerprints have been developed on objects made of bare wood, such as wooden boxes, barrels, ladders, hammer and ax handles; on paper objects such as letters, envelops, checks, cardboard, cardboard boxes, etc.; on cloth such as shirts, collars, cuffs, handkerchiefs, bed sheets, pillow slips, etc.

Fig. 32

How a bottle carrying fingerprints is protected during transportation

Latent fingerprints have not as yet been found on human skin, but they have been found on fingernails and toenails.

Latent fingerprints are impressions of the fingers made with colorless substances which are transferred from the skin to the surface of the object with which the fingers have come in con-

[1] There are quite a few cases on record, where fingerprints on glass have been developed after having been in water for several days. They were then dried and developed in the usual manner.

tact. Under normal conditions the fingertips are constantly covered with natural colorless substances derived by evaporation of the perspiration excreted through the pores. Occasionally, latent fingerprints are encountered where foreign colorless substances due to one's occupation become incorporated in the natural secretion of the fingers, making it possible to develop such latent impressions several years after their natural ingredients have completely disappeared. The natural secretion from the fingers, palms of the hands, toes, and soles of the feet, unlike that from other regions of the skin, contains no oily matter. The minute quantity of fat or oil found on the skin of the fingers and palms comes from frequent and unconscious contacts with the fatty portions of the skin, *i.e.,* the hair, the face, etc.

Fig. 33

How a piece of glass carrying fingerprints is protected during transportation

The secretion from the sweat pores on the fingertips contains 98.5-99.5% water and 0.5-1.5% solid material. Of the latter, about one-third is composed of inorganic matter, usually salt, and two-thirds of organic substance, consisting mostly of urea, volatile fatty acids (formic, acetic and butyric acids), and at times a very small quantity of albumin (0.045%).

The production of fingerprints depends upon the fact that the skin of the fingertips of the criminal committing the crime is generally dirty, even if he avoids all contact with blood or dust. When committing a crime, the criminal is generally nervous, and the perspiration on his hands is more abundant than normally. This perspiration, mixed with the dust found on dusty objects and with dirt, produces the film and the impression. Contact with the burglar's tools and weapons also causes the hands to become greasy. In drilling, the criminal often uses oil. We must also consider the fact that the criminal type is not prone to be very clean.

Some experts search for fingerprints in darkness, using a flashlight, the rays of which are allowed to fall obliquely on the object. The examination can, however, be carried out just as well in daylight. It is only necessary to breathe on the object to produce a thin film of vapor and examine it obliquely. All fingerprints will thus be brought out clearly and persist as long as the vapor film remains.

B. The Transport of Objects Carrying Fingerprints

Objects carrying fingerprints should, if possible, be taken to the identification bureau. At the scene of the crime one ascertains only the presence of fingerprints on the object, but powdering and photography should be done at headquarters. Even if the transport proves to be difficult at times, the advantage gained is great enough to balance the work undertaken. If the objects are too large to be transported and the gravity of the crime warrants the trouble, one should take apart pieces of furniture and carry away that portion on which fingerprints are found; cut with a diamond the necessary parts of a window, etc. If such an operation will destroy the prints, or if it is impossible to cut away or transport the object, as, for instance, when the fingerprints are on a large safe or a wall, they should be photographed at the scene or transferred on a foil.

The object should be packed with the utmost care, to avoid breaking. It is not to be exposed to friction from the wrapping material; and of course the prints themselves should not be even so much as touched. It is a serious mistake to wrap pieces of glass or put them in paper or fabric.

The packing varies according to circumstances and the resourcefulness of the policeman, but there is in most cases, at each scene of a crime, enough material to pack any object. Figures 32, 33, 34 and 35 show some of these packings. Bottles are surrounded by a wooden crate which is fastened in a strong cardboard or wooden box. Glasses are put between two squares of wood and made firm by four nails in each square, whereupon the whole thing is fastened in a small cardboard box. Pieces of glass are put in a pasteboard box with the corners of the glass penetrating the sides of the box. A string is tightened around the box, so that the whole thing will remain firm. One may also put pieces of glass in an upright position in a wooden box, where they are fastened with nails and slabs. Knives and pistols are fastened to a board or a piece of strong cardboard, with strings threaded in holes made in the cardboard or board to keep the object in place.

C. How to Develop and Photograph Latent Fingerprints

Coloring the Fingerprints—The most valuable of the chance impressions are the "latent" ones, which must first be made visible before they can be photographed or transferred on foils. They are developed through the medium of colored powders which stick to the more or less smeary fingerprints.

Theoretically, it is not very important what powder is used if it be fine-grained and devoid of lumps. It should have a different color from that of the background. If, for instance, fingerprints appear on a white background, such as porcelain, the use of lampblack, powdered graphite, or a specially prepared black powder is advisable. For dark objects and for glass, white lead, chalk, chalk and mercury, plaster of Paris, kaolin, aluminum powder or the special white powder marketed for developing purposes may be used. Recently "dragon's blood" has been found advantageous. This consists of a powder made by grinding the resin obtained from the rattan palm tree. The powders mostly used are the white, the white lead and the aluminum powder. The aluminum powder has the advantage of having very fine grains and great power of adhesion. The disadvantage lies in its lightness. It is blown about by the slightest whiff and soils the fingers.

If fingerprints are detected on both surfaces of a glass plate it is necessary to develop them separately. The print found on one of the surfaces is first treated with white lead, then photographed and finally colored black by allowing the vapors of ammonium sulfid to act on it for a few minutes. The print on the opposite surface is next covered with the white-lead powder, a dark-colored paper is applied against the print previously blackened so as to render it invisible, and a photograph of the whitened surface is finally taken.

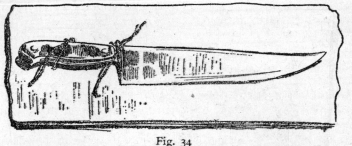

Fig. 34

How a knife carrying fingerprints or bloodstains is protected during transportation

The powders are deposited over the spots where the prints are visible or suspected to exist. These are to be completely covered. The excess powder is then removed by allowing it to fall on a sheet of paper and the print is carefully gone over with a fine camel's-hair brush until all the details are brought out. Should the object carrying the prints be too large to be moved, the brush may be dipped in the powder and passed directly over the suspected place. This latter method is, by the way, used by many fingerprint experts on all occasions.

Development of Fingerprints on Paper—Any of the previously mentioned black powders will give a fairly satisfactory result in developing fingerprints on paper, altho it is preferable to use powdered metallic antimony. Metallic antimony can be purchased from wholesale chemists. It comes in small lumps which must be ground to a fine powder in a mortar. Metallic antimony does not stain the paper to the same degree as charcoal and gives clearer impressions.

The best method of developing fingerprints on paper is by the use of a 10 per cent solution of silver nitrate. This is applied in an extremely thin uniform layer by passing the paper through two rollers moistened with the solution. The paper is allowed to dry and is then exposed to sunlight or ultra-violet light, which reveals the prints in a few seconds. Ordinary daylight will develop the prints, but the time required is longer. Such prints photograph

Fig. 35
How a pistol carrying fingerprints is protected during transportation

extremely well and can be preserved for a year or more if kept in absolute darkness. The process used to fix the prints for permanent record requires considerable skill and training and should be attempted only by those who have had instruction in it.

A very good method of developing fingerprints on paper is by the use of iodin fumes. Some fingerprint bureaus recommend the use of hot iodin fumes. Crystalline iodin has the property of evaporating at common room temperature, and if only a little heat is applied to it the evaporation is greatly increased. There are quite a few kinds of apparatus on the market for heating the iodin and allowing the fumes to condense on the surface of the paper. When the fumes come in contact with the cold paper a thin coat of iodin spreads over the entire surface. The organic content of the paper is simultaneously attacked. All stains on the paper, especially those of a greasy nature, and even impressions and certain secret inks, will then be revealed and show up more or less brown against the paper. If the process is allowed to continue, the whole paper becomes dark brown and nothing more can be seen. The success of the process depends upon the time during which the iodin is allowed to act on the paper. This time should be just long enough to bring out the prints and not long enough to allow the paper to darken. The action of the hot iodin fumes on the paper is very quick and harsh. Good results are obtained only after much training.

In our opinion only cold iodin fumes should be used. By this latter process a quantity of iodin is spread over the bottom of a flat glass container and the paper to be examined is placed in the container about half an inch above the iodin. Two pieces of wood, or preferably glass or porcelain, to hold the paper, should be placed on the bottom of the container. The paper should not be allowed to touch the iodin. The container should then be covered and the paper left therein for a few minutes. About five minutes of this treatment will usually reveal all fingerprints.

Since iodin sublimes at room temperature, the revealed prints will soon fade away; hence it is necessary to photograph them as soon as possible. This property of rapid sublimation, which leaves the paper blank again after a certain time, may be an asset in some respects; as, for instance, when the examination of fingerprints on paper should not be revealed, or where spies are concerned, and an intercepted letter is to be examined without the knowledge of the receiver. In order to get rid of the prints, treating the paper with ammonia fumes is all that is necessary.

In criminology, however, it is often necessary to show the fingerprints to the courts, and there have been several different methods invented for preserving the prints, such as the treatment with gallic acid, nitrate of silver, etc. Most of these methods require considerable skill for good results, but there are two we shall mention because of their relative simplicity. The first consists in putting the paper between two glass plates and gluing the edges together.

The second method, developed by Professor Popp,[2] consists of treating the prints with a solution of chlorid of palladium, made up of 1 gram of chlorid of palladium and 1,000 cc. distilled water. The paper is allowed to float with the prints face down in a flat glass container filled with this solution. The solution may also be applied with a small spray or atomizer similar to those used by artists in treating charcoal drawings, or it may be applied with a piece of cotton. If there is writing on the paper due to an indelible pencil or indelible ink a small quantity of alum or tannic acid should be added. When the solution has been mixed with these last ingredients it should not be poured back into the stock solution.

When treated with this chlorid of palladium solution the prints slowly turn dark brown. As soon as the color is dark enough the treatment is discontinued, the superfluous chemical is washed away with water, and the paper is allowed to dry slowly. The traces are preserved indefinitely, but if it should be necessary to remove them a weak solution of ammonia is used.

The color of the prints is increased by applying this treatment, and even indistinct prints on an unsuitable background may be photographed.

The question many times arises as to whether fingerprints on cigaret stubs can be developed. It is seldom possible to get good impressions from cigaret paper. In most cases the pattern will not show up clearly enough, and in other cases the patterns are superimposed on each other. In still other cases no fingerprints at all will be seen. Of course, there are cases in which clear impressions have been found and identified. The best impressions are obtained in cases where a cigaret holder has been used. The fingerprints then only appear once, namely, when the cigaret is inserted into the holder. When the cigaret has been smoked it is usually either blown out by the smoker or pulled out by its edge. Black powder or iodin fumes will then develop the fingerprints.

Fingerprints on Cloth—Shirts, collars, cuffs, handkerchiefs.

[2] *Kriminal. Monatsh.*, Jan. 1931.

sheets, etc., are dipped in—or sprayed with—a 10 per cent solution of silver nitrate in distilled water, to which has been added a small percentage of acetic acid; or they may be dipped in a 10 per cent acetic acid solution after immersion in the silver nitrate. The material is then left to dry in a dark room. When thoroughly dry it is exposed to sunlight or ultra-violet light. The fingerprints thus revealed are then photographed. The material is afterward washed in water and the fingerprints are fixed by treating them with a 5 per cent solution of ammonium hydrosulfid. The material is finally washed in

Developed by silver nitrate process and fixed

Technical Laboratory, New York City Police, Dr. E. M. Hudson collaborating

Fig. 35a
Latent impression on white cloth, natural secretion

running water again for an hour, wrung out, and allowed to dry, preferably in direct sunlight.

Miscellaneous Fingerprints—Fingerprints have been developed on black satin by sprinkling the material with calcium sulfid powder. The satin material should be stretched on a frame and excess powder removed by tapping the frame. Protect the powdered fingerprints by keeping the cloth on the frame. Of course, the fingerprints should be photographed. The material with the prints on it should be kept where it will not be touched by anybody. The prints should last indefinitely unless the satin is touched or wrinkled.

Copper powder may be found useful in developing latent fingerprints on metallic surfaces and on leather, in instances where aluminum powder has formerly been used. The copper powder will be found to have the advantage of being heavier than aluminum powder; therefore, it is not apt to blow around, a tendency which has been found to be a disadvantage in the use of aluminum powder. Copper powder will be found to have practically the same adhering qualities as aluminum powder.

Dr. Arnaldo Amado Ferreira, Assistant Professor of Legal Medicine, São Paulo School of Medicine, Brazil, reports success in developing latent fingerprints on fruits by the use of a carbonate-of-lead powder applied in the usual manner. Prints have been successfully found on apples, pears, plums, oranges and bananas. Other fruits of a similar nature, especially those having a hard rind, such as watermelons, pumpkins and citrons, will produce like results.

Fingernails and Toenails—Copper powder will be found to be particularly useful in developing a fingerprint of a person on the fingernails and toenails of another person. Manicured fingernails are considered an ideal surface upon which latent fingerprints may be found and developed by the use of copper powder.

Photographing Fingerprints—Plastic and visible fingerprints are photographed directly, but latent fingerprints must be developed to be photographed. Numerous special cameras may be purchased, but only common reproduction ones are used.

Fingerprints on paper are photographed directly, after development. Bottles carrying fingerprints are filled with some black liquid, as, for instance, ink, which produces a black background, and glasses may be filled with black paper. Window panes that are frosted on one surface and carry fingerprints on the other must have the frosted portion colored with printer's ink or some other black substance.

Sometimes fingerprints may be found on backgrounds that render development and photography by the common methods impossible. The aid of a specialist should then be sought, but if a detective is called upon to do the work, he should first perform experiments on his own fingerprints produced on the same material before attempting to obtain results with the suspected fingerprints.

If the fingerprints are located on a sticky surface—for instance, on a greasy tool or similar object—they cannot be developed with powder because it would stick everywhere. The print should be photographed directly with oblique light, without further development. Heindl recommends the use of the old method of the Belgian criminologist Stockis—that of transferring fingerprints to moist photographic paper—a sheet of chlorid or bromid of silver paper—which is fixed directly and well washed and dried. Before the paper is used, it is immersed in water for a few minutes to soften it completely, after which it is placed between filter papers to cause absorption of all the superfluous water. The paper is then pressed gently with the skeleton side against the fingerprint and cautiously lifted away. The fingerprint thus transferred to the paper may be photographed in the usual manner. Foils (see page 110) cannot be used for this work.

Fingerprints on lacquered window frames are developed with common powder, but should always be photographed first, as the foils may in certain cases give unsatisfactory results. If fingerprints are on dry greasy paper, they should not be developed with iodin fumes (see page 105) but with powder.

Visible fingerprints in dust and plastic fingerprints should be photographed directly with an oblique light.

A plaster cast may be made of the plastic fingerprint after it has been photographed. The surface is then hardened with shellac (see pages 139 and 140). The moulage method (page 435) may also be used advantageously in some cases.

Bloody fingerprints against a colored background are often difficult to photograph. The background at times has approximately the same actinic influence on the photographic plate as the fingerprints, so that sufficient contrasts in the picture cannot be obtained. Here the choice of plates and light filters is very important. If the background is white, light blue, light gray, very light yellow or light green, ordinary plates without filters are used.

If the background is black, dark gray, or dark blue, common plates and blue light filters are used. If the background is red, dark yellow or dark green, orthochromatic plates with yellow light filters are used.

When dealing with fingerprints found on multicolored objects, photography in filtered ultra-violet light may be used advantageously. The fingerprints are then penciled with a material of strong luminescence, as, for instance, anthracene. Photography in ultra-violet light is described on page 433. Fingerprints on mirrors or other reflecting backgrounds—for instance, on glossy metals—often give blurred photographs. Many complicated methods have been proposed to improve such photography, but they do not give better results than a rational light and good focusing. If the mirror is of little value, a simple procedure is to scrape off the reflecting surface and use a black background.

Fingerprints should always be photographed. Only a photograph gives effective proof that the fingerprints have been found on a certain object. This is of great importance in court proceedings. The photograph should always be made in natural size and later enlarged to convenient proportions.

In recent years a special apparatus has been constructed to photograph fingerprints at the scene. A camera of this kind is very useful when the fingerprints are located on inaccessible places. It saves time and produces good pictures regardless of circumstances. Such a camera consists of a conical wooden box covered with cloth, four miniature electric bulbs, a lens, an electric battery and a few plate-holders.

The Use of Foils—The foils found on the market consist of two celluloid foils with a layer of transparent paste between them. One foil is very thin and serves as a cover for the paste layer. When the foil is used, the thin cover is taken away. The foil is then gently and uniformly pressed against the developed fingerprints. The colored material on the fingerprint will adhere to the paste on the foil. The foil is then very cautiously removed by lifting it first from one corner and then from the other. The thin cover is then very carefully put back on the foil and the fingerprint taken away. There are two different foils on the market—black and transparent—and it may be a matter of choice which of the two is preferred. The transparent is the more practical, because it may be used directly as a photographic plate for printing and enlarging. When transparent foils are used, black powder should be applied to develop the fingerprints. This is to obtain the strongest contrast possible against the slightly yellow color of the celluloid.

If the fingerprints are on a dark background, a black foil is used. This is later photographed.

The foils may also be used to transfer footprints in dust on linoleum and similar material.

In recent years, foils have been used more and more extensively. Their popularity among detectives is easily explained, if one considers the time saved and the fact that they are at times indispensable for fingerprints located on places difficult to photograph. The use of foils is justified in crimes of minor importance, altho many risks accompany their use. For instance, the whole print, or part of it, may be destroyed if any particle finds its way between the foil and the print, or if the foil slides during the transfer of the print. This sliding is fairly common. Thus major crimes require photography. In such cases no risks should be taken, either because of the possibility that the fingerprints may be destroyed or because of a possible objection on the part of the defense attorney, who might contend that the fingerprint on the foil had no relation to the object on which the fingerprint was found. Foils should therefore be used only when photography is impossible.

D. Examination of the Chance Impression

Determining the Finger and the Hand—The chance impression has now been powdered, photographed or transferred to the foil and is ready to be identified. There may be one or more suspects from whom comparison prints have been taken, but generally one refers to the single fingerprint registration. In all cases it is necessary to determine from which hand and from which finger the chance impression originated. It should be noted that white powder on a black surface makes the ridges appear white on the photo, thus making a reverse.

Chance impressions seldom appear alone. They usually occur in groups, the most common combination being the index and the middle finger or the middle, ring and small finger. One of the most difficult interpretations in fingerprinting is to determine which of the fingers of the hand we are dealing with. One has to visualize the manner in which the criminal has touched the object and the different positions which his fingers have assumed during the maneuver. To gain experience, it is advisable to practise on bottles, glass panes, etc., placing the fingers of the hand in various positions.

The following rules—with few exceptions—may be useful:

If the fingerprints are loops, and have the following pattern, they will in all probability originate from the index, middle finger, ring finger, and small finger of the right hand:

or

If the prints are loops and have the following pattern, they will in all probability originate from the index, the middle finger, ring finger, and little finger of the left hand:

or

Statistics show that generally all fingers have ulnar loops, or the index has a radial loop and the other fingers have ulnar loops. Statistics also show that the whorls usually appear on thumbs and ring fingers and that the little finger almost always presents ulnar loops. The most certain sign, however, is the position of the fingers in relation to each other and the size of the prints, as described above.

In order to determine the origin of the single print, both a trained eye and long experience are necessary. The following advice will be found useful:

The Thumb—This is recognized by its large size and the great distance between the core of the pattern and its tip—a distance conspicuously larger than in the other fingers. The upper ridges in the print always slide in the same direction as that of the hand. The ridges on the right thumb will slide to the right and the ridges on the left thumb will slide to the left. If the pattern of the thumb happens to be a loop, the loop will open to the right on the right thumb and to the left on the left thumb.

If the pattern on the thumb is a twin loop, the *under* loop opens to the right on the right-hand thumb and to the left on the left-hand thumb.

Right thumb   Left thumb

Fig. 36

If the pattern on the thumb is an "egg-shaped" whorl, the "egg" slopes to the right or left, according to which hand is used.

If the pattern of the thumb is a common whorl, the spiral

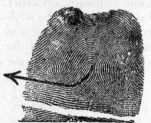

Left thumb	Right thumb	Right thumb
The under loop in the twin loop opens to the left	"Egg-shaped" whorl sloping to the right	Ordinary whorl turning to the right

Fig. 37

turns to the right when made by right thumbs and to the left by left thumbs.

The Index Finger—This finger is curved to the left or to the right according to the particular hand. All types of patterns may occur here.

The Middle Finger—These prints are recognized by the length and size of the pattern. The possibility of confusing them with prints from the index finger does not arise, but there may be a

possibility of confusion with the prints from the ring finger.

The Ring Finger—The print of this finger can easily be confused with the middle finger if it occurs singly.

The Little Finger—The little finger is recognized by its small size.

Left index   Right index

Fig. 38

Analysis and Identification of Fingerprints—The characteristic points found in the pattern of friction ridges are described in Figure 39.

By the identification, the patterns naturally are compared first and their similarity must be established. If the patterns are not the same, identity is out of the question. Outward similarity does not, however, prove anything, and one must, in order definitely to establish identity, make a careful examination of the characteristic details. Such examination can be made with the aid of a magnifying glass, altho most fingerprint experts use the naked eye. In difficult cases, the magnifying glass is indispensable.

In determining the ridge characteristics one must first determine their positions in relation to one another. This is done by counting the ridges between two characteristics. The shapes of certain details play a less important rôle. Forks, abrupt endings and beginnings, and especially lake formations, may not be the same in appearance in different prints. If dirt, small fibers or the like find their way between the fingers and the object, a ridge may, for instance, appear as one or two islands, etc. As a rule, however, the fingerprints are similar to the shape of the friction ridges. The above-mentioned cases are exceptions which teach us to show a certain tolerance towards the absolute form of the characteristics.

The most important parts of the pattern from the viewpoint of identification are the core and the delta. The ridges between the point of the delta and the point of the core are counted first. The result of the ridge counting is a good foundation for further identification. Very valuable signs are scars and other constitutional or accidental deformations of the patterns.

The absolute sizes of the fingerprints should not be compared. By the curving of the finger, the difference in the pressure and

Fig. 39

The characteristic points in the pattern of the friction ridges: (a) the eye, (b) the island, (c) the fork, (d) the contra fork, (e) the hook, (f) the contra hook, (g) the abrupt beginning, (h) the abrupt ending

Fig. 40

Changes of the characteristics in the chance impressions: (a) is an abrupt ending; in some cases it may form a fork with the lower ridge (b) or with the upper ridge (c). The "eye" (g) may form an island (d), a thick point on a ridge (f) or may look as two different ridges (e, h)

a possible future change in the size of the finger due to growth or increase of fat in the finger, the size of the fingerprint may change slightly, altho naturally the pattern and the details remain unaltered. Because of these eventualities the older identification methods founded upon conformity of size and requirement of the two prints to cover each other, are now extinct.

How to Present Fingerprint Testimony—When the identity of the fingerprints has been established—by examination of the patterns, the characteristics and their position in relation to each other, and, if present, by the constitutional or accidental deformations—the fingerprints are photographed by the methods already mentioned. Enlargements are now made, generally five to six times the natural size, and pasted, side by side, on cardboard. The characteristics are marked with corresponding numerals at the edge of the enlargement. The ciphers are connected with the characteristics by fine lines in red or black ink.

E. Value of Fingerprints as Evidence

The first rule of dactyloscopy (page 59) holds that there are no two identical fingerprints. This of course concerns only the well-prepared rolled fingerprints taken at the various bureaus of identification. But can we say the same about the blurred or indistinct chance impressions found at the scene of the crime?

We have already described how the fingerprints are analyzed and how the conclusion on identity is arrived at by considering the similarity of the patterns, and the shape and position of the characteristic points. How great must this similarity be in order to draw a conclusion of identity between the chance impression and the real print?

It has been a longstanding rule that a minimum of twelve identical and characteristic details must be found. One should not, however, adhere too closely to this rule. The identification does not consist only in searching for identical points, such as forks, abrupt endings and abrupt beginnings, but also in estimating the angles of the forks, the length of the ridges forming the forks, etc. When the core of the pattern is missing, the appearance of the details must be examined with the utmost care. In such a case only one difference (not originating in the above-described natural alteration of certain details) is sufficient to declare that the impressions are not of identical origin.

The demand for twelve similar details is the result of the opinion of bygone days, founded on the belief of scientists such as Galton, Remus, Balthazard, and others. All recent scientists working in the field of dactyloscopy, as, for instance, Locard, De Rechter and others, share the opinion that the number of characteristic points which can be noted at the edge of an enlargement is a matter of little importance. A rare detail is an identification sign one hundred times more important than a whole series of forks; four to five details in the core of an unusual pattern have more value as evidence than twelve to fifteen forks in the periphery. Some ridges with unusually grouped pores have more weight than the classical twelve points.

Thus we see that even in judging fingerprints a certain subjectivity must be exercised where the fingerprints are fragmentary. One must, in other words, to a certain degree rely on the judgment of the fingerprint expert as to the rarity and value of evidence of the different details.

Three sets of conditions are possible: [3]

1. If there are more than twelve characteristic points and the fingerprint is clear, there is absolute proof of identity.

2. If one has succeeded in determining eight to twelve points, the value of the identification as evidence now depends on:

    (a) The clearness of the impression.
    (b) The rarity of the pattern.
    (c) The presence of the core or the delta of the pattern to be examined.
    (d) The presence of pores.
    (e) The obvious identity between the breadth of the ridges, the direction of the ridges, and the angles of the forks.

3. If only a small number of characteristic details are found, the fingerprint has no absolute value as evidence, but identity can be surmised with some degree of probability, proportionate to the number and the clearness of the characteristic points.

If there is a series of impressions and no one print is of sufficient value as proof, the total value of the evidence is figured in the following manner:

(a) Let us suppose that the same finger has left several chance impressions. If certain details can be seen on one print and not on another, they may be added. Suppose, for instance, that the right index print is found on a bottle three times; one impression has ten characteristics, the second, five, which are already present in the first impression, but with two additional characteristics. The third has four characteristics already present in the first and second impressions but with the addition of three

---

[3] See also Locard, *L'Enquête Criminelle*, Paris, 1925.

new ones. The identification is then complete because we have fifteen details altogether. The identity is only probable with the first print, but becomes a certainty when all are examined.

(b) Let us suppose that there are several different impressions, each of which—with a degree of probability, but not with certainty—is identical with the fingerprints of the suspect. It is, however, impossible to determine the fingers from which the fingerprints originate. Such an occurrence is common, for example, when one impression is found on the neck and another about the middle of a bottle. By looking at the position of the impressions it is impossible to determine if they originate, say, from the index and middle finger or from the ring finger and little finger. If the first impression has six characteristics which are identical with the suspect's right index finger, and the second impression has four characteristics identical with his left ring finger, identification may be a probability but not a certainty. It may simply be a matter of chance occurrence.

(c) Let us assume that there are impressions of several fingers in their natural position. These cases are the most frequent and occur when an object is touched with the whole hand. One may then find, in natural order, the impressions of the index, the middle finger, the ring finger, and the small finger, and on the other side of the object the impression of the thumb. One of these impressions, taken alone, may not lead to identity; yet if they have respectively seven, nine, eight and eleven characteristics identical with those of the impression of the suspect, one may without hesitation conclude that the identity is established. In such a case, the proof is not only based on the characteristic details in the impressions but also upon the coincidence of two series of the same details.

F. Single Fingerprint Registrations

A good single-fingerprint classification where each finger is classified by itself is an absolute necessity. The ordinary ten-finger classifications are, as a rule, not suited for single-fingerprint search. The suitability of the ten-fingerprint registration for the search of the single-fingerprint varies, however. For instance, in the large registration of the Galton-Henry system, it is almost impossible to search for a single fingerprint inasmuch as the patterns from the ten fingers are transformed into a formula which pays very little attention to the patterns of the single fingers, and none at all to the details of the patterns. Successful attempts at identification have been made, but the tremendous amount of labor involved constitutes a great handicap. When several impressions from the same hand are found, there is some possibility that the Galton-Henry system may be of help; but in any event much time is required.

The system of Vucetich (page 59) and its modifications have more possibilities for identifying a single fingerprint because the patterns of the individual fingers are noted in the principal formula. Identifications can sometimes be made without much loss of time, but if the impression from the scene is of a very common type—for instance, a loop—much time is needed.

Attempts to register single fingerprints are of quite long standing. The Spaniard Oloriz[4] and the Belgian Stockis[5] were the pioneers, but their systems were not practical and did not meet with much favor. The first usable single-fingerprint registration was invented by a Dane, Hakon Jörgensen.[6] His ideas were first made public at the Conference of Legal Medicine in Brussels in 1921. Since then other systems have been developed.[7]

A good system, which in the past few years has been adopted by many identification bureaus, was invented by Harry Battley,[8] Chief Inspector in charge of the fingerprint bureau of Scotland Yard. In Vienna and Berlin new means of single-fingerprint classification which deserve attention have been adopted.[9]

[4] Ferrer, *Manuel de Identificacion judicial*, Madrid, 1921.
[5] Stockis, "Le classement monodactylaire," in *Revue de Droit Penal*, April 1914.
[6] Jörgensen, *Distant Identification and One-Finger Registration*, New York, 1923. Jörgensen was Commissioner of Police of Copenhagen, Denmark, and may be regarded as the foremost criminologist of Scandinavia. He was born in 1879 and died in 1927.
[7] C. S. Collins (London, 1921), J. L. Larson (New York, 1924), Fr. Born (Bern, 1926).
[8] Battley, *Single Fingerprints*, New Haven, 1931.
[9] See Riisnaes, "Nye Veier i Daktyloskopien," and Sveen, "Det nye monodaktyloskopiske system ved Scotland Yard," in *Nordisk Kriminalteknisk Tidskrift*, 1931.

The value of the single-fingerprint classification is proportional to the numbers of prints classified; *i.e.,* the fewer the prints the more effective the classification. For this reason, only those categories of criminals who leave fingerprints on the scene are classified: burglars, certain classes of thieves, etc.

As this manual does not deal with classifications of fingerprints, we refer those interested in further details to the works mentioned in the footnotes.

G. Poroscopy

The sweat pores, which in many chance impressions appear in rows of small white pin-points on the ridges, may also be used in identifications, especially in fragmentary impressions where the number of characteristic details is not sufficient for identification. Identifications by means of sweat pores have been made when only a minute part of the pattern could be utilized. Identification through the sweat pores is called poroscopy and was discovered by Locard.[10] The sweat pores have the same properties as other details in the patterns of the friction ridges, *i.e.,* they are absolutely individual as to shape, size, position and number for each human being and for each finger. They do not change during life, and if the skin is injured in any manner, they will reappear in identical form after the skin has completely healed.

Fig. 41

Friction ridges in strong enlargement

The sweat pores have another important property. Contrary to the alterations occurring in details of the fingerprint pattern, they are not subject to any changes as the result of the pressure

<hr />

[10] "La Poroscopie, procède nouveau d'identification des criminels par les traces des orifices sudoripares," in *Arch. d'Anthr. Crim.,* Lyons, 1913.

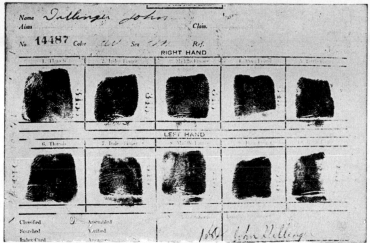

JOHN DILLINGER'S FINGERPRINTS BEFORE THE ATTEMPT TO CHANGE THEM

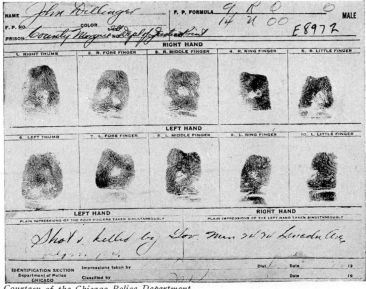

DILLINGER'S FINGERPRINTS TAKEN AFTER HIS DEATH

Note the slight destruction of a limited area: they can easily be identified

[PLATE 6]

Federal Bureau of Investigation, U. S. Department of Justice

IDENTIFYING FINGERPRINTS IN THE TECHNICAL SECTION OF THE GOVERNMENT BUREAU AT, WASHINGTON

[PLATE 7]

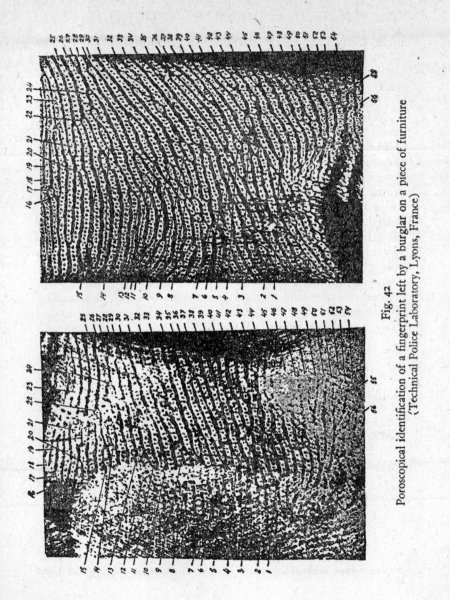

Fig. 42

Poroscopical identification of a fingerprint left by a burglar on a piece of furniture
(Technical Police Laboratory, Lyons, France)

used. They keep their form under all circumstances. On prints taken with ink, the shape of the sweat pores can be seen only with difficulty. They may be seen quite clearly on uncolored fingerprints or on fingerprints taken by special methods.

The size varies greatly, even in the same individual. The diameter varies between the 0.08 and the 0.25 part of a millimeter and is much smaller in women than in men.

The arrangement of the sweat pores on the ridges varies to a great extent. In some individuals they are placed so close together that the distance between them is less than the diameter of the opening. In other cases, the distance between them is seven to eight times larger than the openings. They may be placed in the middle of the ridge, or so far out to the sides that the edge of the ridge has a ragged appearance. According to Locard, in normal cases there are from nine to eighteen pores on each millimeter of a ridge.

As already mentioned, the common impressions made with printer's ink are not suited for poroscopical identifications, and a special method must be used. The police laboratory of Lyons, France, used the following formula: [11]

> 4 grams of yellow wax
> 16 grams of Greek resin
> 1 gram spermaceti
> 5 grams tallow

The mixture is allowed to solidify in a flat receptacle of glass or metal where it can be kept for some time if the container is covered. The finger, which has been cleaned with ether or xylol, is rubbed against the surface of the mixture and then against a highly glossed paper or against celluloid. The print is colored with oxid of cobalt. If it seems advisable, the final print may be fixed with a mixture composed of the following:

> 25 grams of gum arabic
> 10 grams of alum
> 5 grams of formalin (40%)
> 300 grams of water

[11] The method originated from the Spanish dactyloscopists Maestre and Lecha Marzo.

In order to smooth the surface of the wax before use, it may be passed over a flame.

Heindl recommends, instead of this somewhat complicated method, the rolling of the clean finger against the glass plate and the developing of the print with iodin fumes.

H. Personal Traits in Fingerprints

Many dactyloscopists, as Forgeot, Pottecker, Galton and others, have tried to gather information about the personality of the criminal by studying his fingerprints. Such information would be of great value in cases where the fingerprints originated from an unknown person. The results, however, are insignificant. Most valuable, from a practical viewpoint, are the examinations made by Forgeot on the size of the friction ridges.[12]

We have already remarked about the growth of the friction ridges during the normal development of a person, altho nothing is altered in the relative proportions of the fingerprint. Forgeot drew a perpendicular line over a certain number of parallel friction ridges and calculated the number of intersecting lines on five millimeters of the perpendicular line. On this length of line newborn infants had fifteen to eighteen ridges; children of eight years, thirteen ridges; children of twelve years, twelve ridges; and adults nine to ten ridges. Adults with very large hands often have only six to seven ridges. There is then the possibility of approximately determining the age of the person, even by fragmentary impressions.

Determination of race, intelligence, etc., by fingerprints is not possible, altho numerous efforts have been made to establish such relationships. Some have tried to determine the profession of the person by marks on the fingerprints and on the hands. Only in very pronounced cases (see page 68) is such a determination possible.

[12] Forgeot, *Les empreintes latentes*, Lyons, 1891.

I. Trickeries Employed by Criminals to Avoid Leaving Fingerprints

Cases have occurred where arrested criminals have tried to avoid having their fingerprints taken by continuously rubbing their fingertips against the rough walls of the cell until the friction ridges were worn off, leaving only a smooth surface. Other criminals have injured their fingertips with incisions, scarifications and burns. In such cases it is only necessary to put the person in handcuffs and gloves for a few days until the friction ridges have grown back or the wounds have healed. The friction ridges will normally regrow in a few days.

In recent years newspapers have dealt extensively with attempts of criminals to have the skin of their fingertips removed and new skin transplanted by means of plastic surgery. Three such cases were reported in New York City in 1934. On closer investigation all three cases proved to be entirely without foundation of fact. The arrested persons simply had scars on their fingertips as the result of accidents.

Recently the notorious felon John Dillinger and some of his accomplices were reported as having made *unsuccessful* attempts to alter their finger patterns by plastic surgery.[13]

The most eminent authorities on plastic surgery are unanimous in saying that the grafting of skin on the fingertips is practically impossible if the operation is to be carried out on all ten fingers. Very little imagination is needed to picture how closely an arrested person is scrutinized if his fingertips have been tampered with. In cases of plastic surgery, the question of expense, time wasted, difficulty in obtaining a skilled surgeon, and last, but not least, the physical courage and stamina to withstand those ten painful operations will always prove deterrents to this method of procedure.

The cases mentioned above are very rare, but this cannot be said of the methods used to avoid leaving chance impressions at the scene of the crime. The most common method is probably the one in which gloves are used. It is, however, difficult to

[13] See Plate 6 reproducing John Dillinger's fingerprints before and after such an operation.

find one's way in the dark or to use tools with gloved hands, and many criminals who have at the beginning of the act used gloves, finally have been compelled to discard them, leaving fingerprints behind. It cannot be denied, however, that the use of gloves has hampered investigations not a little. Criminals nowadays seldom leave fingerprints unless drunk, very excited or inexperienced.

In recent years many attempts have been made, especially abroad, to identify criminals from glove impressions. The gloves are often greasy and may in many cases leave a perfect impression of the glove fabric on smooth surfaces. The pattern of the fabric, especially the presence of possible defects due either to the manufacture or wear or accidental tears, are used for identification.

Fig. 43
Glove prints developed with white lead
(Detective Division, Oslo, Norway)

In such a case the glove prints are either photographed directly if visible, or colored with "white powder" or white lead. Comparison prints from the suspect's gloves are made by inking them with a roller and pressing them gently against white paper.

In this regard, attention is called to the necessity of examining the dust on the suspect's gloves. In one case, for instance, a man was arrested for burglary. The dust found on the gloves, when examined, contained a small quantity of glass particles. A windowpane had been smashed by the burglar and the glass from the gloves was compared with the glass from the pane. It was finally determined that the glass on the gloves did not derive from the windowpane in question. Hence the assumption that the burglar had also committed other burglaries and had smashed other glass panes. In this case the glove gave more information than would a chance impression found at the scene.[14]

Small quantities of paint, fibers, etc., may also be found on the gloves and may give valuable information as to past burglaries committed by the thief. As a rule, therefore, all gloves found on arrested burglars should be thoroughly examined.

There are also other methods of avoiding leaving fingerprints, but we do not find it advisable to divulge them in a book so easily accessible to the general public.

During the last decade the question of forged fingerprints has been discussed quite frequently. Even before the World War Reiss in Lausanne and Minovici in Bucharest studied this question. After the war, Wedhe [15] published a book describing methods of forging fingerprints. In all these cases the fingerprints were reproduced on a stamp which was pressed against the object. Such forgeries must, however, be considered of rare occurrence. They not only require a large amount of skill but the fingerprints of another person must be available. Enlargement of the forged print will surely bring out the fact that the ridges in the forged print do not have the same fine arrangement of the pores as the natural print possesses.

J. Palm Prints

Chance impressions of the palm of the hand will be seen very often at scenes of crime, either alone or accompanying fingerprints. If the fingerprints alone do not lead to identification, or if the palm impression is the only one found, one must use the latter for identification. If the suspect has already been arrested, impressions of his palms should be taken for comparison with the print from the scene of the crime. If the perpetrator is unknown, a thorough search in the palmar register should be made. However, such classifications are very rare, tho they are as necessary as the single-fingerprint classification. At the moment palm classifications are found only in a few places. Sometimes

---

[14] Lochte in *Arch. f. Kriminol.,* Vol. 88.
[15] Wedhe and Beffel, *Fingerprints Can Be Forged,* Chicago, 1924.

the classification of palm prints is also used to subclassify arch prints because of the inability to subclassify the latter by common methods.

The best method of taking palm prints is to use the device invented by the Belgian criminologist, Stockis, which is shown in the accompanying sketch. The block is of common wood, about 15 x 6 inches. The upper surface of the block is curved. Half of the curve is covered with an aluminum or copper plate which is inked in the same manner as in taking finger-prints. The other half of the curved surface is covered with a piece of white paper. The hand is pressed lightly, first against the inked plate and then against the paper. The fingers must be slightly spread and pressure must be exerted especially against the knuckles and the wrist. This is most easily accomplished if the operator's hand is pressed across the hand which is being printed. Some bureaus of identification use a rubber air pillow instead of the device just described.

Fig. 44
Stockis' device for the taking of palm prints

The identification is made in the same manner as with finger-prints. It is very common to have more than one hundred characteristic points in an identification; but, on the other hand, the interpretation of the palmar print is difficult for the untrained, especially if only fragmentary evidence is available.

Palm prints have been especially studied by Stockis,[16] Ferrer,[17] and Wilder and Wentworth.[18] The study of some of those clas-

[16] Stockis, "Les empreintes palmaires," in *Archives de medicine legale,* Bruxelles, 1910.
[17] Ferrer, *La identificacion personal por medio de las impresiones palmares,* Madrid, 1917.
[18] Wilder and Wentworth, *Personal Identification,* Boston, 1918. Harris Hawthorne Wilder, Professor of Zoology at Smith College, famous anthropologist, known for his extensive researches on various problems of identification, died in 1928. Bert Wentworth, former Police Commissioner of Dover, New Hampshire, has invented a code for distant fingerprint identification and can be regarded as one of the foremost experts on fingerprints.

sification systems is recommended, especially the one of Wilder and Wentworth. Such a study will lead to a better knowledge of the patterns in the palm and will simplify identifications.

K. Prints of the Soles of the Feet

From the viewpoint of criminology, sole prints are not as important as finger and palm prints, but occasionally they may have

Fig. 45
Bert Wentworth

some measure of importance. One of the authors of this book has knowledge of a suicide case where a sole print solved the problem.

A recently married pair had frequent quarrels which were noticed by the neighbors. One morning, the nude body of the young wife was found hanging from a rope attached to an iron hook in the wall. The body was swinging. The husband had left the house a few hours earlier, following a violent quarrel which had been overheard by the neighbors. He had, without doubt, mistreated his wife, whose body and clothing showed signs thereof. There was a strong suspicion that the husband had murdered his wife and then hanged her body to simulate a well-planned suicide. He was arrested. A sewing machine with a highly polished wooden top was standing on one side of the hanging body. According to the husband the death of the young woman was the result of suicide, the act having been carried out after the husband had left the home. A close examination of the top of the sewing machine showed clear sole prints of the naked feet of the dead woman. This discovery resulted in the release of the husband.

The burglar or murderer may, at times, also remove his shoes and socks, thus making sole prints important in such cases.

Prints of the sole of the foot have also been used in maternity hospitals for identification purposes. Classifications for this purpose have been invented by Wilder and Wentworth and Dr. Emil Jerlov of the Maternity Hospital of Hälsingborg, Sweden.

QUESTIONS

1. Describe the different types of chance impressions.
2. How are chance impressions produced?
3. Describe methods for developing fingerprints on paper.
4. How would you photograph a fingerprint on a multicolored background?
5. Which are the most common fingerprint patterns?
6. Describe the characteristic points found in the pattern of friction ridges.
7. Has the absolute size of the fingerprint any importance in identification?
8. What is your opinion of the value of fingerprints as evidence?
9. What is meant by poroscopy?
10. Is there any possibility of identification if the criminal used gloves?

VIII

FOOTPRINTS

A. The Walking Picture

K NOWLEDGE of footprints and their nature is not as widespread among policemen as it should be. Footprints are generally not used sufficiently by investigators of crime. Practical work is needed to gain an understanding of footprints. Theoretical speculations, however clear, can neither explain the mechanics of walking and running nor impart knowledge of the traces. Experience is needed and the only way to gain it is to carry on practical experiments under different conditions. It is especially important to study footprints while out walking. At first they will not reveal much information, but once the eye has become accustomed to observe minute details, a composite picture of interesting facts will stand out very clearly.

The investigator often satisfies himself with a mere examination of the footprints at the scene of the crime or in the immediate neighborhood, not taking into account the fact that curious onlookers or perhaps the criminal himself may have walked upon and destroyed the prints. The chances of finding the footprints of the criminal are greater in a suburban or country neighborhood, and here the difficulty of differentiating from footprints not pertaining to the crime is less. The criminal, during his escape, will be quite likely to use unfrequented roads. In rural districts a check-up of the restricted numbers of persons responsible for making the footprints is easily made. Prints left by a running person are more suspicious, especially if he has tripped over stones or bushes, an indication that he does not possess knowledge of the neighborhood.

Walking Pictures—In walking, the heel of the foot is first brought down to the ground, to be followed by the sole, which is pressed to the ground from the heel forward to the toes. The foot is then raised by exerting a final pressure against the toes. The pressure is strongest against the heel and the foremost part of the foot. A cross-section of the footprint resembles a bow.

Fig. 46
Normal walking line

In walking, the weight of the body exerts greater pressure on the outer and rear portions of the heel and sole. Examination of a group of soldiers, for instance, disclosed that 98 per cent had their shoes worn out along those parts, while the remaining 2 per cent wore them out on the inner and anterior portions of the heel and sole. This latter peculiarity should be kept in mind.

Footprints produced by someone running are less visible on

Fig. 47
Broken walking line

account of the sliding of the foot and because of the dirt and sand thrown over the print by the rapid movement of the foot. Many persons run on their toes only, but experienced runners, especially when tired, are said to put down the whole foot.

By the expression *"walking picture"* is meant the whole ensemble of footprints left by the walker. The principal components of the walking picture are the direction line, the walking line, and the foot line.

The *direction line* indicates the direction in which the walker is moving.

The *walking line* is an imaginary line which in normal and

ideal walking fuses with the direction line and runs along the inner sides of both heelprints. The walking line, however, is often irregular, varying with each step because of the manner of putting down the foot. It is more broken by stout persons and pregnant women, who walk with their feet unusually far apart in order to maintain their equilibrium. In general, it can be said that the broken walking line is especially suggestive of phlegmatic persons, strollers and women.

The *foot line* shows the angle at which each foot is put down and is a straight line through the longitudinal axis of the footprint. The angle between the foot line and the direction line is called the *foot angle*. It can be very characteristic and does not change much except when the subject is standing still, runs, walks up and down slopes, or carries heavy weights. The foot angle of a man is often larger than that of a woman. The normal foot angle is 30 to 32 degrees.

The *step length* is the distance between the centers of two successive heelprints. It depends upon the size of the walker, the habits of the walker, and the speed of the walk. Generally a large person takes longer steps than a small one walking at the same speed. One should not, however, arrive at positive conclusions so readily. Persons with hernia or pelvic disorders often take steps which are very short in proportion to the length of the legs. Railroad workers, on the contrary, are accustomed to taking exceptionally long steps on account of walking on railroad tracks. The step length varies from 20 to 40 inches. Twenty-seven inches is said to be the average for slow walking and 35 inches for fast walking. Step lengths over 40 inches are in most cases taken by persons running.

A changing step length in the same walking picture is an indication that the person limps. The normal leg takes a longer step than the shorter one.

By looking at the accompanying picture it will be found that an imaginary line which runs along the inner sides of both heelprints to the left or to the right will be straight and parallel with the direction line. If those lines are also broken—that is to say, if the distance between the heelprints on the left and the right sides changes, there is some fault with the walking apparatus of the person. The simplest explanation is to assume that the gait is that of a drunken person, but it may also be caused by wounds or illness, such as paralysis. Certain diseases such as syphilis or Parkinson's disease, in which there is interference with body equilibrium, have fairly characteristic walking pictures.

When the walker has stood still in one place, it may be pos-

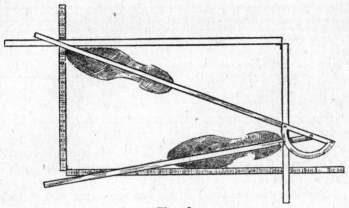

Fig. 48

Müller's method of measuring the "walking picture"

sible to determine if he has stood there for some length of time by noticing the number of times he has shifted his weight from one foot to the other. Jumping to one side, sudden changes to slow walk, steps taken previous to jumping, turnings, etc., may be of great importance and should be noticed.

Measuring the Walking Picture—In recent years attempts have been made to measure walking pictures and record them in a formula. In cases where the footprints themselves are plain and without characteristic details, the formula of the walking picture may be of value as evidence. At least two consecutive footprints of the left and right foot are necessary for such measurements.[1]

[1] Müller, *Kriminal Monatsh.*, No. 1, 1932.

For measuring, two squares and a compass are used. Each square is a right angle operating on a hinge. One of the two has a scale marked in inches. When a usable picture is found, the graded square is put in such a position that the longer side lies against the outer and longer side of the left foot and the short side touches the front tip of the right foot. If the right foot is in the rear of the picture, the procedure should be reversed. Then the second square is put so that the short side touches the rear tip of the left foot and the long side touches the outer side of the right foot, or the contrary if the right foot is in the rear. The squares should frame the feet in such a manner that they make four right angles.

The compass is now placed so that one arm is parallel with the longitudinal axis of the left footprint and the other arm with the longitudinal axis of the right footprint. The axis may be determined by putting a right angle against the straight line which connects the two corners of the heel. The angle of the arms gives the position of the feet in relation to one another. In the formula this angle is called the "principal" angle and the designation is H.

Experience has shown that the two feet often make different angles with the walking line of the individual, and the angles which the arms of the squares make with the footline are also measured. Those angles are called l for the left foot and r for the right foot.

The following measurements are also made:

1. The step length is called S and is measured from the rear edge of the left heel to the rear edge of the right heel. It is read directly on the graduated rule. S varies, and is dependent upon the kinds of steps (jumping, running, walking).

2. The breadth of the step, which is called B, is measured from the outer edge of the long side of the left foot to the outer edge of the long side of the right foot and read directly from the graduated rule. B does not vary if the walking line is straight. It is always larger when made by stout, old persons and pregnant women, and smaller by younger and lighter individuals.

3. ll, length of the left foot, and lb, greatest width of the left foot.

4. rl, length of the right foot, and rb, greatest width of the right foot.

Other peculiarities may be found in the footprints and should be examined and described. Particular attention should be paid to evidence of wear on the heel and sole. They are described in the following manner:

Left Foot

Impression sole forward	—	*lv*
" " outside	—	*la*
" " inside	—	*li*
" " rear	—	*lh*
Impression heel forward	—	*laa*
" " rear	—	*lah*
" " inside	—	*lai*

Right Foot

Impression sole forward	—	*rv*
" " outside	—	*ra*
" " inside	—	*ri*
" " rear	—	*rh*
Impression heel outside	—	*raa*
" " rear	—	*rah*
" " inside	—	*rai*

Special peculiarities should also be described, *e.g.*, repairs, nails, rubber heels, etc. They come under heading X in the formula. The formula has the following arrangement:

$$H\frac{r}{l} \ BS \ \frac{ra \ rv \ raa}{la \ lv \ laa} \ \frac{ll}{rl} \ \frac{lb}{rb} \ X$$

In this formula $\frac{ra \ rv \ raa}{la \ lv \ laa}$ is a sample, showing how the formula should be used.

H, r, l and B are constant values. The values $\frac{ll}{rl} \frac{lb}{rb}$ and X depend on the shoes. The value S also varies, but as far as is known has no influence on the other factors. When a walking picture is to be identified it is easy to determine the speed of the walk by allowing the suspect to walk either quickly or slowly.

Experience shows that walking pictures are highly individual and that one can identify the person who makes them without difficulty. For instance, several persons have been made to walk side by side. It has then been possible to determine the walking picture of each person after having taken comparison prints of them.

B. Surface Footprints

The slight interest shown by policemen in footprints may be attributed partly to the fact that almost all shoes are of the ready-

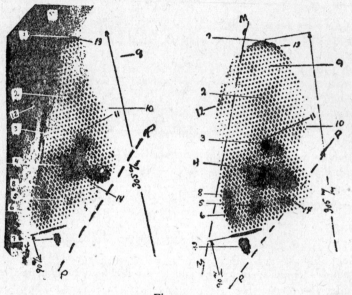

Fig. 49

Identification of a surface footprint left by a burglar's rubber-soled shoe on a painted floor: left foot (Police Department, Skien, Norway)

made type, which vary very little in the design of the sole. Apart from exceptional sole designs on fancy shoes, most soles vary only slightly from one another. In olden times it was quite different. Shoes were usually made to order and often not only repaired many times but also studded with nails, protected with heel irons, etc. Such shoes may still be found in rural districts and may leave footprints which are as valuable as fingerprints for identification purposes. With the ever-increasing use of rubber soles and rubber heels, new and highly valuable means of identification have been added to the identification of prints. Millions of rubber heels will be quite uniform in the manufacture when sold in the shop, but after only a few days of wear will develop individual characteristics.

Prints from rubber heels can be left on almost all floor coverings, *i.e.,* linoleum, cork, parquet floors, painted wooden floors, and on papers lying on the ground, etc. Continental identification in recent years can boast of convictions aided through prints of rubber heels and rubber soles on the various materials named above. Sometimes these prints are nearly invisible to the eye, but skilful photography brings them out. Surface footprints are sometimes difficult to find, especially wet prints on floors. In such cases they are searched for with a strong oblique light.

Surface footprints are photographed with a scale by the side. Comparison prints from the suspect's shoes may be obtained by inking them with a common fingerprint roller and making the suspect walk over white paper.

C. Footprints in Plastic Materials

Generally all footprints should be photographed before attempting to make casts. The risk of an accident while making the cast is ever present. The photographs are taken with the camera in a vertical position above the footprint, supported by a reversible tripod. A cardboard or paper scale graduated in inches, stained black, should be placed beside the footprint and at the same level if possible. It goes without saying that the lens must be absolutely parallel with the object to be photographed to avoid false perspectives. It was formerly the rule to photograph prints on as large a scale as possible, preferably on a half plate (5 x 8 inches). Today, owing to the improvement of the miniature camera, footprints are successfully photo-

graphed on film of motion-picture size and subsequently enlarged to natural size.

The technique used in making casts differs according to the
nature of the footprints. Some authors—for instance, Gross,
Reiss, Frecon, Hofmann and Hugoulin—recommend plaster of

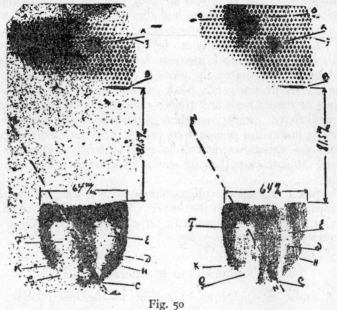

Fig. 50
Same case as in Fig. 49: the burglar's right foot

Paris and different materials such as wax, sulfur, glue, concrete
blends, etc. Our experience shows that plaster of Paris is the
best medium. Only the very best plaster—art plaster of the
finest grade—should be used. The technique used by dentists
in mixing plaster of Paris with water should be followed. A
rubber cup is filled with one pint of water (approximately
enough for one footprint) and the plaster of Paris is spread
over the water. No stirring is permitted. The plaster of Paris
is allowed to sink to the bottom spontaneously. Enough should

be added until the water is unable to absorb any more. The mixture is then ready for use.

Before using, it should be stirred thoroughly and then placed on the footprint. When a layer about one-third of an inch thick has been applied, portions of twine, sticks, twigs, or some similar material should be put on for reenforcement. This reenforcing material should not extend past the print, and should be put on carefully and without pressure to prevent it from touching the bottom of the print and thus destroying the details. A new layer of plaster is then put upon the reenforcement, and the cast allowed to harden completely before it is taken away. A sure sign of hardening is that the plaster is getting warm.

If rapid hardening is desired, a small quantity of salt may be mixed with the plaster. On the other hand, if slow hardening is desired, some sugar or dextrose should be added. In order to prevent the spreading of the plaster of Paris over the sides, a frame of cardboard, wood or similar material is built around the print. To prevent air bubbles, the first layer of plaster should be put on slowly and carefully, preferably with the aid of a spoon.

About twenty ounces of plaster of Paris are needed for one footprint. In cases of great emergency, sulfur, tallow, lard, porridge or flour and water may be used.

It is always advisable to prepare the surface of the footprint before the plaster cast is made, and this is especially the case when the footprints are in dust, fine sand or other soft material. This is done by spreading a thin coat of shellac over the surface. The shellac hardens quickly and renders even a very sensitive surface hard enough to bear the weight of the plaster. In order to spread the shellac a Flit can or similar spraying device may be used, but it is advisable to have a special sprayer for that purpose. The complete outfit used by the New York City Police Department for preparing the surface of footprints and for making the casts is shown in Figure 51.[2] It consists of the

[2] This outfit was constructed for the units of the Swedish State Police by Söderman in collaboration with Ivan Lindell, instrument maker to the faculties of the School of Science, University of Stockholm.

above-described sprayer, from which the shellac can be easily cleaned. The outlets may be kept clear by inserting and retaining pieces of wire when not in use. There is one container for shellac and another for oil, both of which can be screwed to the sprayer; one shaker for talcum powder, two containers for the plaster, one for water, a rubber cup, a spoon and a spatula.

Footprints in soft or hard earth, dry marsh land and sand are prepared in the following manner: A thin coat of shellac is spread upon the surface of the print. The sprayer should be

Fig. 51	Fig. 52
Complete kit for casting all sorts of footprints	Spraying the surface of the foot-print with shellac

kept at a distance of about one yard so that the shellac may fall like a soft cloud on the surface. Care should be taken that the air stream from the sprayer does not disturb or carry off particles from the print. The shellac dries in a few minutes; a thin coat of talcum is then shaken over the print, and the plaster cast is made in the manner described previously.

Footprints in dust, fine sand, or other soft materials are prepared in the following manner: A coat of shellac is spread with great care over the surface and this is followed by a thin coat of oil which is spread over the dry shellac by means of the sprayer. The plaster cast is made in the ordinary manner, altho the mixture of the first layer should not be so thick and should be applied in small portions with a spoon. When the plaster cast is dry it is possible, in many cases, to peel off the coat of shellac and oil very easily. If the coat sticks to the plaster it can be placed on a hot stove and in most cases loosened. If necessary the cast may also be cleaned by immersing it in alcohol.

Footprints in snow are prepared in the following manner: A thin coat of talcum is first shaken over the print. Shellac is spread over the talcum, and talcum is again shaken over the shellac while it is still wet. This operation is repeated three times. By this time a thin skin-like layer of talcum and shellac protects the print. The plaster cast may then be made in the regular manner.

In cases where water covers the footprints, as, for instance, at the seashore, plaster of Paris should be spread on the water over the print with the aid of a piece of gauze, which acts as a sifter. The plaster will sink to the bottom of the print and form a hard crust.

When it is raining the footprints should be protected pending the arrival of the men from the police laboratory. Empty boxes, etc., may be used for this purpose. If there is a small quantity of water on the prints it should be carefully drawn away with a blotter or filter paper.

D. Prints of Naked Feet

Prints of naked feet are seldom found, altho the history of crime shows that quite a few cases have been reported where a criminal has taken shoes and socks off in order to operate more silently and to avoid contaminating his shoes with blood. In the well-known murder of the banker, Remy,[3] when Bertillon made a very ingenious reconstruction of the crime, the two murderers, Renard and Courtois, had undressed completely and operated in the nude.

Indoors, one will in most cases find surface prints on floors, tables, chairs, etc., and more seldom prints in plastic materials, earth, ashes, etc. Prints of naked feet can be colored or un-

[3] See Söderman, *Brottets Värld*. Stockholm. 1927.

colored. In the first case the feet are soiled with blood, dust, soot, etc. The prints are then visible. In determining the size of the foot care should be exercised, as the pressure and coloring material have a large influence on the size of the prints. One should look for malformations and flat feet.

Uncolored prints of naked feet are dealt with the same as latent fingerprints. (See Prints of the Soles, page 128.)

Traces of Socks—Frequently it is possible to identify traces of socks. They may be visible or latent. Latent traces of socks are dealt with as fingerprints inasmuch as the latent mark is due to perspiration. The identification is based on the structure of the fabric, which can be very characteristic, especially if there are holes or darns.

E. Identification of Footprints

Comparison Prints—For the identification of naked feet and socks the foot is pressed against a glass panel or tin plate covered with a thin layer of fingerprint ink and the suspect is made to walk on a sheet of white paper. In order to get a true picture of the formation of the foot in different positions, it is necessary to take four different footprints, namely, in normal standing position, in walking, in a standing position with pressure on the outer portion of the foot, and in a standing position with pressure exerted on the inner part of the foot.

In making comparison prints of shod feet the suspect is made to walk, if possible, on the same plastic material as that in which the footprints are found. Casts are then made at the scene. If the prints found on the scene have been made with wet shoes, the shoes of the suspect should also be wet when making the comparison prints. It is, however, often possible to make the identification by direct comparison of the cast made at the scene and the suspect's shoes.

The Identification—For identification, it is necessary to have definite starting points for measurements. For naked feet, those points are the rear border of the heel and the tip of the large toe, and for shoes the rear border of the heel and the tip of the shoe. With the aid of those starting points one draws a "Causé's net," which is shown in the accompanying figure. It is advisable to photograph the two prints (suspect and comparison) side by side, including the grad-uated scale, on the same plate, en-large them to natural size, and then draw the net on the photo-graph. It is also possible to photo-graph the two prints separately in exactly the same size and make the comparison between the two prints.

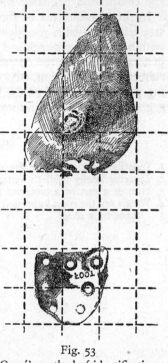

Fig. 53

Causé's method of identification

In the identification of naked feet differences of one one-hun-dredth of an inch are not impor-tant, because the foot becomes larger or smaller according to whether the person stands or walks.

Shoe prints seldom have exactly the same size as the shoes which have made them. This is due to the various movements in walk-ing. Differences of some hun-dredths of an inch in length or width are no indication of non-identity. The substance in which the print has been made is also subject to alterations. Wet earth, for instance, contracts in drying, and this contraction in clay can be more than one-half an inch for a footprint. In such cases experiments must be made and the contraction carefully studied. The drying process is also very often not uniform, and this is especially the case with earth which has been wet and dried several times. Traces in snow can also be subject to changes. In warmer weather the prints become larger. In one case, for instance, the footprints in snow became three one-hundredths of an inch longer with a rise of temperature of only 9 degrees Fahrenheit in half an hour. The process of casting in snow also enlarges the prints and it is then advisable to make the comparison prints in snow.

In the identification of shoe prints it is a general rule that the size has little value for identification, altho it certainly must fit within the above-mentioned limits. The identification is most generally based on the characteristic signs of wear, repairs, nails, rubber heels, heel irons, etc. The method of measuring the walking picture described at the beginning of this chapter also adds a great deal to the identification.

QUESTIONS

1. Describe the elements of the walking picture.
2. Describe briefly Müller's system of measuring the walking picture.
3. How is a cast of a footprint in dust made?
4. Which are the most important points in the identification of a footprint made by a shoe?

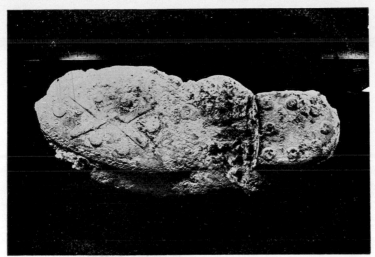

PLASTER CAST OF RUBBER-SOLED SHOE IN FLOUR (Page 139)

MICROSCOPIC IDENTIFICATION OF A BURGLAR'S TOOL MARKS ON A
PAINTED WINDOW FRAME (Page 163)

[PLATE 8]

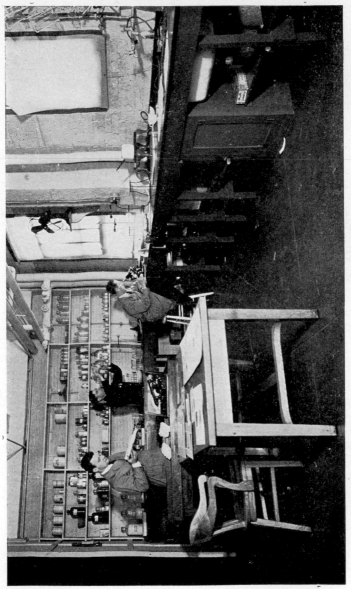

TECHNICAL RESEARCH LABORATORY, NEW YORK CITY POLICE DEPARTMENT

[PLATE 9]

IX

TRACES OF VEHICLES

THE motor car plays a large part in many crimes. The criminal arrives at the scene of the crime in a motor car and escapes in a motor car with his loot. In some cases marks of tires may be found, and these marks are almost always valuable from the viewpoint of aiding the investigation and supplementing other evidence.

Determination of the Direction—The determination of the direction in which a car has traveled is sometimes fairly easy, especially if the road is wet or dusty. Small heaps of dust and dirt are thrown on each side of the tracks in such a manner that they point in the direction the car has traveled.

If the substructure on which the car is traveling is pressed down by weight, it forms a mass more compact than that portion of the dirt in its immediate vicinity and breaks "step-like" along the bottom of the track. The wheel travels in the direction in which the soil has been lifted. There is a simple rule by which to remember this: if one should want to even the track again, the wheel is to be made to turn in the opposite direction to the one traveled.

The distance separating the tracks will give very little information concerning American cars, owing to their standardization. In Continental models, on the contrary, these distances differ very much in the various makes and may constitute valuable clues. For instance, the Italian Fiat has four different distances—1.2 meters, 1.25 meters, 1.4 meters, and 1.42 meters; the Swedish Volvo has respectively 1.3 meters and 1.45 meters; the English Morris has the following distances: Minor, 1.07 meters, Cowley, 1.22 meters, and Cowley 35 horsepower, 1.42 meters.

145

The distance separating the tracks made by a motorcycle with a side-car varies, because an adjustable axle regulates the distance between the motorcycle and the side-car. The minimum distance is constant for the different types. As a rule it can be said that this distance in a motorcycle with side-car is appreciably less than that of a motor car.

Even when a motor car travels on a hard surface, such as an asphalt street, it may leave clear traces of its tires, especially if the street is wet or dusty. In such a case the trace is called a surface print. The traces of tires in loose earth are generally clearer. They are called depressed prints. For the subsequently described classification of tires the difference between surface prints and depressed prints has no importance, because the pattern is then considered as a surface. The depth of the impression in the latter cases is in proportion to the weight of the car and the structure of the soil. If the weight of the car is to be determined, tests must be made on the same substructure to obtain the same type of impression.

The width of the marks will not always disclose the dimensions of the tire. The weight of the car as well as the structure of the soil plays even here a large rôle. Furthermore, there is a third factor, the degree of inflation of the tires. The pattern of the tires and their measurements will generally determine the dimensions.

A motor car traveling in a straight line leaves only traces of its rear tires. In order to see the traces of all four tires the place where the motor car has backed up or has made a sharp turn must be located.

When the direction of travel has been determined, the tracks are carefully examined for traces of injuries and marks of repairs existing on the tires. Such traces are at first photographed side by side with a ruler so that later measurements can be taken on the photographic enlargement. Good pictures of the different patterns should also be made. When the photographs have been taken, plaster casts of the traces are made, following the same procedure used in making casts of footprints. A plaster cast having a length of about 1½ feet for each tire will do. If a car has stopped on the road for some time it is often difficult to determine the exact location from the marks if the car later continued to travel in the same direction. Oil drops[1] on the ground, matches, cigaret butts, etc., may, however, give valuable information.

Classification of Tire Marks—There can be four different patterns of tires left by a given car. As a rule only brand-new cars or expensive cars have the same patterns on all four wheels simultaneously. If we assume that there are only 100 different tire patterns, this gives theoretically 100^4 which is the equivalent of 100,000,000 possible combinations.

A description of the tires will be most valuable in tracking down the car. Even if the tires have been changed after an accident or a crime it is possible in many cases to obtain evidence of this change.

Early attempts to collect tire marks for identification purposes were made by Söderman[2] and Chavigny.[3] In 1931 Dr. Robert Heindl published a classification of tire patterns[4] which represents a very fine achievement in modern police science. This classification has a great value in criminology. Experience shows that the identification of tire patterns by tire dealers cannot be relied upon, as even the most experienced of them is acquainted only with a few patterns. In Heindl's classification the tire patterns are arranged according to their form. When a tire pattern is obtained at the scene of a crime the make of the tire is easily detected with the aid of the classification.

Tires with totally smooth treads are no longer in existence. In the classification different models or types are arranged according to the pattern of the treads.

The patterns are at first divided into *symmetrical* and *asymmetrical* forms. The letters *A* and *B* are used to denote the

[1] The oil drops from a running car will split in the same manner as blood drops (see page 279) and indicate the direction in which the car has traveled.
[2] *Handbok i kriminalteknik*, by Söderman and Fontell, Stockholm, 1930.
[3] M. Chavigny, "Les traces des vehicules" in *Revue International de Criminalistique*, v. 1, 1929.
[4] *Archiv für Kriminologie*, v. 91.

symmetrical and asymmetrical patterns respectively. The sub-classification of these two principal groups is arranged according to the shape of the pattern in the middle portion of the tire. Still another subclassification of the two principal groups is arranged according to the patterns flanking the middle pattern. These two subclassifications are denoted by numbers in fractions. The number for the middle pattern is the numerator of the fraction and the number for the flank pattern is the denominator. For example:

$$\frac{\text{number of middle pattern}}{\text{number of flank pattern}}$$

Consequently there is a formula for each pattern consisting of one letter and two numbers, as, for instance, $A\frac{3}{4}$.

The word "pattern" is used to indicate that part of the tire which touches the ground. In every make of tire the tread is always distinct in pattern.

The first fact to determine is whether the pattern is an A or a B pattern. In answering this question one figuratively splits the pattern longitudinally and folds the halves together. If the two halves of the pattern when brought together exactly match one another it is a symmetrical pattern, or A. If they do not match, it is an asymmetrical pattern, or B.

Middle Patterns (Numerators)—The middle pattern may be as follows:

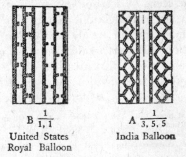

B $\frac{1}{1,1}$ A $\frac{1}{3,5,5}$

United States   India Balloon
Royal Balloon

1. A raised, unbroken band with straight borders.

$A\frac{2}{4,3,6}$

Seiberling
Patrician

$A\frac{2}{3,9}$

Seiberling
Special
Balloon

2. A furrow with straight borders.

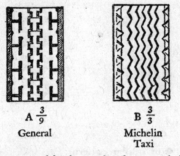

$A\frac{3}{9}$

General

$B\frac{3}{3}$

Michelin
Taxi

3. Raised lines or furrows with zig-zag borders, consisting of a continuous succession of angles, for example: ⌐⌐, ⌐⌐, ⌐⌐, ⌐⌐, ᴧᴧᴧ, ⌐.

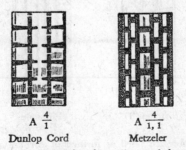

$A\frac{4}{1}$

Dunlop Cord

$A\frac{4}{1,1}$

Metzeler

4. A series of squares or rectangles (not diamond-shaped).

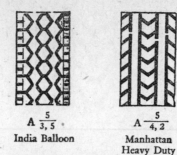

A $\frac{5}{3,5}$

India Balloon

A $\frac{5}{4,2}$

Manhattan
Heavy Duty

5. A series of polygons (the word polygon signifies a surface that has more than four angles and is surrounded by straight borders).

A $\frac{6}{6}$

Goodyear

A $\frac{6}{8}$

Michelin

6. Diamond shapes ◆ or similar patterns.

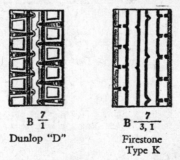

B $\frac{7}{1}$

Dunlop "D"

B $\frac{7}{3,1}$

Firestone
Type K

7. A band with unbroken borders formed of corners *and* curves, as, for instance, ⌐⌐, ⌐.

A $\dfrac{7}{...}$

Englebert
(Belgian)

or a constant succession of figures with borders consisting of straight lines, angles or curves.

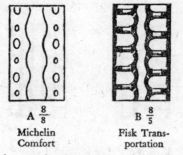

A $\dfrac{8}{8}$ B $\dfrac{8}{5}$

Michelin   Fisk Trans-
Comfort   portation

8. A band where the two borders consist of unbroken lines running in curves $\sim\!\!\!\sim$.

A $\dfrac{8}{8}$

Goodrich

or a succession of round or oval figures (without sharp corners).

The General $A \frac{9}{...}$

9. Other patterns.   Vitalic

Flank Patterns (Denominators)—In examining flank patterns
attention is drawn to the fact that in this classification bands
with straight borders are put under heading 4 and a succession
of squares under heading 1. In the numerator the opposite is
the case.

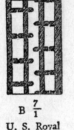   

B $\frac{7}{1}$ B $\frac{1}{1,1}$

U. S. Royal   U. S. Royal
Heavy   Balloon

1. A series of squares or rectangles (not diamond shapes or oblique
parallelograms).

B $\frac{1}{2,2}$ or B $\frac{1}{3,2}$ A $\frac{3}{2}$ or A $\frac{3}{3}$

Dunlop   Dunlop Giant
Fortuna

2. A series of oblique parallelograms ▱ .

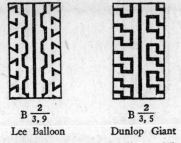

B $\frac{2}{3, 9}$ B $\frac{2}{3, 5}$

Lee Balloon   Dunlop Giant

3. A band bordered by two uninterrupted lines. The lines may either both consist of straight lines and corners or one line may be straight and the other may consist of straight lines and corners.

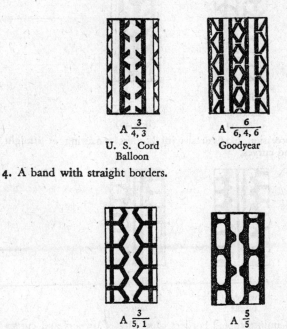

A $\frac{3}{4, 3}$ A $\frac{6}{6, 4, 6}$

U. S. Cord   Goodyear
Balloon

4. A band with straight borders.

A $\frac{3}{5, 1}$ A $\frac{5}{5}$

Firestone   John Bull

5. A series of polygons (see middle pattern 5).

A $\frac{6}{6, 4, 6}$ B $\frac{1}{4, 6}$

Goodyear   Goodrich
Safety

6. Diamond shapes, similar patterns and triangles.

B $\frac{7}{7, 2}$ A $\frac{2}{7}$

Excelsior   Englebert
Balloon   (Belgian)

7. A constant succession of figures with borders consisting of straight lines, angles and curves,

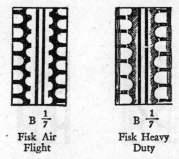

B $\frac{1}{7}$ B $\frac{1}{7}$

Fisk Air   Fisk Heavy
Flight   Duty

or a band with uninterrupted borders consisting of corners and curves (the lines may either both consist of corners and curves, or one may consist of corners and the other of curves, or one may be straight and the other consist of corners and curves).

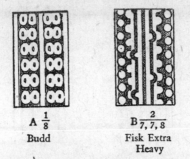

$A \frac{1}{8}$
Budd

$B \frac{2}{7, 7, 8}$
Fisk Extra
Heavy

8. A series of round or oval figures (without sharp corners),

$B \frac{2}{4, 8}$
Goodrich

or a band bordered by two uninterrupted lines which either consist of only curves or one is straight and the other consists of curves (no corners).

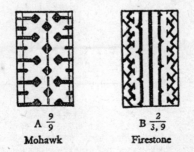

$A \frac{9}{9}$
Mohawk

$B \frac{2}{3, 9}$
Firestone

9. Other patterns.

Some samples of tire-pattern classification:

$A \frac{1}{2}$

Continental
Cord Balloon

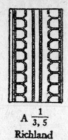

$A \frac{1}{3, 5}$

Richland

$A \frac{1}{4}$

Continental
(Tire for horse
carriage)

$A \frac{2}{7, 9}$

Penn

$A \frac{2}{7, 9}$

Seiberling

$A \frac{5}{5, 2}$

Federal

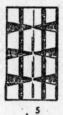

$A \frac{5}{1}$

Dunlop

$A \frac{6}{4, 6}$

Seiberling

$A \frac{6}{6, 4, 6}$

Seiberling

$A \frac{6}{6}$

Michelin
Comfort

$A \frac{6}{6, 6}$

Seiberling

$A \frac{7}{3}$ or $A \frac{7}{7}$

Seiberling
de Luxe

B $\frac{1}{2}$

U. S. Tire
Royal Cord

B $\frac{1}{4, 1, 1}$

U. S. Tire
Royal Cord
Balloon

B $\frac{1}{4, 5}$

Federal
Commercial

B $\frac{1}{9}$

U. S. Usco

B $\frac{2}{4, 8}$

Fisk Trans-
portation

B $\frac{5}{3}$

Kelly Spring-
field

B $\frac{3}{9}$ or B $\frac{3}{3}$

Michelin

B $\frac{8}{8}$ or B $\frac{7}{8}$

Fisk

B $\frac{9}{5}$

Federal
Commercial

In combined patterns, as, for instance, where the middle pattern consists of squares (4) and round figures (8), the numbers are written down, the high ones preceding the low ones, thus,

$$\frac{8,\,4}{\cdots}$$

If the flank pattern is composed of different designs the numbers are written down consecutively from the center to the flank of the patterns. For instance, $\frac{\cdots}{3,\,9}$ or $\frac{\cdots}{7,\,7,\,8}$.

It is not necessary to consider the outermost border or design. And it goes without saying that only one of the flank patterns is to be considered, either the right or the left.

In the formula only the shape of the surfaces and not the shape of the furrows should be noted. Only in one exceptional case does the formula not express the shape of the surface, namely, when the middle pattern is represented by a furrow or raised band (1 or 2).

A furrow on the tire becomes a raised band in the trace. The classification has reference to both the tires and their traces or impressions. Therefore only the surfaces and not the furrows are taken into consideration, except where the furrows constitute the middle pattern.

If there are two bands in the middle pattern, the middle pattern is a furrow with 2 as a numerator. If there are three bands in the middle pattern, the middle pattern is a band with 1 as a numerator. If there is a raised "wall" in the center of the tire and the trace has a furrow, the middle pattern is also 2. The wall is different from the band. The latter has an even surface and the wall has a curved surface. The band is always broader than the wall.

The thin bridges of rubber connecting the different raised surfaces—made to strengthen the pattern—are ignored in the formula. In some cases these bridges are so broad that when the tire is quite worn out doubts may arise as to whether one is dealing with a "bridge" or a pattern such as 3 or 7.

Thin longitudinal rubber threads in the center of the pattern are ignored. They cannot possibly be mistaken for furrows.

"Combined patterns" differ from "combined flank patterns" inasmuch as the combined pattern contains two differently shaped surfaces which follow each other regularly in a longitudinal direction. The combined patterns may be either middle or flank patterns. The "combined flank patterns" are placed side by side in a horizontal direction.

Heindl himself does not regard his classification of tire patterns as final. The influence of wear on the patterns and the alterations to which they may be subjected by wear, must be studied very thoroughly. However, this classification will do in the majority of cases.

It is recommended that the larger municipal forces and especially the State Police always keep up to date with the tire classification. Yearly models are put out by the manufacturers, and the person in charge of the tire classification should become familiar with the new patterns. The table of patterns given here should by no means be regarded as covering the whole field. It contains, however, many common domestic and foreign patterns used in this country.

QUESTIONS

1. How is the direction in which a car has traveled determined from its tracks?
2. Describe briefly the principles of the classification of tire patterns.

X

TRACES OF TOOLS

A NY tools, such as jimmies, hatchets, axes, hammers, cutters, pliers, and knives, will leave markings on material softer than the tool itself. In a burglary, for instance, there may be jimmy marks in the paint or wood of windows, doors, cabinets and drawers. A cut telephone wire will carry markings of the cutter. A hatchet with characteristic marks of wear will leave traces on the skull of the murdered person.

The identification of tools is especially common in burglaries, and it can be said that the new technique for bringing out microscopic evidence in such cases represents the most valuable aid which has been added to police science since the perfection of forensic ballistics.[1] It is nowadays often possible, after a microscopic examination of the surface of a trace of a tool, to identify the tool with the same accuracy with which a bullet is identified with the weapon from which it is fired.

If a screw-driver, a jimmy or any other tool is examined under a suitable microscope, preferably in oblique light, a slight enlargement will show innumerable ridges and irregularities on the surface of the tool. These are caused by the grinding of the tool and by wear, and may be looked upon as being as characteristic as the ridges and grooves of a fired bullet.

When the tool is pressed against a plastic material, generally paint, these characteristic ridges will be molded into the paint, leaving a more or less perfect cast of themselves. These casts can be identified as having been caused by the tool in question.

[1] Luke S. May: "The Identification of Knives, Tools, and Instruments a Positive Science," in *American Journal of Police Science*, v. 1, No. 3, 1930; and Th. Madsen: "Bidrag til Undersögelsestekniken for Skaarspor i Traevaerk," in *Nordisk Kriminalteknisk Tidskrift*, No. 12, 1933.

The procedure to be used in caring for the marks caused by the tools depends entirely upon the manner in which the identification is going to be made. In any case, the position of the trace should be marked on the sketch or photograph of the scene, and a detail photograph showing the whole trace should be taken. A graduated ruler should be placed beside the trace and on a level with it before photographing. If the case is of less importance or there are easily interpreted characteristics of the mark, a cast of the trace should be made. If the case is important and there is reason to believe that a microscopic examination will yield results, the trace should be cut out and taken to the laboratory.

Making Casts of the Impression—The most commonly used casting method consists of pressing a piece of plastelina against the trace. Before its application the plastelina should be kneaded in the hand until it becomes soft. In order to prevent the plastelina from sticking to the trace it is generally moistened with water, altho quartz powder is recommended for this purpose.[2]

The quartz powder should be sprayed with the aid of a small rubber sprayer over the surface of the trace. The plastelina is then pressed gently but firmly into the trace and removed. The cast is transported in a small cardboard box (often an empty wooden matchbox will do) to the laboratory, where a cast of plaster of Paris is made of the plastelina cast. A mixture of plaster of Paris and water is made (see page 138) and put into a small container, whereupon the plastelina cast is placed on the surface of the plaster mixture and allowed to sink to the necessary depth. It can be kept in position by a string attached to a support. In order to avoid air bubbles, which cause holes in the plaster cast, there should be spread, with the aid of a fine brush, a thin coat of plaster over the surface of the plastelina before sinking it into the plaster. The plaster should be allowed to harden completely before the plastelina is removed.

The photographs and the traces on the plaster casts are compared with the suspected tool. In order to make the evidence

[2] P. Christiansen: "Anvendelse of Kvartspulver ved Skaarsporafstöbninger" in *Nordisk Kriminalteknisk Tidskrift*, No. 4, 1932.

as conclusive as possible, experiments with the same tool should be carried out and casts prepared as described above.

Moulage Method—The moulage method, described on page 435, may also be used for making casts of burglars' tools.

Goddefroy's Method—There is still another method of reproducing prints of burglars' tools invented by Goddefroy,[a] which may at times be employed with advantage. A piece of very thin sheet aluminum is cut to fit the size of the trace, which is then covered by it. With the aid of a modeling stick the soft aluminum sheet is pressed into the trace in such fashion that its entire surface is completely gone over with the stick. Experience will show the amount of pressure to obtain a clear impression while avoiding destruction of the trace. One side of the sheet will show the relief of the trace and the other side the imprint. Circumstances will dictate which side should be used for identification.

To strengthen the mold the side of the sheet which is not used is covered with a layer of plaster mixture. If the trace is of a delicate nature, the thinnest possible sheet of aluminum should be used, and the plaster reenforcement molded over the sheet before it is loosened from the trace.

Comparison prints can be obtained by putting a piece of sheet aluminum on a suitable background—for instance, blotting paper—and the part in question of the suspected tool drawn or pressed against the sheet. The comparison is then done in the usual manner, either directly under the microscope or by comparing the photographic enlargements.

This method has some advantages over plastelina, inasmuch as the resulting molds may sometimes be more accurate. They are also easier to transport. On the other hand, the method is absolutely unsuitable for all traces which have been molded in soft material, as the pressure of the modeling stick then causes alterations.

The Microscopic Method—The microscopic method of May and Madsen is founded on the normal occurrence of fine ridges

[a] *Revue Intern. de Crimin.*, No. 3, 1931.

on the surface of the tool. These ridges cannot be seen by the naked eye, because some of them are as fine as 1/100 of a millimeter. A direct comparison of the tool and the trace is difficult because the ridges in the trace are naturally found to be raised while they occur sunken in the tool. In addition, the trace represents a reflected picture of the tool. The examination of such a large object as a tool under the microscope is also difficult—a reason for not examining the tool directly. A cast of the tool in soft lead is made. The tool is wrapped in a piece of soft, thin lead plate and tightened in a vise. The two jaws of the vise are covered with lead so that the pressure may be spread evenly. The print from the scene and the comparison proof are now matched under a binocular microscope. When the identity is established, photomicrographs of the proof from the scene and the comparison proof are made in exactly the same enlargement. Microsummar or Microtessar lenses should be used. A very oblique light will give good results.

An enlargement of about forty times is appropriate. When showing the similarities to the court, one may cut out a characteristic strip of the photograph of one print and place it over the other.

It is strongly recommended that traces of tools from burglaries committed by unknown perpetrators should be classified in the police laboratory. The classification is founded on the dimensions of the tool and some notes on the *modus operandi* of the perpetrator should be added. When tools are found on suspects, they should be delivered to the laboratory, which may be instrumental in establishing whether the same tools have been used in previous burglaries.

QUESTIONS

1. Describe some types of crime where traces of tools will have special importance.
2. How is a cast made of the trace of a tool?
3. Describe briefly the microscope method of May and Madsen and its foundation.

XI

TRACES OF TEETH

ARKS made by the teeth may be found on the skin of the victim in rape and sex murders. In other crimes evidences of tooth marks have been found in food and miscellaneous articles. They are often found in burglaries of grocery stores or dwellings, where the perpetrator has bitten into butter, cheese, fruit, chocolate, or other materials which retain tooth markings. In perishable articles of food the drying process may obliterate or distort tooth impressions. This may be prevented by placing the substance in a ½ per cent solution of formalin until a cement cast can be made.

The marks made by the teeth are first photographed. Comparison marks of the teeth of the suspect are then made. These may be made in different manners. Formerly the suspect was compelled to bite plastelina and a plaster cast was then made of the markings. In recent years, however, compositions generally used in dentistry for making casts of the teeth have been employed. These substances, which are hard and solid, are softened with warm water and then pressed against the teeth. On cooling they harden very quickly, leaving a microscopically exact reproduction of the teeth in question.

Almost without exception the traces of teeth found on the scene of a crime originate from the anterior teeth of the upper and lower jaw, and especially from the incisors. Markings of the posterior teeth will seldom be found. The markings found on the incriminated object may originate either from the cutting edge of the teeth, from the anterior surface, or from the lingual or posterior surface. In many cases the markings will show all three surfaces, as, for instance, bites taken in a plastic

164

material. In most cases, however, they originate from the edge or from the anterior surface.

Markings from the Cutting Edge of the Teeth—The anterior teeth of an adult have more or less smooth cutting edges. Earlier in life, however, before the teeth become worn, three lobes or elevations divided by two developmental grooves may be noticed along the edge. As the distances between the lobes vary, these signs may be regarded as individual. They also indicate that the person in question has not yet reached the adult stage. Sometimes one of the lobes may be divided by an extra groove,

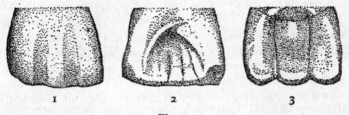

1   2   3

Fig. 54

Characteristics of the front teeth: (1) Labial surface of right upper central incisor, (2) lingual surface of left upper central incisor of adult person, (3) lingual surface of left upper central incisor of youth

thus bringing the total number of lobes to four or five, which can be regarded as a special peculiarity.

In cases of hereditary syphilis the anterior teeth may be peg-shaped and show fairly deep notches on the incisal edge, with semi-lunar notches on the posterior and lingual surfaces. These notches generally last throughout life.

Markings from the Anterior Surface—The anterior surface of normal teeth is usually convex. The above-mentioned notches run on this surface as shallow grooves which may be characteristic of a certain individual, altho they gradually wear off so that in a person over thirty years of age quite a smooth surface is generally the rule. The impressions of these grooves may be found in the tooth-marks.

Markings of the Lingual Surface—The lingual surface of the teeth is concave. This surface is supplied with an elevation called the singulum, whose prominence varies in different indi-

Fig. 54a

Front teeth of adult having hereditary syphilis

viduals. The identification is then based upon the prominence and width of the singulum.

The Making of Casts—Casts of the incriminating tooth-marks may be obtained in different manners. Formerly a direct plaster cast of the marks was made by dipping the object in thin plaster of Paris solution and allowing it to remain there until the plaster hardened. Air bubbles were avoided by penciling the surface of the object with the plaster mixture before dipping it into the container of plaster of Paris. However, the methods employed by dentists are now in vogue. They give clearer impressions, and harder and less perishable casts. For this purpose the tooth impressions should first be carefully varnished with a rapidly evaporating substance which leaves a thin protective film on the impressions. The actual cast is made with some of the substances generally used for this purpose. These compounds consist of a liquid, generally containing phosphoric acid, and a powder. A small quantity of the liquid is put on a cool smooth glass slab. An amount of powder equal to that of the liquid is added. After the rough mixing additional quantities of powder are incorporated into the mixture by means of a spatula. The entire process should not take longer than a minute or a minute and a half. If these precautions are not followed the setting of the mixture will be retarded or may fail entirely. If the object to be cast is soft and easily deformed, the mixture should be of a thick, creamy consistency. If the object, on the contrary, is hard and will withstand some pressure, a thicker mixture can be used. The hardening process takes from five to ten minutes, but the full crystallization takes place in about twenty-four hours.

The Identification—When the casts have been obtained in this manner they should be carefully scrutinized as to the following points: The kind and number of teeth; the arrangement and position of the teeth in the arch, which may be more or less irregular; the width of each individual tooth; the distance between the teeth; the measurement of the lobes (if they are present), and the measurement of the grooves on the surface if these exist.

The evidence thus obtained may be presented to the courts in the form of photographs of the casts after the respective measurements and the characteristic points have been marked with red ink, as is being done in fingerprint work.

QUESTIONS

1. Describe a case out of your own or others' experience where tooth prints have played a rôle.
2. At what age are the teeth most characteristic? Why?
3. What are the most characteristic points to be examined in tooth prints?
4. Tell briefly how a cast is made of a tooth print.

XII

HAIR

A. Places Where Hairs Are Found

THE examination of hairs may at times be important in criminal investigation. At the scene of the crime, and especially at the scene of a homicide, a careful search for hair left by the criminal should always be made.

In homicides where a struggle has occurred between the victim and the murderer, hair from the murderer may be found in the hands or on the clothing of the victim, or hair from the victim will adhere to the clothes of the murderer or to his weapon. Fingernails should be carefully examined, particularly in cases of sex crimes. Hair may be found on all kinds of things—clothes, beds, floor, carpets and furniture. It has happened that some of the burglar's hairs have been caught by a safe door. In rape and in sex murders the genitals of the victim and of the perpetrator should be carefully searched by a physician for traces of foreign hairs.

Hairs also may play a rôle in robbery, assault, illegal hunting, and generally on all occasions where it can be shown that a human being has been at a designated place or has had anything to do with a certain object. A stolen coat may, for instance, carry hairs of the thief and a stolen fur coat will sometimes leave traces on its bearer.

As will later be shown, the identification of hairs is not as easy and sure a matter as is generally thought, altho the importance of a search for hairs at the scene of a crime should not be underestimated. The floor of any room when cleaned with a vacuum cleaner will yield hair probably from dozens of persons. Places where one can reasonably expect to find hairs from the perpetrator should be searched.

168

Examination of hairs in criminal investigation was made for the first time when the Duchesse de Praslin was murdered in Paris in 1847. An examination was made of a hair which clung to the pistol used, altho the examiner satisfied himself with making some general remarks about the character of the hair and did not make any attempt at identification. Among cases in crime history where examination of hairs has played an important rôle can be mentioned the sixfold murder in Chursdorf, 1867, where a medical expert, Dr. Lender, identified the weapon and from the appearance of hairs drew important conclusions regarding the *modus operandi* of the murderer; the well-known murder of the tax collector, Gouffer, in 1889 by Gabrielle Bompart and Eyrand; the murder of Germaine Bichon in 1909, where the victim fought with the murderer and pulled hairs from her head, which were identified by Dr. Balthazard in Paris; and finally, the investigations made by the German scientists, Sonnenschein and Kutter, into the finding of animal hairs on perverts after unnatural acts with dogs and horses.

Comparison Hairs—Comparison hairs from the scalp of living persons, dead bodies and furs should not be cut, but pulled with the aid of forceps so that the roots may come out with them. Comparison hairs should be taken at each autopsy of a person who is the victim of an unknown murderer, or when the investigation is not yet completed. The comparison hairs should be as complete as possible. Hairs from the head, beard, eyebrows, eyelashes and genitals should be kept in different containers, properly labeled.

The necessity for taking comparison hairs before burial of the body cannot be too greatly emphasized. For example, in an actual case in which a woman was murdered with a hatchet, the woman lived for a few hours and was taken to a hospital where all the hairs on her head were shaved previous to the performance of an operation. This hair was thrown away. A few days after burial the hatchet was found with some hairs attached to it. In order to get comparison prints it became necessary to search the murdered woman's hair-brushes and hats. Unfortunately, she had had a girl friend living with her who had hair of the same color. This friend had also worn some of the murdered woman's hats. It became almost impossible to connect any of the hairs found with those of the dead woman. This part of the evidence, therefore, had to be discarded.

Transport of Hair—Hair should be kept in clean white paper which should be folded in the same manner as druggists fold powders, or even better in test tubes. Hairs to which blood or sperm is attached should be kept with great care so that they may not be subjected to friction. If the hair has become brittle and dry it can easily be broken and damaged. In such cases, when examining the hair false conclusions may be reached as to the manner of assault.

B. The Structure of Hair

Outer Aspect—Among mammals, including human beings, there are two kinds of hair—real hair (here called "hair") and fuzz. Hairs are generally long and stiff, compared with fuzz, which is generally short, fine and at times curly or woolly.

The hair consists of the root, tip and shaft.

The root does not give much information as to the origin of the hair. Very often the root is missing on hair found on clothes at the scene of the crime, on weapons, etc.

There are two kinds of roots, living and dry roots. The living roots, which are often found on hair in full growth, are very different from the roots of hair that is dry and dead. An examination of the root gives the clue to a very important question, namely, whether the hairs have been pulled away by force or have fallen out spontaneously. There are three possibilities:

1. *All hairs have living roots.* In this case they have not fallen out themselves but have been pulled away by force.
2. *All hairs have dry roots.* In this case they have most certainly fallen out themselves.
3. *Some hairs have living and some dry roots.* In this case they have been pulled away by force, the living hairs with the dry ones.

The tips may be natural or cut. In animals that live in freedom and whose hair has never been cut the original primitive form of the tip can be seen. The same is the case with certain domestic animals, and also with women whose hair has never been cut.

The form of the tip varies greatly on different parts of the body and on different animals. In some animals the hair has the same thickness from the root to the tip. Sometimes it has a very fine point. Between these two extremes there are all kinds of variations.

A cross-section of a hair of a human being differs according to the part of the body from which it is procured. Hairs from the head are generally round, altho curly hairs are sometimes oval. The hair of the beard is triangular, with concave sides. Hair from the torso is usually oval or kidney-shaped. These characteristics should not be looked upon as final, as the appearance of the cross-section is fairly variable. On animals many different types of cross-sections can be found.

Inner Structure of the Hair—If a hair is examined under a microscope three parts may be observed: The medulla, the cortex, and the cuticle. Of these three the medulla is the most important from the viewpoint of investigation.

Certain hair has no medulla. Therefore, hair can be divided into two categories—that without medulla and that with medulla. The hair of a very few animals belongs to the first category.

The medulla begins more or less near the root. In hairs that are full-grown and nearly falling out, the medulla begins fairly high up, its appearance varying to a high degree. In some animals it starts with a row of cells which continue the whole length of the hair to the tip, or the medulla makes one or more bifurcations and continues in several rows of cells side by side.

The medulla can be *continuous* or *interrupted*. It is continuous in a large number of animals and very often interrupted in humans, monkeys and horses. The diameter of the medulla can be absolutely constant but may also in the same hair at times be alternately narrow and broader. The actual diameter of the medulla is of very little importance, but the relation between the diameter of the medulla and the diameter of the whole hair is of great importance. This relation should always be calculated at the point where the hair is thickest. The diameter can be measured under the microscope with an eyepiece micrometer, or by microphotography with a ruler. This relation is named I (= medullary index).

The Medullary Index—1. Hair with narrow medulla (*i.e.*, less than 0.5). In this group belong human and certain monkeys' hairs.

2. Hair with medium medulla (*i.e.*, approximately 0.5). In this group belong the hairs of the cow, horse, and others.

3. Hair with thick medulla (*i.e.*, larger than 0.5). The hairs of almost all other animals belong in this group.

Certain human hairs show a very narrow and often interrupted medulla, and others, especially hairs from women's scalps, are often entirely without medulla. The following values of I are approximate:[1]

	Man	Woman
Neck	0.115	0.163
Forehead	0.132	0.148
Eyebrows	0.236	0.233
Eyelashes	0.095	0.146
Beard	0.260	....
Genitals	0.153	0.114
Armpits	0.102	0.179

High values will be found in most domestic animals.

The cuticle consists of translucent scales, laid one on another as shingles on a roof, with the free end pointed toward the tip of the hair. In humans about four-fifths of each scale is covered by the adjoining scale.

Preparations for Examination—It happens fairly often that at the scene of a crime hair-like fibers are collected and believed to be hair. A simple microscopic examination is in most cases sufficient to determine their origin. Fibers which show a similarity to hairs are wool, cotton, silk, hemp, linen, straw, and sometimes insects' legs. There is a simple method of differentiating between fibers of animal and vegetable origin—by boiling them about ten minutes in a 5 per cent solution of sodium hydroxid;

[1] Lambert and Balthazard, *Le Poil de l'Homme et des Animaux*, Paris, 1910.

if they are of animal origin, they will dissolve. Fibers of vegetable origin remain intact.

The first examination is made with the naked eye and includes
the determination of color, curliness and length. Thereafter a
microscopical examination should be made. The hairs are examined, especially from the viewpoint of adhering dirt, which often
gives valuable information as to the part of the body from which
the hair comes, the profession of the bearer, and the nature of the
crime. Many professions leave characteristic dust on the hair.
The mechanic will have metal dust; the miller, flour dust; the
bricklayer, brickdust, etc.

For the microscopic examination the hair should be mounted
on a glass slide. In most cases mounting in water or in a
very diluted solution of gelatin or glycerin is quite sufficient.
If there are several hairs to be examined they may be placed on
the slide side by side so that they can be studied at full length.
If the hairs are very long they should be cut in pieces, and in
order to avoid getting them mixed they should be marked with
small lumps of different-colored wax. Sometimes it may be
necessary to wash the hairs before the final examination if they
are very dirty. They are washed with alcohol or ether, but this
should not be done until a thorough examination of the adherent
dirt has been made. In some cases the hairs are so strongly
pigmented that the cells in the interior and the details in the
cuticle do not show up. For the purpose of bleaching the pigment the hairs are treated in acetic acid or strong peroxid of
hydrogen. The treatment requires from ten minutes to half an
hour and should be controlled by examination from time to time
under a microscope so as to avoid overtreatment. When the de-
colorizing process has reached the desired degree the hairs should
be washed repeatedly in water. Hairs on dead bodies at times
assume a reddish color on account of the action of the humus
in the soil.

Deformation of Hairs—Deformation of hairs sometimes leads
to very interesting conclusions as to the kind of weapon used. If
the head of a person has been hit only once with a hatchet or
an ax there are seldom deformations of the shaft of the hair in

the longitudinal direction, but it can very often be broken in the neighborhood of the root. The condition of the hair may disclose whether more than one blow has been struck; if so, longitudinal splits can be seen in the shaft. Such splits, then, are a sign of several blows.

The following description of conclusions which can be drawn from deformation of hairs may serve to show the importance which they may have in an investigation.[2]

Deformations Caused by Cutting—Sharp, right-angled or oblique cutting surface without splits denotes sharp cutting tool, such as knife or scissors.

Uneven, stepped cutting surface, with splitting or crushing of the end of the shaft, denotes a blunt cutting tool, such as a dull knife, hatchet, ax or similar weapon.

Deformations of the Surface of the Shaft—The deformed part of the shaft shows a flattening, which denotes crushing between two even surfaces. If the flattening is long and has the form of a bobbin, the hair has been crushed between one even and one round surface.

If the flattening is short and like a bobbin, the hair has been crushed between two round surfaces.

If the shaft is broken or bowed at an angle it has been crushed between an even or round surface and a corner.

If the flattened part at the cut end is long, it indicates a blow from a dull weapon with a straight edge.

If the flattened part at the cut end is short and bobbin-shaped, it denotes a blow with a blunt round weapon.

Deformations Caused by Shooting—Here sometimes particles of powder and metal may be found and also the natural consequences of burning, such as blackening, curling and charring.

Deformations Caused by Burning—These can be the result of an open flame, lightning, electric current, curling iron, and, as above mentioned, shooting. Singeing only causes curling, a slight swelling and a gray color. Burning in all its degrees up to complete charring leaves an odor like burnt horn, great swelling, gray, brown, red or black color, brittleness and transparence.

[2] Leers, *Gerichtsärztliche Untersuchungen*, Berlin, 1913.

Sometimes also air bubbles, arranged like the beads of a necklace, can be seen in the interior of the hair. Treatment with a curling iron sometimes also gives those results, altho generally it only splits the hair.

Deformations Caused by Scalding—These deformations are caused by hot water or steam. In the latter case, if the temperature has not gone above 350 degrees Fahrenheit, the hairs are reddish and show streaks in the longitudinal direction caused by the shriveling of the cells of the medulla. Up to 480 degrees Fahrenheit the hairs curl and become brittle, the reddish color becomes red-black, the hair is more transparent, and air bubbles form the typical "necklace."

C. Does the Hair Come from a Human Being or an Animal?

When studying this problem it should not be forgotten that none of the properties described below are alone and of themselves absolutely certain indices of origin. One or more of them can be found in hairs of certain animals, but never all together.

The medulla is missing in the fuzz of humans and often even in the hairs. I is always less than 0.3. The air network is irregular. In examining the hair in water the air is driven out and it is generally found that no pigment exists in the cells of the medulla. In animals, on the contrary, round, oval or many-cornered cells of the medulla are found. The grouping of these cells is different in each class of animals. In the equine, bovine and canine animals there is a granulation which at first sight resembles that of human hairs. In such cases I gives a definite solution. Except in some very rare cases the value of I in animals is always higher than 0.5.

The cortex is more developed in humans than in animals, and the pigment is equally divided over all the cortex in the form of fine grains. In almost all animals the pigment grains are irregular and larger than in humans.

The details of the cuticle in human hairs can only be found when the hair has been highly magnified. In animals, where they are much larger, they can be seen under a medium enlargement. The following table gives a survey of the principal differences in human and animal hairs: [3]

TABLE OF THE MAJOR DIFFERENCES BETWEEN HUMAN AND ANIMAL HAIR

HUMAN	ANIMAL
Medulla	
Air network in fine grains.	Air network in form of large or small sacks.
Cells invisible without treatment in water.	Cells easily visible.
Value of *I* lower than 0.3.	Value of *I* higher than 0.5.
Fuzz without medulla.	Fuzz with medulla.
Cortex	
Looks like a thick muff.	Looks like a fairly thin hollow cylinder.
Pigment in the form of very fine grains.	Pigment in the form of irregular grains—larger than the human.
Cuticle	
Thin scales, not protruding, covering one another to about four-fifths.	Thick scales, protruding, not covering one another to the same degree as the human.

D. From What Part of the Body Does the Hair Come?

This is a very delicate problem, which may not be solved in cases where there are only a few hairs. The length and diameter, shape of the tip and foreign particles are examined.

The fuzz has short length (not more than a quarter of an inch), and is very fine (0.025-0.04 mm.); there is no medulla or pigment. It is impossible to tell from what part of the body such bits of fuzz come because they are always alike.

In the adult male, hairs longer than 8 cm. come from the head,

---

[3] This table, as well as the one that follows, is taken from the excellent work of Lambert and Balthazard, *Le Poil de l'Homme et des Animaux*, Paris, 1910. This book is recommended for one who desires to enter more deeply into this study. Of especial value are the illustrations showing microscopic studies of the hairs of almost all animals.

or possibly from the beard. Hairs with a length of 3 to 4 cm. may originate from the different parts of the torso. They may also come from the head or the beard. Hairs of a length less than 3 cm. and with a natural point may come from the eyebrows, eyelashes, nostrils, breast, arms or legs. The first clue is given by the length of the hair, altho it should be taken into consideration that in certain cases, on the torso, legs and arms, the hair may show an abnormal development.

In the woman, hair longer than 8 cm. originates from the head. Hairs of lesser length come from different parts of the torso, but because of the mode they may also be from the head. Short hairs are either from the eyebrows or eyelashes.

E. Does the Hair Come from a Man or a Woman?

In the following survey some of the most important differences between male and female hair are described. A study of the table will show that the problem of determining the part of the body from which the hair has come is intimately connected with the determination of the sex.

TABLE SHOWING APPEARANCE OF THE HAIR ON DIFFERENT PARTS OF THE HUMAN BODY

Clipped Hair

Average diameter less than 0.08 mm. ....Male or female head hairs
"   "   greater than 0.1 mm. ....Beard

Original Hair

Length more than 8 cm. ....Female head hairs

Length 3 to 8 cm.
- Hair covered with grease..............Armpits
- Curly and Coarse
  - Knobby root...............Male genitals
  - Fine root ....Female genitals
- Wavy
  - Diameter larger than 0.1 mm. ....Mustache
  - Diameter less than 0.1
    - Cuticle intact ......Scrotum
    - Cuticle split ....Genital orifice

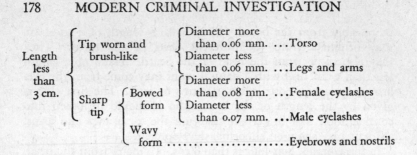

F. How Old Is the Person from Whom the Hairs Come?

Hairs from minors have the same appearance as from adults and are differentiated only by the smaller diameter and the more feeble pigmentation. The problem is in a certain respect simplified by the fact that head hairs are the only ones which are found on children. The German scientist, Oesterlen, gives the following average diameters:

Age	Diameter
12 days	0.024 mm.
6 months	0.037 "
18 months	0.038 "
15 years	0.053 "
Adults	0.07 "

If, therefore, a few hairs similar to head hairs are found and if the average diameter is much less than 0.07 mm. justification may be found for the belief that they come from a child. The less the diameter the greater the possibility of the child's being young, altho it is impossible to determine the age exactly.

In old persons the hair has a tendency to become finer, altho it is impossible to base any determination of the age on this fact. More important is the lack of pigment. If a hair is found with a living root where there are almost no pigment grains in the cortex it is probable that the hair comes from an old person.

G. How Long a Time Has Elapsed Since the Hair Was Cut?

Hair from the head which has been recently cut shows a clean-cut surface, especially if the scissors were sharp; but after a short time—not more than 48 hours—the cut begins to grow round from the friction of the hat or other covering. Naturally, it never acquires the characteristic appearance of hair that was never cut. Even in animals whose hair has been cut, this is the case. There is a possibility of showing approximately the time which has elapsed since a hair was cut. Figure 55 shows the tips of hairs cut 2, 8, and 20 days previously, and the tip of a hair which was cut only 24 hours before.

In some older medical manuals one may find calculations concerning the date of death based on the assumption that the hair has grown 0.2 to 0.5 mm. each day since the last shave. These calculations are uncertain because hair also continues to "grow" after death, owing to the drying and contraction of the skin.

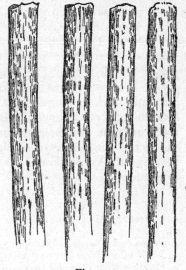

Fig. 55

From left to right, tips of hair cut 24 hours, 2, 8 and 20 days previously

Is the Hair Dyed?—In order to answer this question one must make a micro-chemical examination. It is possible to determine if it has been dyed with salts of bismuth or lead, nitrate of silver, permanganate of potassium, pyrogallic acid, paraphenyldiamin, henna, etc.

H. Does the Hair Belong to a Certain Individual?

Identification of hairs is very difficult, especially if only a few hairs, or, as it often happens, only a few pieces of hair are at the disposal of the expert. In almost all cases it is only possible to reach conclusions with great difficulty. One measures the length of the hairs, the average diameter of the medulla, and compares the colors. The diameter should be measured at the thickest places, and this has in itself little value for identification. *I* should be calculated. The color is determined after the *portrait parlé*. If all those signs are alike there is a probability of identity, but only a close examination can strengthen this probability. Examination of the medulla is important; likewise that of the root, the point, and the pigmentation of the cortex. It is difficult to describe the degree of similarity which should exist in order to arrive at a conclusion of identity. Here only wide experience can guide.

QUESTIONS

1. In what types of crime does the examination of hair especially play a rôle?
2. When and how should comparison hairs be obtained?
3. What information can be obtained from the roots of the hair?
4. Describe what is meant by the medulla index and its importance from the viewpoint of identification.
5. Describe some cases where adhering dirt on the hair will give information.
6. Tell briefly what information can be obtained from deformations of the hair.
7. What are the general differences between human and animal hair?
8. On what factors is the identification of hairs based?

XIII

PROBLEMS OF ATTACKS WITH FIREARMS [1]

THE first attempts to identify a bullet as having been discharged from a certain firearm were made hundreds of years ago, and it is quite possible that some such identifications may have been successful simply because the projectiles in those days were usually manufactured by the shooter himself. However, when factories began to produce ammunition, the possibility of identification on that score disappeared, at least as far as pistols and revolvers were concerned.

A. Revolvers and Pistols

The revolver is a hand firearm having at the rear of the barrel a revolving cylinder, provided with a number of chambers which, by the revolution of the cylinder, are brought successively into alinement with the barrel and the firing mechanism for successive and rapid firing.

In modern revolvers the cylinder-revolving mechanism is connected with the firing mechanism, the cocking of which automatically revolves the cylinder.

In double-action revolvers the pulling of the trigger performs the double function of cocking the hammer and revolving the cylinder to present a fresh cartridge to the firing mechanism.

An automatic pistol is a firearm from which the shell of a fired shot is ejected and a fresh cartridge pushed from the magazine into the breech by means of the gases generated by the pre-

---

[1] This chapter deals exclusively with small arms, *i.e.,* revolvers and pistols. Attention should be called to the fact that identification of bullets and shells fired from rifles and submachine guns is founded on the same principles and differs in no essential respect from the methods here described.

181

ceding explosion. The magazine usually fits into the butt or frame of the pistol but may also be a permanent part of the mechanism.

From the viewpoint of construction revolvers can be divided into three categories:

1. Revolvers with barrel firmly fixed to the frame, and a revolving cylinder which may be swung out to the side for the purpose of loading.

2. Revolvers with barrel hinged to frame, and carrying revolvable cylinder which may be broken open to load by releasing the barrel latch.

3. Revolvers with barrel firmly fixed to the frame, and revolving cylinder which may be removed by taking out the cylinder pin on which it rotates.

An obsolete type of revolver known as the "pepper-box" had a group of barrels which was revolvable.

From the viewpoint of identification the revolver should be classified first by caliber and secondly by percussion. We then have the three following primary groups:

1. Revolvers with center fire, where the percussion cap is placed in the center of the cartridge.

2. Revolvers with rim fire, where the percussion composition is placed around the inside of the rim of the shell.

3. Revolvers with pin fire, where the hammer strikes a needle which is placed at the rim of the shell and presses on a percussion cap in the interior of the cartridge. This type is obsolete now, and is very rarely found.

Revolvers with center fire are most prevalent for individual purposes. In the United States the following are the arms using center-fire revolver and pistol cartridges:

Firearm	Diameter of Bullets
25 Automatic Colt	(.251 inch)
32 Smith & Wesson	(.315 ")
32 Smith & Wesson Long	(.315 ")
7.63 Mauser	(.3105 ")
7.65 Luger	(.3095 ")
32 Short Colt	(.315 ")
32 Long Colt	(.313 ")

32 Long Colt	(.300 inch)
32 Colt N.P.	(.314 ")
32 Automatic Colt	(.3125 ")
32 Winchester	(.312 ")
9 mm. Luger	(.3555 ")
38 Short Colt	(.375 ")
38 Colt N.P.	(.359 ")
38 Colt Special	(.358 ")
38 Colt Long	(.358 ")
38 Automatic Colt	(.359 ")
380 Automatic Colt	(.357 ")
38 Smith & Wesson	(.359 ")
38 Smith & Wesson Special	(.3585 ")
38 Winchester	(.3595 ")
41 Short Colt	(.406 ")
41 Long Colt	(.387 ")
44 Smith & Wesson Am.	(.420 ")
44 Smith & Wesson Russ.	(.431 ")
44 Smith & Wesson Special	(.431 ")
44 Winchester	(.4255 ")
45 Colt	(.455 ")
45 Colt Automatic	(.4505 ")
455 Colt	(.458 ")

On the Continent the following calibers are found:

5	mm.	
5.5	"	(.2165 inch)
6.35	"	(.250 ")
7	"	(.276 ")
7.63	"	(.300 ")
7.65	"	(.302 ")
8	"	(.315 ")
9	"	(.354 ")
11	"	(.433 ")
12	"	(.472 ")

Revolvers with rim fire are not much in evidence today, altho the rim-fire .22 caliber cartridge is used to a large extent in target practise. Single-shot pistols are used by professional shooters in target practise. The Derringer .41 caliber may be found in many places throughout the United States.

It should be added that some of the above-named revolvers with rim or center fire can be loaded with bird shot, but the custom is by no means common.

Automatic pistols may be classified according to the number of grooves and impressions made on the bullets (see page 193). The common calibers in the United States are as follows:

.25 caliber (.251 inch)
.32   "   (.312 ")
.35   "   (.350 ")
.38   "   (.356 ")
.380 "   (.356 ")
.45   "   (.451 ")

On the Continent the following calibers are used:

6.35 mm. (.250 inch)
7.63   "   (.300 ")
7.65   "   (.302 ")
9   "   (.354 ")
11.5   "   (.451 ")

Of these the 6.35 mm. and the 7.65 mm. are the most generally used. The 7.63 is a special type of cartridge used only for the Mauser automatic pistol of military type. The 9 mm. is almost exclusively used for military and police purposes. The 11.5 is extremely rare on the Continent and only used for imported pistols (.45 Auto Colt for the Colt M. 1911 and .455 Auto for the Webley & Scott). One may also find on the Continent some other calibers of automatic pistols—the Lilliput 4.25 mm., the Clement 5 mm., the Steyr and Roth 8 mm. (.315 inch), etc.—but these are now becoming obsolete.

Calibers are calculated differently in English, American and Continental firearms. In order to understand this important difference we will introduce the terms, "real caliber" and "nominal caliber." In Continental arms (with the exception of arms without rifling—as, for example, for buckshot) the real caliber, *i.e.*, the diameter of the bore, is measured between two opposite lands. In other words, the bore is looked upon, in measuring, as having no grooves. The measurement is taken at the muzzle and not at the breech, where the cartridge chamber is located. The nominal caliber is purely a conventional measurement which has only an indirect relation with the bore. American and English calibers are nominal and are expressed in decimals of an inch. The following table shows the relation between American, English and Continental calibers:

American Caliber		English Caliber		Continental Caliber in Millimeters
.22 inch		.220 inch		5.5
.25 "		.250 "		6.5 (6.35)
.28 "		.280 "		7
.30 "	(.32 Rev.)	.300 "	(.303)	7.65
.32 "		.320 "		8
.35 "	(.351)	.350 "		9
.38 "		.360 "		9.3
.38 "		.370 "		9.5
.38-.40-.41 inch		.410 "		10
.405 inch				10.5
.44 "		.440 "		11
.45 "		.450 "	(.455)	11.5

B. The Caliber of a Fired Bullet

When the Bullet Has Its Original Shape—One would perhaps expect a bullet to have a caliber absolutely corresponding to the arm. This is not the case. If one tries to introduce the bullet back again into the firearm after it has been fired, it will be found to be impossible. If the lands are to make markings on the bullet, the latter must be larger than the bore. In bullets of small caliber (.22-.32) the difference between the diameter of an unfired bullet and the real caliber of the arm is about .008 inch. In the arm of larger caliber (.35-.45) the difference may be as great as .015 inch.

The caliber is determined with the aid of a micrometer, calibrated to .0001 inch, and measured on two opposite grooves.

When the Bullet Has Been Deformed—If a bullet has completely lost its original form, there is a possibility of determining its caliber by measuring the width of the land or groove, and in

rare cases by noting the letters affixed to the bottom of some foreign bullets, and by the weight.

In order to determine the caliber and the origin by the weight

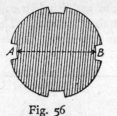

there should be a complete collection of
information about all bullets. The weight
of the bullet varies with the manufacturer and the materials used.[2]

If the bullet has been split in the body,
all parts should be carefully collected at
autopsy. When weighing these parts
there are three alternatives. In the first
case, the weight may tell the supposed
caliber if, for example, the firearm has
been seized. This is, at any rate, interesting information. In the second

Fig. 56

Schematic cross-section
of a fired bullet: the caliber is measured between
A and B .

case, the parts may weigh more than a bullet from the suspected arm. In this case, no identity is possible. Finally, they
may weigh less, in which case identity is not excluded because
one may not have collected all the small parts.

To try to determine the origin of a bullet by chemical analysis
is almost useless. In some cases special alloys are used, notably in
jacketed bullets, but this is rare. As a rule both bullets and
jackets from different manufacturers are of uniform composition.

Bullets are made either of lead or, with regard to jacketed
bullets, of hard metals, generally of gilding metal coated with
nickel, and with a lead core. There are, also, jackets consisting
entirely of copper and zinc, and coated with nickel or tin.

C. The Identification of Bullets

Examination of a bullet should lead not only to the determination of identity with the firearm from which it has been fired
but also to a thorough knowledge of the marks produced on it

[2] Fairly complete tables regarding the weight and chemical composition of bullets
are given in Söderman's book, *L'Expertise des armes a feu courtes*, Lyons, 1928.
This information embraces only modern ammunition on the market. Some stocks
of old cartridges no longer manufactured are even now, without doubt, in the possession of some individuals.

by its discharge. Under certain circumstances it might be possible to identify a bullet by examination of an object which it has touched on its way. De Rechter and Mage,[3] for instance, succeeded in identifying a bullet by studying a tooth which it had hit. Lead bullets may also be identified by the marks left on them by the fabrics which they have pierced.[4]

All modern small arms have rifled bores. The grooves are necessary because modern bullets possess a long or cylindrical section and a more or less conical shape. If they were not put in rotation around the longitudinal axis through the pitch of the grooves they would probably turn end-over-end in the air. The number of grooves varies according to the manufacturer, but there are generally five or six. In all modern firearms the grooves are made with an automatic cutter, and it would seem natural to assume that all barrels of a certain serial would be absolutely identical. However, this is not the case. While irregularities might have no influence whatever on the value of the arm, they have great importance in criminological examinations. The grooves are made with a small special cutter, their width and depth changing very slightly.[5]

Another important fact is to be considered. The tools become worn while in use and produce numerous microscopical ridges in the grooves, which are still more accentuated when small metal alloy particles are ground between the cutter and the steel. Defects in the material may also make characteristic marks. All in all, the width, the depth and the pitch of the grooves, the ridges in the grooves, and other peculiarities due to defective material, wear and tear, and accidents, individualize the barrel and render possible the identification of the bullet which has passed through it. On a bullet we find *the sum total* of the peculiarities of the particular barrel. Generally speaking, it is useless to compare the barrel or its parts directly with the bullet

[3] De Rechter and Mage, in *Revue de Droit Penal*, March, 1927.
[4] Piedelièvre, "Les empreintes de vêtements relevées sur les balles de plomb" in *Étude Criminologique*, Paris, 1927.
[5] For further information about tools used for cutting, *The Modern Gunsmith*, by James V. Howe, New York, 1934, should be consulted.

as was formerly done. The comparison should be made with comparison bullets.

The bullet to be examined is at first inspected for adhering particles, and these, if necessary, should be analyzed microscopically. Such an analysis may give important information. If the bullet is deformed, one tries to determine how the deformation came about—eventually by performing practical experiments. If the bullet is deformed to such a degree that it has completely lost its original form and does not show any grooves, it is only possible to determine the caliber and perhaps the make.

If, on the contrary, the bullet has retained its shape or is only partly deformed, the grooves are examined with the comparison microscope. The comparison microscope is double—two separate microscopes—fitted with a comparison eyepiece, which, when placed on them, merges them together like one microscope. The comparison eyepiece fuses the images of two bullets or shells into one image. One may see the front half of one and the rear half of the other bullet, and they appear to be one in the microscope.

When a fatal bullet or shell is set in the microscope with a test bullet or shell fired from the arm used, they can be rotated either independently or together, and any marks left on them by reason of any condition of the rifling of the barrel used, or any marks left on the primer of the shell from the breech-block or firing-pin, are bound to match in the composite image of the two bullets or shells, thereby making identification positive. This eliminates any possibility of guess-work.

This instrument was first used to identify bullets by the Americans, Graville and Waite, but many modifications, especially concerning the bullet holders, have been made. It goes without saying that a great deal of experience is a prerequisite to complete success. The able expert may often detect signs of identity or non-identity where the amateur sees nothing at all.

In some cases it may be advisable to photograph each groove individually. A special bullet-holder should then be used for the purpose of turning the bullet continuously. The focus of the camera should not be altered after the first groove of a bullet has been photographed. If sharper details are to be brought out, this should be done by means of the movable bullet-holder. The light should be as constant as possible and put in such a position that the best relief is obtained. When the groove on the incriminating bullet has been photographed, the same procedure is carried out on the comparison bullet. Again, we must emphasize that the focusing of the camera must not be changed. In order to get the necessary depth of focus, a common portrait lens with a very long bellows on the camera, or some other special attachment, should be used.

This last method of photography was at first used by the Belgian scientists, De Rechter and Mage. In recent years the tendency has been to obtain "rolled photographs" of the bullets, *i.e.*, the whole circumference of the bullet is photographed on one plate. An apparatus of this kind was constructed by Professor Bruning of the police laboratory in Berlin in 1928.

Comparison bullets can be obtained by shooting them into water. A high, thick barrel filled with water may be used for this purpose, altho a steel cylinder, one foot in width and about two yards high, is preferable. Many ballistic experts shoot into cotton or wax. In order to facilitate the comparison of the bullets a little trick can be employed to establish their position in the chamber. With a file a thin scratch is made at the side of the top of the bullet and this scratch is placed topmost when introducing the cartridge into the firearm.

Two cases from the ballistic bureau of the St. Louis Police Department, submitted to the authors by Thomas Lewis, research officer, will illustrate the use of identification of firearms:

1. About 10 A.M., August 31, 1928, a man was seen running from a store located at 3217 Cherokee Street. A police officer gave chase and captured the man, who was later identified as David Valasco. Upon returning to the store with Valasco the officer found that the proprietor, Nathan Brodden, had been held up and shot. An investigation at the scene disclosed the fact that a .38-caliber Smith & Wesson revolver, No. 57404, had been dropped by Valasco after he had shot Mr. Brodden. Valasco admitted participating in the holdup and implicated two other Mexicans, Mike Aguilera and Joe Martinez. At the hos-

pital Mr. Brodden, before dying, identified Valasco. Valasco and
his two accomplices confessed to the crime but refused to sign
written statements. As there were no eye-witnesses to the crime
it was necessary to assemble all circumstantial evidence possible.

The bullet was removed from Brodden's body and compared
with the test bullets fired from Valasco's pistol. The identification was complete, as the photographs showed. Mike Aguilera
and Joe Martinez were tried together, found guilty and sentenced
to be hanged. At a later date David Valasco was tried and found
guilty and sentenced to life imprisonment in the Missouri State
Penitentiary, Jefferson City, Missouri.

2. On the evening of December 24, 1928, a "home brew" party
was in full swing at the home of August Greving at 1943 North
Ninth Street. One of the guests, Calvin S. Harper, became intoxicated. Upon being told to leave because he paid too much
attention to Greving's wife, Sybil, he became quarrelsome and
had to be put out. Harper let it be known at this time that he
was always "heeled."

About 11:45 P.M. of the same evening he returned to Greving's
home, and when Greving opened the door, Harper shot at the
silhouette upon the stained glass of the door. There were three
eye-witnesses to the shooting, Sybil Greving, Alice Stone and
Opal White. Harper, in making his getaway, boarded an inter-
urban car bound for Granite City, Illinois. In his intoxicated
condition he dropped his pistol on the floor of the car, upon
which it was discharged, the bullet striking Pete Simos, another
passenger. Upon the car arriving at its first stop in Granite City,
Illinois, Harper was arrested and later brought back to St. Louis
to answer to a charge of murder.

Some time later and prior to his trial the three eye-witnesses,
Sybil Greving, Alice Stone and Opal White, were riding in an
auto driven by Carl Carey, who was in an intoxicated condition
at the time. While driving he swerved the car to the right and
crashed into a telephone pole. Opal White was killed instantly
and later Alice Stone died at the hospital. When the case was
called Sybil Greving could not be located and a search for her
proved to be in vain. This left the State without any eye-

witnesses and the trial was set back until a ballistic examination could be completed. The State's Attorney offered to accept a plea of murder in the second degree with a sentence of ten years, which Harper refused. However, after learning of the ballistic evidence assembled against him, Harper's lawyer advised him to take the plea, which he gladly did. He is now serving his time in the Missouri State Penitentiary.

Three cases from the ballistic bureau of the New York Police Department, prepared by Henry F. Butts, ballistic expert, further illustrate the value of identification of firearms:

1. Francis Crowley, also known as "Two-Gun Crowley," who was electrocuted for the murder of Patrolman Hirsch in Nassau County, New York, had committed an earlier crime in the Bronx and was wanted by the detectives there. Information was obtained that Crowley frequented an office on Broadway. A detective was assigned to cover the office and finally found him there. As the detective was searching Crowley and taking one gun away from him, Crowley drew another gun from the sleeve of his coat and shot the detective in the abdomen and escaped. The shells discharged from the weapon used by Crowley, and the bullets removed from the detective's abdomen, showed that they had been fired from a Colt .380 caliber automatic pistol.

During a holdup in an apartment on the upper west side, several shots were fired by one of the robbers, all of whom made their escape. Examination of the shells and bullets recovered showed that they came from Crowley's gun. A coal company office was the scene of a holdup, where several shots were fired. The robbers escaped. Examination again showed that Crowley's gun had been used.

Detectives in a police motor-car had a running pistol fight with the occupants of another automobile, and the bullets found imbedded in the squad car showed that some of them were fired from Crowley's gun. The bandits' car was found later, and it developed that this car was the one in which Virginia Brannen was killed by Fat Durringer, who was executed for that crime. The car was found abandoned; on the floor lay several discharged shells, and in the rear cushion was found the bullet that had gone through Virginia Brannen's body. These also were identified as having been fired from Crowley's pistol. Later, it developed that Crowley had lent Durringer his pistol.

Patrolman Hirsch was shot and killed in Nassau County by the occupant of an automobile whom he was about to question. A number of shots were fired. Examination of the shells and bullets recovered from the scene and from Patrolman Hirsch's body showed that they, too, had been fired from Crowley's gun.

When Crowley was captured in an apartment in the west-end section of Manhattan, his gun was found and test bullets and shells were obtained from it. Comparison of the test bullets with all the bullets and shells mentioned above showed that the identifications made before the gun was recovered were absolutely correct.

2. Early in October, 1933, Vito Caruso was held up in his drug store on Graham Avenue, Brooklyn, and the robbers took from him a .32 caliber revolver. On October 30, Sigmund Berkowitz was shot and killed during an attempted holdup in his haberdashery store on Eighth Avenue, Brooklyn. In November, Detective Sweeney, of the Second Detective District, arrested four occupants of an automobile who had in their possession, without permit, a .32 caliber Colt revolver, with the numbers filed off. The arrest was made at Canal and Center Streets, Manhattan.

Examination at the ballistic bureau showed that the serial number of the revolver was 182921, and that it was the revolver that had been taken from Vito Caruso. The usual tests were obtained from the revolver, and microscopic comparison showed that the bullet removed from the body of Berkowitz was fired from this weapon. This information was forwarded to the commands concerned, and confessions were obtained from the men. They were charged with the murder of Berkowitz. In January, 1934, the four defendants were tried for murder in the first degree, and during the trial three of them pleaded guilty to murder in the second degree; the fourth, who had actually fired the shot that killed Berkowitz, was convicted of murder in the first degree.

3. On April 18, 1931, the dead body of one John Little (alias

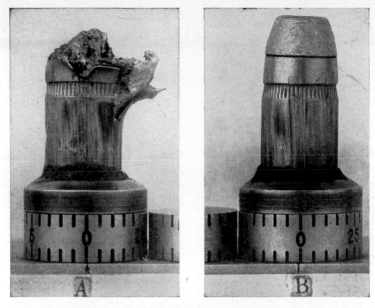

IDENTIFICATION OF BULLETS

A is the fatal bullet. B is a test bullet. The barrel markings match.
(Page 186)

IDENTIFICATION OF COLT REVOLVER SHELLS

The upper five shells were fired from the "crime gun" after it was recovered. The lower six were found at the scene of the murder. The breech markings match. (Page 197)

[PLATE 10]

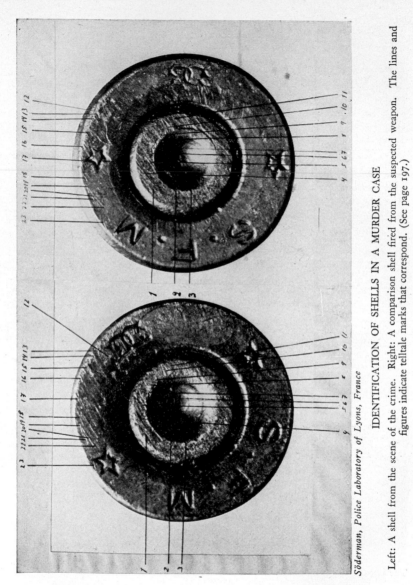

Söderman, Police Laboratory of Lyons, France

IDENTIFICATION OF SHELLS IN A MURDER CASE

Left: A shell from the scene of the crime. Right: A comparison shell fired from the suspected weapon. The lines and figures indicate telltale marks that correspond. (See page 197.)

[PLATE 11]

Burke) was found lying in the gutter outside of a warehouse in Long Island City. A .38 caliber bullet was recovered from his body at the autopsy.

Information was received by the New York Police Department that there had been a pistol battle between holdup men and Patrolman Maurice Kenman of the Watervliet Police Department, Watervliet, New York. Patrolman Kenman was requested to bring his revolver to the ballistics bureau at the New York City Police Headquarters for test. Microscopic comparison showed that the bullet removed from the body of John Little had been fired from Patrolman Kenman's revolver at Watervliet.

D. Possibilities of Determining the Make of an Unknown Firearm by a Bullet

In order to determine the make of an unknown arm from which a bullet has been fired a classification of bullet marks must be at hand. Early attempts at such a classification were made in the U. S. A. by Charles Waite and continued by Lieut.-Col. Calvin Goddard. In 1926 in Lyons, France, Dr. Söderman began a classification of European automatic pistols, and at the same time Professor Metzger, Dr. Heess and Inspector Haslacher in Stuttgart, Dr. Kraft in Berlin, and Major Wittman in Nuremberg, Germany, undertook a similar classification. The work of Metzger, Heess and Haslacher has been published in an *Atlas of Arms* which contains photographs of more than 100 different automatic pistols and can be classed as one of the achievements of police science in modern times.[6] In many police departments of the United States there now exist comprehensive classifications of revolvers, pistols, etc.

Determining the make of an unknown firearm is accomplished by examining the grooves on the bullet, their number and width, as well as the direction (right-hand or left) and the leed (rate of twist) of the spiral. These four factors will be found constant in the same make of pistols, or at least in the better-known ones.

[6] The text of the *Atlas* was published in the *Archiv für Kriminologie*, v. 89. Dr. Walther Heess, Forststrasse 18, Stuttgart, Germany, published the photographs.

Unimportant European manufacturers of pistols will often have the barrels made by a "barrel maker" (home industry). In these cases the measurements are seldom exact, and home manufacturers do not record changes in measurements. This gives rise to uncertainty regarding the date of manufacture and the exact calibers. In addition, when large orders have been received, the manufacturers frequently begin a new series of numbers for arms, beginning with No. 1, or some other low number, to avoid the extra work of making four ciphers.

For the sake of simplicity all rifling heads have one cutting tool, and almost all pistol barrels have an even number of grooves. In the .25 and .32 caliber automatics there are usually 6 lands (smooth surfaces between the spiral grooves). Only about one-half of the Continental pistols of the .25-caliber group and only one-third of the pistols of the .32-caliber group have 4 lands. Very few pistols of European make have 5, 7 or 8 lands. In the survey made by Metzger and Heess there were only 8 automatics having 5 lands. In the .25-caliber group there are the Express, Floria, Pickert, Princeps & Waldman. In the .32-caliber group there are the F. N. Model 1900, Helios, and the Stenda pistols. The Schmeisser Model No. 2 .25 caliber has 8 lands. Up to No. 105,000 the Schmeisser pistol had 6 lands. Such variations have also been noted in the Walther Model 5 and 7 and in the Stenda. Walther has changed from 4 to 6 lands.

Pistols with the same number of lands may also be differentiated by the direction of the *leed* or twist of the rifling, which may be either to the left or to the right. The direction of the leed is figured from the breech to the muzzle. There are very few automatics with leed to the left, with the exception of Spanish pistols of .25 and .32 caliber. The Bayard and Colt, calibers .25, .32, .38 and .45, also have left leed. All pistols known so far to have left leed have 6 lands.

The leed can be expressed by measuring the distance a land must travel to turn one complete circle, or it may be expressed by the angle of leed. The angle of leed is the angle which the land forms with the longitudinal axis of the bullet. If that angle is large, the leed is small. To measure the angles a special measurement microscope has been manufactured. A complete description of the technique of measuring is given in the above-mentioned work of Metzger and Heess.

The angle of leed is an important sign but it is not always constant. Small defects may arise by a readjustment of the cutter. The angle of leed will, however, often give sufficient information for distinguishing different makes of pistols.

The width of the lands must be judged even more carefully than the angle of the leed. This is necessary because of the manufacturers' practise of making the cutter about .002 of an inch wider than standard and using the cutter until it has worn down to .002 of an inch below standard, causing a difference of .002 plus or minus. Therefore, differences in the same make of pistol may occur. The width of the lands is measured with the same microscope mentioned above.

In the classification, the bullets are divided at first by the caliber and then according to the number of lands and the direction of leed. The following classification may be found in the *Atlas of Arms:*

Table No.	Caliber		No. of Lands	Direction of Pitch or Leed
1	.25	with	6	right
1A	.25	"	6	left
2	.25	"	4	right
3	.25	"	5, 7 or 8	right
4	.32	"	6	right
4A	.32	"	6	left
5	.32	"	4	right
6	.32	"	5	right
7	{ .38 / .380 }	"	4, 6 or 7	right and left

In these tables the individual makes are arranged according to the degree of the leed. In tabulating, the authors of the *Atlas* have considered only the smallest angle of the leed. If two pistols of the same make vary more than .3 degree (angle of leed) the pistols are tabulated separately. In the tables one will also find minimum and maximum width of the lands.

The possibilities of determining a certain make when dealing with the most common combinations—for instance, .25 caliber with 6 lands and right leed—are small and only in exceptional cases are results obtained. The possibilities of determining the makes of rarer combinations in the table, such as 1A, 3, 4A, 6 and 7, are greater. As a rule, it may be said that only in a few cases is it possible to determine an individual manufacturer.

The following is a table of rate of twist and groove diameters of American-made revolvers:

TABLE OF RATE OF TWIST AND GROOVE DIAMETERS OF AMERICAN-MADE REVOLVERS

Name and Caliber	Make	Leed in Inches	Groove Diameter Inches
22 Long Rifle	S. & W.	15R*	.2235
22 Colt	Colt	14L†	.222
25 Automatic	Colt	16L	.251
32 Colt Automatic	Colt	16L	.311
32 Smith & Wesson	S. & W.	18¾R	.313
32-20 Colt	S. & W.	12R	.312
32 Colt	Colt	16L	.312
38 Smith & Wesson	S. & W.	18¾R	.357
38 Smith & Wesson Special	S. & W.	18¾R	.357
38 Colt Special	Colt	16L	.354
38 Colt Automatic	Colt	16L	.356
38 Colt Revolver	Colt	16L	.354
38-40 Colt	Colt	16L	.402
41 Colt	Colt	16L	.402
44-40 Colt (old models)	Colt	16L	.424
44-40 Colt (new models)	Colt	16L	.427
44 Smith & Wesson	S. & W.	20R	.431
44 Colt	Colt	16L	.427
45 Automatic Colt Pistol	Colt	16L	.451
45 Colt	Colt	16L	.452

*R indicates right or clock-wise rifling twist.
†L indicates left or counter-clock-wise rifling twist.

The Colts have six grooves. Most of the Smith & Wesson have five grooves, except Smith & Wesson Government 1917 model and Smith & Wesson Automatic, which have six grooves.

E. Identification of Shells

In order to understand the process of identification of shells it is necessary to know what happens when a shot is fired.

The revolver is a firearm with a rotating chamber which allows the successive firing of five or more shots. The chamber is put in rotation by a hand or prawl, often connected with the trigger. It is the shooter himself who makes the necessary movement to fire the cartridge from the revolver and to introduce a new cartridge.

In the automatic pistol, on the contrary, as the name implies, this series of movements is absolutely automatic. The cartridges here are in a magazine which is lodged in the butt. When a cartridge is fired, the empty case is forced backward by the recoil; the slide around the barrel is movable and retreats a certain distance, due to the pressure of the recoil. This causes the slide to open, thus permitting the empty shell to come out. The empty shell is drawn backwards with the slide and the extractor. At the moment when the slide is opened the cartridge strikes the ejector and is thrown free of the extractor and slide. The slide goes back to its original position with the aid of a spring. The spring of the firing-pin has in the meantime been contracted again, and it is now only necessary to pull the trigger in order to repeat all the movements of firing, recoiling, throwing out the empty case, and contracting the spring of the firing-pin.

Because of the difference in the construction of pistols and revolvers the examination of the fired shells differs according to the arm. We will first deal with automatic pistols, which from the viewpoint of identification are the more interesting.[7]

Automatic Pistols—Let us assume that a murder has been committed and that some empty shells have been found by the side of the victim. These are given to an expert to be compared with the automatic pistol seized from the suspect. The first step to be taken is to determine whether the shells belong to an automatic pistol and whether the calibers are equal. Both facts

[7] See also "Identification of Shells," translated from *Revue Internationale de Criminalistique*, Vol. 4, No. 5, *Journal of Criminal Law and Criminology*, Vol. XXIII, No. 3, Chicago, 1932.

may be determined without difficulty, but care should be taken not to introduce the incriminating shell in the pistol while mak-

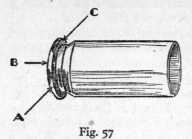

Fig. 57

A shell for automatic pistols: A, rim; B, head; C, front of the rim

ing the comparison, as the small scars found on the shell, necessary for the identification, may be destroyed during the manipulation. Anyone who is familiar with firearms is usually able to tell the caliber at a glance. Should there be any doubt about the caliber, as, for example, calibers 7.63 mm. and 7.65 mm., Mauser and Parabellum pistols, respectively, measurements on a special test shell should be taken, the test shell being fitted into the incriminating pistol and then compared with the incriminating shell. Knowledge of the calibers commonly used in different countries is of importance to the expert on firearms.

When the caliber has been determined the actual examination takes place. We have already sketched, superficially, the procedure of firing an automatic pistol. It goes without saying that all those operations must leave marks on the shell. Of these the following are of importance: [8]

Marks from the Firing-pin—The pin leaves an impression in the percussion cap which is sometimes characteristic of the arm but often varies according to the hardness of the metal in the cap.

Marks from the Extractor—These are of great importance because they are the starting point in observation of the shell. The position of the shell previous to being fired is determined by the trace of the extractor. The trace of the extractor is found in front of the rim of the shell and will show up bright and glossy in an oblique light against the sooty background of the shell.

[8] See also *Identification of Firearms and Forensic Ballistics,* by Burrard, London, 1934; *Firearms Identification,* by Hatcher, Marines, N. C., 1934, and "Scientific Identification of Firearms and Bullets," by Goddard, *Journal of Criminal Law and Criminology,* Vol. XVII-2, 1926.

This sootiness around the trace will enable one to differentiate between the trace of the extractor which is made when the shot is fired and such traces as will occur when a cartridge is inserted in the weapon and later extracted but not fired. The fact that no soot is present at the opening of the breech where the extractor is located may be explained by the fact that the powder gas finds its way out at this point and is not condensed. Sometimes the extractor when extracting the shell will slip over the rim and make distinctive scratches on it. Only the traces in the front of the rim should, however, be taken into consideration. Other traces may easily be mistaken for scratches from the magazine.

Traces from the Ejector—The trace of the ejector is found on the head of the shell. When examining these traces it is essential to have a clear idea of the position of the shell previous to the firing. This will, as already mentioned, be determined by the trace of the extractor on the rim. The shell is thrown backwards a relatively long distance before it is pivoted against the extractor, thus altering its position to some minute degree on its way.

Sometimes the marks of the ejector will be distinctly imprinted, sometimes it will touch the edge only very slightly, and in some cases it will not leave any marks at all. Owing to such variations the amateur will probably have difficulty in finding these traces, altho it is always possible to note where the marks of the ejector should be found by looking for the marks of the extractor. Generally the ejector has a position directly opposite the extractor, altho this may not be the case in all instances.

Marks from the Breech Block—These are most important. The breech block is very often finished by hand and bears the characteristic ridges from the file or from other tools used. These ridges are pressed into the soft metal of the shell and often give identification marks of great value.

The identification is made in the following manner: A few shells are fired from the incriminating arm, collected and marked. The incriminating shell is also marked to avoid confusion. They are then carefully washed, first with soap and water, and then with diluted ammonia, to free them from all adhering grease and dirt.

With the aid of a strong magnifying glass or a low-power microscope, preferably of the binocular type, the traces of both the ejector and the extractor are compared. If they are in the same position in relation to one another and their general appearance is the same, one may conclude that they have been fired from a pistol of the same make. An absolute conclusion about the origin of the shells, however, can be reached only after a photomicrographic examination of the markings from the breech block on the rear of the shell.

For this purpose a common photomicrographic apparatus of vertical type with a special shell-holder is used. A mikrosummar with a focus of about 65 mm., or similar lens, may be used.

Usually it is sufficient to photograph the incriminating shell and two comparison shells.

Each shell is placed in the holder so that the head is absolutely parallel to the lens. In order to facilitate the identification, care should be taken that the markings from the ejector have an absolutely identical position before photographing each shell. A line mark may be made on the shell and holder with a fine lead pencil. The lines should touch each other when the shell is inserted in the hole.

Oblique light from a small powerful arc lamp should be made to fall on the shell. A condenser concentrates the light on the head of the shell. There should be as much relief as possible. An enlargement of about 10 times is sufficient, the enlargement covering about three-quarters of a half-plate.

Identification, with the aid of the enlargement, should not prove difficult. The characteristic scratches can be easily seen. A photograph of the incriminating shell and one of a comparison shell should be pasted side by side on cardboard, and the characteristic marks should be recorded with lines and ciphers, following the same method as that used in the identification of fingerprints.

The identity of the shells may also be shown by printing photographs of the shells on negative films instead of on paper. If, when the negatives are held up to the light, the details cover each other, the identification is established.

Revolvers—When a shot is fired from an automatic pistol the shell, in most cases, will be found on the scene, as the criminal seldom thinks of disposing of this important piece of evidence. On the other hand, when a revolver is used, the empty shell remains within the chamber. It is seldom thrown away on the scene unless the criminal is forced to reload.

Revolvers with Center Fire—Cartridges of calibers .32 and .45 for automatic pistols may in rare cases be used in revolvers. But a doubt about the type of firearm used should never arise because of the presence of traces from the ejector and the extractor when an automatic has been fired. Mistakes are possible with certain automatic pistols, as, for instance, the German D-pistol, where the firing-pin serves as ejector, and where the usual marking on the edge of the rim is missing. A careful examination, however, will disclose a microscopically small oval scratch on the percussion cap near the mark of the firing-pin. This scratch is due to the second striking of the firing-pin against the shell, denoting clearly that the shell has been fired from an automatic pistol.

The identification of a shell with the revolver from which it has been fired is often difficult. The following characteristic marks are available for identification: the mark of the firing-pin,.the mark of the breech-block and the mark of the firing-pin hole.

The mark made by the firing-pin varies according to the shape of the pin, the hardness of the metal in the percussion cap, and the force of the blow dealt by the firing-pin. If all these three factors were constant, characteristic marks should be found on all fired shells, but this is not the case. On account of the varying degrees of hardness of the metal in the cap, the depth of the mark changes often, and if the ignition cap is not deformed in some manner it is, in most cases, difficult to arrive at positive conclusions. By firing some cartridges from a revolver and then comparing the marks the difference in the shapes of the marks will be easily seen. Some of them are fairly similar, but some show such great variations from the true form that they cannot be identified. Some of the marks may be similar to those on cartridges fired from other revolvers, and some are so different that they may lead to the conclusion that no identity is possible. It is therefore necessary to make a very painstaking investigation to determine the true shape.

Revolvers with Rim-Fire Cartridges—The identification is based upon the markings of the breech-block. In rim-fire revolvers the marking of the hammer may sometimes be characteristic.

F. Possibility of Determining the Make of an Unknown Arm by a Shell

In order to determine the make of an unknown arm from which a seized shell has been fired, a classification of marks on shells must be available. Such a classification of automatic pistols will be found in the *Atlas of Arms* by Metzger and Heess.

The shell receives the first marks from the sharp guide lips of the magazine in the form of very fine scratches on two opposite sides of the cartridge, parallel with its longitudinal axis. When the cartridge enters the chamber there will be one more mark caused by the magazine slide or the following cartridge which presses the first cartridge down. This trace consists of a faint mark between the two aforesaid marks. None of these marks have importance from the viewpoint of examination, but it is necessary to know them so as not to confuse them with other marks.

If the cartridge is inserted directly into the chamber a secondary extractor mark will occur which comes from the extractor touching the rim when the slide is going forward.

Other marks are the above-mentioned impressions of the breech-block.

In order to be able to judge the possibilities of determining the pistol system, one must study the different phases of the procedure of repeating.   The traces may be studied by covering the shell with a coating of black enamel containing a little resin oil to make it more elastic.   All the traces on the shell will then be easily seen.

The traces of the extractor may sometimes serve as a basis for the determination of the system, as there are at least two automatic pistols made without extractor—the Steyr .25 and .32.   This

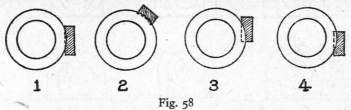

1   **2**   **3**   **4**

Fig. 58
The principal forms of extractors

fact is very interesting.   It shows that the extractor in reality is not needed to draw out the shell after firing.   The pressure exerted by the powder gas will do that by itself.   The extractor is useful only when the cartridge misfires, or in pistol instruction.

The extractor varies a great deal in different pistols, and a distinctive print of the extractor will often afford some ground for the determination of the pistol system.   Generally speaking, there are four principal forms of extractors.   Figure 58 shows graphically these forms which are seen at the front of the rim of the cap.

Starting from the mark of the extractor and looking at the rim on both sides, a trace of the rear of the chamber, in case the shell has rested against it, will be seen.   In many pistols the marks of the rear of the chamber will be found whether the cartridge has been deposited in the chamber by hand or has slid up from the magazine automatically.

The lower part of the rear of the barrel is cut in a certain fashion in order to facilitate the sliding of the cartridge from the magazine to the chamber. There is also a notch for the extractor. The shell does not rest against these two latter portions of the rear of the barrel, hence no marks are produced.

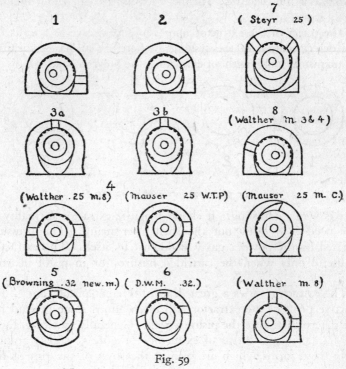

Fig. 59
The principal forms of the rear of the barrel

The presence of the above-mentioned marks will determine whether the extractor has been in the middle or to the right or left.

This observation is of highest importance in determining the pistol system. There are eight principal forms of the rear of the barrel. They are shown in Figure 59. In the figures, the shells are in the chambers, and that part of the rear of the barrel which will cause marking is indicated by a dotted line.

If we now turn to the marks on the head of the shell we notice first the marks of the ejector. As already mentioned, its position is determined by the trace of the extractor. The drawings in Figure 60 show the different principal forms of the traces of the ejector and their relationship to the extractor. The extractor is marked *E*.

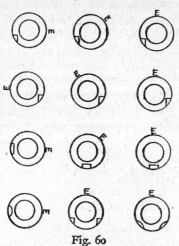

About two-thirds of the automatic pistols on the market have a special ejector, and the different systems of relationship of ejector and extractor will serve to differentiate them.

Examination of the head of the shell can be looked upon as an attempt to reconstruct the picture

Fig. 60

The principal forms of the traces of the ejector

of the breech-block. The traces of the extractor and the ejector, as well as the outline of all holes in the breech-block—for example, the hole for the firing-pin, notches in the periphery of the breech-block for the extractor, ejector, etc.—will aid in this reconstruction.

The print of the firing-pin on the primer is important in determining the pistol system. The diameter of the firing-pin is distinctive in different makes of automatic pistols and its width is approximately constant in the same make. If the firing-pin has left a clear mark on the primer it is measured directly with the measuring microscope. If only sections of the marks are found the measurement may be made in the following manner: The shell is placed before a photographic apparatus and enlarged 10 times on the ground glass. A cellophane paper upon which concentric circles have been drawn with China ink is then placed on the ground glass. An attempt must now be made to pick out a circle corresponding with the mark on the primer. With this method the measurement can be taken to within ±.002 inch.

Traces of tool marks on the breech-block may also be characteristic for certain pistols. These traces may be arranged in three different categories: (1) parallel linear traces, (2) concentric traces, and (3) irregular traces of the file.

Some of the above-described marks may not be found at all on a cartridge, while at times other traces, characteristic of certain makes of pistols, will be found. There is, for example, the Swiss Chylewski pistol, .25 caliber, which leaves a broad resting mark across the primer.

The first classification of shells is based on the caliber and on the presence or absence of the ejector. In the *Atlas of Arms* the following tables will be found:

Table No.	Caliber	Description
8	.25	with ejector
9	.25	without ejector
10	.32	with ejector
11	.32	without ejector
12	.38	....

In Table 12 are included all pistols of .38 caliber because of their rarity. In all the tables the cartridges of the same caliber and the same marks caused by the ejector are arranged according to the diameter of the mark of the firing-pin on the primer. In cases where the mark of the firing-pin is not clear another classification based on the principal form of the rear of the chamber may be used.

Table No.	Caliber	With Principal Form of Rear of Barrel
13	.25	1
14	.25	2
15	.25	3
16	.32	1
17	.32	2
18	.32	3

In these tables the shells are divided into two categories: those with and those without ejector. A simpler and more practical division than that in Tables 8 to 11 is obtained.

A separate classification is given to the pistols which have right-angled traces of the ejector of principal form No. 3.

The possibility of determining the pistol system from a fired shell is in direct relation to the construction of the arm and the clearness of the impression. If the automatic pistol system is characteristic with some individual markings the work is not only greatly facilitated but the identification can be made with a greater degree of certainty.

Automatic pistols which cause individual marks on the shells, making them easy to identify, are:

Sauer & Sohn, .25, .32 caliber; the Spanish pistols, Victoria, .25, .32 caliber, Astra, .25 caliber, Alkar, .32 caliber, Ydeal, Waldman and Kaba-Speziel, .25 caliber; the Swiss Chylewski, .25 caliber; the German Titanic and Walther Model 2, .25 caliber; as well as the Belgian F.N., .32 caliber. The Mann pistols with a broad extractor embracing about one-fourth of the rim of the shell, and the Steyr, .25 and .32 caliber, both without extractor, are also easily identifiable. The principal forms of the rear of the barrel 4, 5 and 6 can also give information concerning the following pistols: Mauser Vest-pocket Model, Walther Model 8, German D.W.M., and the Belgian F.N. Model 1910. Fairly easy of identification are the following pistols, characterized by their ejectors: Oewa (principal ejector form 4), Webley without hammer (principal ejector form 6), the pistols Delu, .25 caliber, and Praga, .32 caliber (principal ejector forms 5), as well as the pistols with the ejector to the right (principal form 2) as in the German Walther, Models 3 and 4, and the Spanish Star pistol. Other characteristic pistols are the Frommer Stop and Frommer Baby, Savage, Walther Model 9, .25 caliber; and Stock, .25 caliber; F.N., .25 and .32 caliber, Model 1900; Bayard, .32 and .380 caliber; Schwartzlose, .32 caliber, and Ortgies, .32 and .38 caliber.

The photographs in the *Atlas of Arms* give clear information about the above-mentioned characteristic details in the pistols. In conclusion it may be stated that the determination of the pistol system is, in most cases, not difficult. The difficulty arises when the make of the pistol is to be identified.

G. Examination of the Powder

There are two different types of powder used in firearms, black and smokeless powder. Black powder is still employed in some revolver cartridges, especially in those used for revolvers of Continental make, but the smokeless powder is now almost exclusively used.

The composition of black powder is classical: nitrate of potassium, sulfur and charcoal. The proportions of these ingredients vary in different countries within the following limits:

> 60 to 78% nitrate of potassium
> 10 to 18.5% sulfur
> 12 to 21.1% charcoal

The base of all smokeless powders is generally nitrocellulose and nitroglycerin. There may also be included non-explosive ingredients, as, for instance, stabilizers to absorb traces of free acids and nitric gases, substances which facilitate gelatinization of the powder, substances to prevent muzzle flame or to render the powder less sensitive to friction and less inflammable. There may also be substances to lower the temperature and speed of combustion.

The smokeless powders may be divided into two large groups: (1) powders containing nitroglycerin gelatinated with nitrocellulose and (2) powders containing pure nitrocellulose as an active ingredient.

Necessity for analyzing powders in criminological investigations may arise when:

(1) Powder is found on the victim or otherwise on the scene of the crime.

(2) Powder grains are found in the so-called "tattooing" around the wound to establish the kind of powder employed.

(3) The residue is found in the interior of the barrel to establish the sort of powder employed and the probable time elapsed from the firing of the shot.

Analysis of Powder—When a substantial quantity of powder is to be analyzed and compared with another powder there are numerous chemical and microchemical methods at our disposal. Such an analysis may in many cases lead to the identification of

Philadelphia Police Department Laboratory

EXAMINING PISTOL BULLETS UNDER THE COMPARISON MICROSCOPE

[Plate 12]

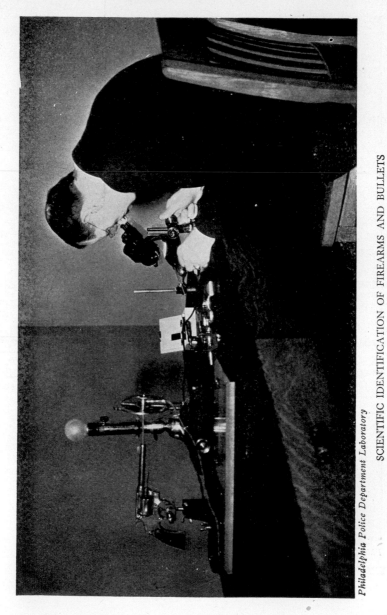

Philadelphia Police Department Laboratory

SCIENTIFIC IDENTIFICATION OF FIREARMS AND BULLETS

[PLATE 13]

the manufacturer. A collection of comparison powders would be advisable for the laboratory.[9]

Analysis of Powder Tattooings—In spite of the high temperature and the instantaneous combustion of the powder in the barrel, the unburnt or partly burnt powder grains are in most cases flung out so violently from the barrel that they become deposited on nearby objects, as in shooting cases, on the clothing or the skin.

The black powder produces the heaviest deposits. Owing to the similarity to real tattooing (particles of charcoal are deposited in the epidermis) this is called "powder tattooing." There is no possibility of mistaking the characteristic tattooing of black powder for that of smokeless powder.

Owing to the uniformity of the composition of black powder, an analysis would be fairly useless. The skin is examined under the magnifying glass, and the grains may be picked out with forceps and examined under the microscope in order to determine the minuteness of the grain.

The tattooing produced by smokeless powder is very insignificant in comparison with that inflicted by black powder. This is due to the nearly complete combustion of the smokeless powders. However, semi-smokeless powder will produce tattooing at short distances. In all cases where shots have been fired at short distances, *i.e.*, less than 10 or 12 inches, grains may be found with the magnifying glass during the examination of the surface fired upon. The search for powder grains may sometimes be of the utmost importance, as, for instance, in cases of doubtful suicide.

When the shot has been fired from a very short distance several powder grains from the tattooing may in most cases be retrieved. Generally a microscopic examination is sufficient to determine, with certainty, the powder used. At times some of the grains may be broken or only partly burned. The color and the size of the powder grains is often very characteristic for a particular manufacture.

[9] For more detailed information see Brunswig, *Das rauchlose Pulver*, Berlin, 1926; Söderman, *L'expertise des armes à feu courtes*, Lyons, 1928.

Analysis of Powder Residues—Only a very minute residue of the combustion products will be found inside of the barrel. Black and smokeless powders are easily distinguished, but the only possibility of determining the specific powder used is to carry out a spectrographical examination. Spectrography, however, gives useful results only when we are dealing with powders containing bichromate of potassium or nitrate of barium; included in this category are the British powder Schultze, Imperial Schultze, Amberit, E.C. and E.C.3 with nitrate of barium, the German Walsroder with nitrate of barium, the French poudre J with bichromate of potassium and bichromate of ammonia.

In collecting the residue, the barrel is cleaned with a small piece of cotton soaked in alcohol. The quantity of cotton should be as small as possible to avoid dispersing the residue which is already present in very minute quantities. The cotton is incinerated at the lowest temperature possible in a platinum crucible. The ashes are now evaporated by the electric spark in the spectrograph and the spectrum is photographed.[10]

Time Elapsed Since Shooting—Before the above-mentioned cleaning of the barrel takes place, the residue in the barrel should be examined for the possibility of determining the time elapsed since the firing. Very often the literature dealing with the examination of firearms gives information concerning the examination of the residue from this viewpoint. Chavigny [11] has studied this question carefully. The expert will in most cases establish approximately whether the weapon has been fired recently or not, especially when black powder has been used; the visible changes in the residue are, however, not typical and characteristic enough to permit decisive conclusions.

If essential, tests to determine the time necessary for the experimental residues to assume the same physical characters as the incriminating one should be carried out. Such tests should be made under the same circumstances as the incriminating residue

[10] For detailed information about spectrographical analysis of powder residues see Söderman, *L'expertise des armes à feu courtes.*

[11] Chavigny, *L'expertise des plaies par armes à feu*, Paris, 1918. See also Fleury-Silvera, *Détermination de la date d'usage des armes à feu et des munitions*, São Paolo, 1926.

was supposed to have been subjected to, but even under such conditions the conclusions concerning the time elapsed can only be made with great reserve.

H. Determining the Distance from Which the Shot Has Been Fired

The examination of the wound and its aspects in relation to the distance from which the shot has been fired should be left to

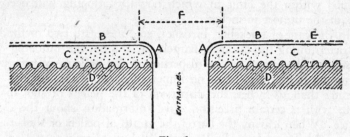

Fig. 61

Schematic cross-section of wound (after Chavigny): A is the flame zone, B is the second zone, and E the third zone. C represents the powder grains embedded in the corneum, which can be washed away; D represents the powder grains embedded in the mucosum, which cannot be washed away. F is the diameter of the bullet

the medical examiner or coroner. Among the duties of the expert on forensic ballistics is that of determining by the powder tattooing the distance from which the shot has been fired.

The tattooing consists of three zones:

1. The first zone, also called the flame zone.

2. The second zone, where the real powder tattooing is to be seen.

3. The third zone, where powder grains and combustion products are sparsely scattered.

The second and third zone will change entirely if the wound is washed. Washing will alter the color and aspect of the second zone and may entirely dispose of the third zone. It is therefore important to ascertain whether the powder tattooing to be examined has been subjected to washing or not.

The aspect of the three zones will alter with the slant of the shot and the distance. Only practical tests can guide in cases where the distance is to be determined. The tests are generally carried out on white paper or linen sheets, using the same firearm and ammunition as those used in the original shooting attack.

The distance which a bullet has traveled can only be determined within the limit in which powder tattooing will occur, *i.e.,* at the utmost 16 inches.

In the case of buckshot, birdshot, etc., there are two methods of determining the distance, namely, by the powder tattooing as described above and by the dispersion of the pellets. When the tattooing is found to be of no importance, *i.e.,* if the distance is greater than 16 inches, the dispersion of the pellets or shot may still, with a certain precision, give information about the distance. When leaving the barrel the group of pellets or shot may be regarded as a large bullet that will immediately start to disperse in a fairly regular manner. The scheme of the dispersion can be established experimentally and will be highly characteristic for various distances and for types of ammunition.

I. Errors Caused by Acoustics in Determining Direction of Shooting

When a shot is fired, the air in front of the barrel is driven away so forcibly by the bullet and the powder gases, that the sound vibrations produced are heard as a report. This report is usually called the muzzle blast and occurs in all cases. Sound vibrations travel spherically with the speed of 1,090 feet per second.

When a person hears the muzzle report he gets an idea of the approximate direction of the sound, *i.e.,* the place of the shooting. The person perceives the source of the sound from a direction which is at right angles to the sound waves. The exactness with which the direction of the sound is determined depends very much upon the development of the sense of hearing of the person in question (a person who is deaf in one ear cannot as a rule tell the location of the shooter) and upon his experience.

Bullets which have a very high initial velocity, higher than the velocity of sound, will, as long as the speed is great enough, hurl aside the air particles along the trajectory with such a speed that sound waves are produced. An ear, against which these vibrations are directed, will perceive a sharp report, called the bow-wave report. This report, from some point in the trajectory, travels like other sounds, spherically, and with the same speed of 1,090 feet per second. Because the person perceives the source of sound to be at a right angle to the sound waves, this bow-wave report does not tell the shooter's position, but only the direction from which the sound originates. If a person is placed in such a relation to the shooter that the bow-wave report will be perceived by his ear before the muzzle report, the person will first hear the bow-wave report and the direction from which it came. If the ears under this act of perception also are encountered by the muzzle report the person has no time to perceive the direction from which the latter came. Most persons do not know of the existence of the bow-wave report, and therefore, trusting their ears, assume that the direction whence the first sound came is the one leading to the shooter.

A practical example may illustrate this.[12] If a gun has been fired at a victim, designated by B in the accompanying sketch, the phenomena of sound in different moments will occur as follows: The gun is 160 meters distant from B. The bullet will then reach the victim in 0.25 second after it has left the muzzle. By this time the muzzle report has traveled 85 meters in all directions, the speed of sound being about 340 meters per second. The bow-wave report at this moment has the form of a cone with its apex directed toward B and its sides aiming at the circumference of the muzzle report. After one-tenth of a second the radius of the muzzle report is 34 meters larger and the bow-wave report from each point of the trajectory has also traveled 34

[12] See special report submitted to *Adalskommissionens rapport* by Capt. Birger Ekstroem, Stockholm, 1931, and Hermann, in *Archiv für Kriminologie*, v. 92, 3-4.

meters, but it is now mutilated and without apex, because the bullet has reached its destination. The bow-wave report is still a cone tangential to the circumference of the sphere of the muzzle report. The observer in the sketch gets the impression that the shot has been fired from a direction far away from the true one.

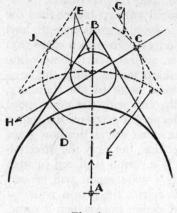

Fig. 62

Acoustic errors in perceiving direction of shooting: A, gun; B, victim; C, person hearing bow-wave report; D, muzzle report at the moment the bullet hits the victim; E, bow-wave report at the moment the bullet hits the victim; F, muzzle report 1/10 second later; G, bow-wave report 1/10 second later; H, direction from which the person believes the shot to have been fired; J, point in the trajectory where sound perceived by the person originated

The bow-wave report does not occur when pistols and revolvers are fired because the speed of the bullet is too slow.

The sound of the bow-wave report will deaden the "whizz" of the bullet. At first, at long ranges, on account of the resistance offered by the air, the speed of the bullet is less than the speed of the sound; hence the bow-wave report disappears and the "whizzing" can be heard. If, for instance, a bullet fired from a military rifle passes close to a person at 2,000 meters from the point where the shot was fired, he will first hear the bow-wave report originating from the first part of the trajectory of the bullet, then the whizzing of the bullet, and finally the obtuse sound of the muzzle report. At short ranges, when the speed of the bullet is higher than the speed of sound (for military rifles on ranges less than 800 meters), the sound of the friction of the bullet against the air, the "whizzing," is deadened by the bow-wave sound. If the bullet has touched any object on its way so that its speed is less than the speed of the sound, it may also be heard at shorter distances, especially if it travels more or less transversely to the direction of the wind.

J. The Reappearance of Obliterated Numbers

Experience shows that professional criminals nowadays generally file the numbers off the machine guns, pistols and other weapons used, in order to avoid tracing their origins. Stolen motor cars also very often have the motor numbers filed off or changed.

In most cases the numbers may be brought out again, even if the filing has penetrated deeply. When the original numbers were punched into the steel, its molecular structure underwent changes which were not confined to the immediate vicinity of the numbers but extended also to the portion underneath. By grinding down the surface with emery, highly polishing it, and then treating the smoothed surface with one of the etching fluids generally used in metallurgical work, the numbers can be made to reappear.

For obvious reasons it is not deemed advisable to record in these pages any of the formulas of the processes used for the above purpose.

It has also been found that the inexperienced have temporarily injured their fingers with some of the chemicals in the course of their attempts to make the numbers reappear. It is therefore suggested, to those who are studying in technical lines of detective work, that in such cases they will do well to consult with a recognized metallurgist until they have acquired proficiency in the processes in question.

QUESTIONS

1. What revolver calibers are used in the United States?
2. How is the caliber of a fired bullet determined?
3. Describe briefly the methods used in identifying a bullet with the firearm from which it was shot.
4. On what factors is the determination of the make of an unknown firearm by a bullet founded?

5. Describe briefly the traces left by an automatic pistol on a shell
6. On what factors is the determination of the make of an unknown firearm by a shell founded?
7. Is there any possibility of determining, from examination of the gun, how long a time has elapsed since the last shot was fired?
8. Describe the appearance of the powder tattooing around the wound and how the distance from which the shot was fired is determined.
9. What is meant by a bow-wave report and how does it influence the determination of the direction of the shot?

XIV

PROBLEMS OF BROKEN WINDOWS

SOMETIMES it may be of the utmost importance to determine whether a bullet has entered a windowpane or whether a windowpane has been smashed from within or without. The latter question frequently arises in connection with arson cases and insurance frauds in the form of faked burglaries. These questions were first studied by Gross and lately by the Russian criminologist Matwejeff.[1]

Generally it may be said that the hole produced by a bullet with a strong charge has the sharpest edges; but if a bullet has been fired from a very long distance and has come to have a low speed it will break the pane in the same manner as will a stone. A shot from a very short distance will produce the same result, because the pressure of the powder gas

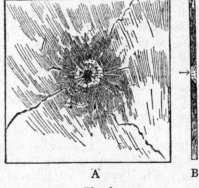

A   B

Fig. 63

Determination of the direction from which a shot was fired through a windowpane. A shows the typical appearance of the exit side. B shows a cross-section of the hole

itself will smash the glass. In important cases, test shootings should be made on the same sort of glass and under as nearly identical circumstances as possible.

It is easy to determine the direction from which the shot was

[1] *Archiv für Kriminologie*, Vol. 2-3, 1930.

fired. On one side of the hole only, numerous small flakes of glass will be found to have been blown away, giving to the hole the appearance of a volcano crater. Such an appearance indicates that the bullet was fired from the opposite side of the hole from which the flakes are missing. If the bullet strikes the glass at right angles, the flake marks are evenly spread around the hole. If the shot is fired from the right of the pane, very few flake marks will be found on the right side of the hole. Most of them will be on the left side. It is even possible to calculate approximately the angle of the shooting. The more acute the angle the more flakes will be blown away. It should be added that bullets passing through glass generally deviate and continue their flight spinning around their longitudinal axis, thereby causing large, more or less rectangular wounds in the case of pointed bullets, and oval wounds, larger than the caliber of the bullet, if the latter is round. This fact is important from a medico-legal point of view.

It is not so easy to determine from what side a blunt object—a fist or a stone—has smashed a windowpane, altho the experienced can still solve the problem.

If one makes test shots on a windowpane and then pieces the broken glass together, one will see that the fractures produce a network consisting of radial rays running out from the center (the bullet hole), crossed by concentric lines. The radial fractures precede the concentric ones, as may be seen by noting that the radial rays are continuous while the concentric are interrupted at the crossings.

If the same experiment is carried out by smashing a windowpane with a blunt object, one will find by putting the pieces together that an analogous pattern of radial and concentric fractures occurs, altho it is not as regular. To facilitate matters, the glass may be marked on the side which receives the blow with a net of rays and circles made with grease crayon. The surface of the glass gives no evidence as to where the blow was struck, but if a cross-section of one of the pieces of glass is examined a relief consisting of a series of curved lines will be found. Sometimes this relief is very evident, at other times quite difficult to detect, but with a little training it can always be found.

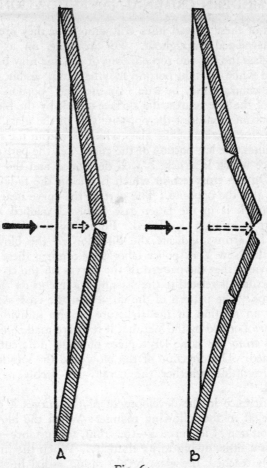

Fig. 64

Schematic drawing of the order of occurrence of the radial and concentric fractures by smashing windowpane with blunt object. A shows how the radial fractures at first occur at the side opposite to the destroying force. B shows how the secondary concentric fractures occur at the same side as the destroying force

Studies of these curved lines will show that they are not uniformly developed throughout. For example, on a particular piece of glass the left and top portions of the line may be strongly developed while its right portion may be barely visible. In other panes the contrary may be true. By the "left" portion we mean the part of the line nearest the surface struck by the blow. The "right" portion is nearest the opposite side of the glass.

On the cross-section of the glass which is within the concentric fracture lines, the left portion of the curve, *i.e.,* the part nearest to the surface which is struck, is well developed and the right one feebly. On the cross-section which is within the radial fracture lines it is just the opposite. The part of the curve nearest to the surface struck is in the latter case feebly developed while the other part is strongly developed. Figure 65 shows this graphically. The arrows indicate the direction of the blow. Tests made at the New York police laboratory confirm these findings.

It is obvious that the pattern of the curves on the cross-section of the fractures is related to the missing fragments on the surface of the glass. The pattern of the curves on the cross-section has, however, no relation to the structure of the individual glass. This is corroborated by the fact that if tests are made on windowpanes cut from the same large piece of glass, different patterns are obtained. The direction of the blow and the location of the pattern determine whether the curves are feebly or strongly developed.

The difference in the development of the curves is explained by Matwejeff in the following manner: When the blow strikes the glass on one of its surfaces—the front, for instance—the glass first bends a little, owing to its elasticity. When the limit of its elasticity is reached, the glass breaks along radial lines starting from the point where the destroying force is applied. These radial fractures originate on the opposite surface of the glass, because this is the surface which is more subjected to stretching by the bending. The front surface is only pushed in. This may be illustrated by folding a piece of thick cardboard: its back side breaks first.

While the radial fractures are taking place, the newly cre-

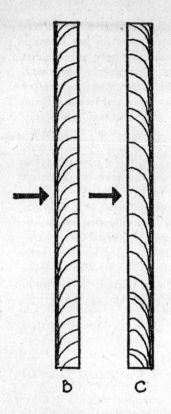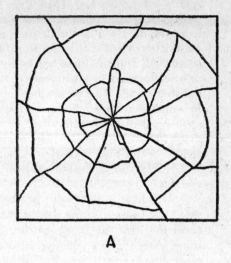

Fig. 65

(A) Broken window glass showing the radial and concentric fractures
(B) Radial edge showing more developed part away from the side struck by the destroying force
(C) Concentric edge showing the more developed part toward the side struck by destroying force

*See Federal Bureau of Investigation Bulletin, Vol. 5, No. 10,
October 1, 1936*

ated glass triangles between the radial rays will also bend away from the direction of the destroying force. By this bending the glass is stretched along the front surface, the limit of elasticity is reached, and the glass breaks in concentric lines. These concentric fractures originate on the front of the glass, because of the stretching. This occurrence may be illustrated in the following manner: Radial lines running in all directions are drawn on a piece of thick cardboard. These are then cut out with a sharp knife. If pressure with the finger at right angles is exerted against one of these triangles so that it is pushed backward as far as possible, the cardboard will break anteriorly in a concentric manner.

Only fractures which can be shown to be radial or concentric should be utilized. One should avoid considering small fractures occurring near the frame, as the resistance offered by the latter complicates matters. Matwejeff is of the opinion that only fractures showing their points of origin (where the destroying force has been applied) should be considered. In these cases it should be possible immediately to determine whether the glass has been broken from within or without.

QUESTIONS

1. Tell briefly how it is determined through which side a windowpane was shot.
2. Describe briefly the rôle of the radial and concentric fractures in determining from which side a windowpane was shattered with a blunt object.

XV

STAINS OF BLOOD, SEMEN, ETC.

A. Where Blood Has to Be Searched For

THE search for bloodstains must be made very carefully.

Bloodstains on walls sometimes do not have their usual reddish-brown color, but may be black, green, blue or grayish white. This change of color is due to the fact that the dyes in wallpaper and paint sometimes are dissolved in the bloodstains, with the result that the latter change color. Bloodstains on golden-brown wallpaper, for instance, often turn green because of the forming of oxid of copper. Blood on certain fabrics turns gray if it is exposed to the action of the sun.

On a dark background bloodstains are often difficult to recognize. When searching for bloodstains in such cases, one should use a searchlight, even in the daytime. Under artificial light the dried bloodstains will appear against the dull background as a glossy varnish.

Blood is often found in places which are not directly visible, *e.g.,* under the edge of a table where the criminal may have wiped his hands, a common custom in rural districts; under drawers in a table or cabinet where the criminal may have searched for money; in the watertrap of a sink where the criminal may have washed his hands and where there still may be blood remaining in the water. In this latter case, the remaining water in the watertrap should be drawn off by unscrewing the valve under the trap and letting it drop into a clean bottle. Blood may also be found on paper, on stoves, toilets, wastepaper baskets, etc.

Of great importance are the bloodstains on the body of the suspect, where especially the fingernails, the edges of the beard and the hairline should be searched. For this sort of examination a magnifying glass is used, and the blood is scraped with a knife onto white paper. Pockets should be carefully searched. On clothing that has been recently washed the seams should be cut open to ascertain if any blood may be there. Even on well-rinsed clothing it may be possible to detect blood. An absolutely white handkerchief may still contain blood. Examination under the light of the ultra-violet lamp will show this.

In certain cases it is also possible to ascertain the presence of blood on a scrubbed floor, altho such examination must be made with great care. When the floor has been scrubbed, blood may also still be present in the cracks between the floor boards. It is important if one is able to show that the floor had been scrubbed with some etching substance, as, for instance, strong lye, sulfuric acid, etc. Also, the position, size and form of the bloodstains should be carefully determined (see pages 279-282).

Transport of Bloodstains—When the stains are very large and located on easily transported articles, only a part of them is used at the examination; in this case it is not necessary to describe them so carefully, because one can always, with the aid of the remaining blood, reconstruct the original appearance of the stains. Smaller stains, where all the blood must be used for the examination, should be photographed or sketched, and their position noted on the photograph of the scene. (Instructions for some methods of photography of bloodstains on dark or otherwise unsuitable backgrounds are given on page 109, where the photographing of bloody fingerprints is described.)

Smaller objects carrying bloodstains are transported in clean cardboard boxes or in glass containers, which are packed in wooden boxes with straw or sawdust. On larger objects, bloodstains are protected by clean white paper, which is kept over the stains with thumb-tacks or strings, whereupon the whole object is carefully packed in thick wrapping paper. On wearing apparel, the pieces of clothing are rolled tight and the stains are protected by tissue paper. Firearms or other weapons which carry bloodstains are packed as described in the transport of fingerprints (page 103).

In packing, one should take care never to place newspapers directly on the object.

When the object cannot be transported, the dry blood is scraped away with a clean knife and put on clean white paper, which is folded in the same manner as a druggist folds powders. This paper is put in a glass container. The place where the bloodstain has been found must be photographed or sketched before this operation takes place.

Certain authors, such as Gross and Schneickert, recommend that such stains be dissolved in water or, better, in a physiological solution of salt (0.85%), which is then absorbed by blotting paper, and the latter turned over to the expert for examination. In emergencies, a policeman may be justified in applying this method, but it is always best if the expert can do this work.

As a general rule, preferably the whole object which carries the stains should be given to the expert. Following this principle, wallpapers should be torn down, pieces of wood cut away, parts of floor sawed away or surfaces of floors planed, pieces of stucco taken away, etc. In many large cities as well as in other localities specific instructions are followed as to the proper procedure in delivering promptly to the medical examiner or coroner articles for examination and analysis, especially in homicide cases.

Blood that has been absorbed by earth is dug up and put in glass or enameled containers. All the blood should be collected, because sometimes it may be important to make quantitative blood tests in order to determine the quantity of the blood.

Several questions are put to the expert in connection with blood examinations. These will now be dealt with in a definite order.

B. Does the Stain Contain Blood or Another Substance?

There are two different groups of methods to determine the character of the stain. The first group embraces the preliminary tests, often carried out at the scene of the crime; the second embraces the microscopic and spectroscopic methods used in the laboratory.

Preliminary Tests—The preliminary test may be made by a policeman or detective in cases of emergency and where there is enough blood left for a later expert examination. The most commonly used are the benzidine test, the guaiac test, and the leuco malachite test. In some countries the peroxid of hydrogen test is used. This method, however, cannot be recommended: it has more sources of error than other tests and makes the treated parts of the bloodstain unsuited for further examination because of the formation of white hemol.

The benzidine test is sensitive (1 to 300,000). The reagent is made fresh each time by filtering a saturated solution of benzidine in glacial acetic acid added to a few drops of a solution of perborate of sodium (0.1 N) which can readily be purchased. In making the test, blotting paper soaked in water is carefully pressed against the stain, whereupon a few drops of the reagent are put on the part of the blotting paper that was in contact with the stain. If there is blood, the paper turns blue or green. However, fresh fruit and milk give the same color.

The guaiac test is less sensitive (1 to 50,000 or 100,000). The reagent consists of a newly made filtered solution of guaiac resin in alcohol or pyridin, to which have been added a few drops of old, ozonized turpentine. The blotting paper should turn blue after a few seconds if blood is present. Rust and iron salts, milk, cheese, potatoes, saliva, perspiration, pus and other organic substances will give a similar color.

The leuco malachite test is the most sensitive and the most specific of preliminary tests, and is looked upon by many as an almost final and absolute test. The reagent is prepared according to the following formula: [1]

Leuco malachite green................	1 gr.
Glacial acetic acid....................	100 cc.
Distilled water.......................	150 cc.

The reagent has a slightly greenish color. The stock solution should be kept in a dark brown bottle with a paraffin cover over the glass stopper. It will then keep indefinitely.

When making the test one mixes 8 cc. of the stock solution

---

[1] Pierre Medinger: "Contributions au diagnostic de traces minimes de sang," in *Revue Intern. de Criminalistique*, No. 7, 1931.

with 2 cc. of a 1-per-cent solution of peroxid of hydrogen. This mixture will keep for a few days. Before making the actual test the reagent is tested on a minute quantity of old blood, which is put on absorbent paper soaked with a drop of the reagent. After ten seconds at most, there should appear a green stain which should become a dark greenish blue after the lapse of not more than one minute.

When performing the actual test a piece of filter paper is placed as near the bloodstain as possible, and with the aid of a knife a small amount of dried blood is scratched from the stain onto the paper. With the aid of a glass rod a drop of the reagent is placed on the side of the powdered blood, and in a short time it will be soaked with the reagent. The coloring of the stain should then follow in the above-described manner.

Owing to the surprizing sensitiveness of the reaction, the articles used (knife and glass rod) must be absolutely clean in order to avoid error. Even an infinitesimal amount of blood from a former operation, adhering to them, may lead to false conclusions.

The reaction is so sensitive that small traces of blood may be detected by the following procedure: A thin glass rod is moistened in water and pressed for a few seconds against the trace, whereupon the glass rod is pressed against the filter paper soaked with the reagent. A green stain is immediately produced in the presence of blood. Small isolated green points, which may appear on filter paper of bad quality when soaked with the reagent, should not be mistaken for the reaction.

By searching large surfaces, as for instance mudguards of motor-cars in "hit and run" cases where no blood is visible, a filter paper soaked with distilled water should be pressed against the surface, whereupon it is pressed against another paper soaked with the reagent.

As a check on the reagent, one should, when blood is found, try to make a test only with a drop of the stock solution. No stain should then appear, but when a drop of peroxid of hydrogen is added a green stain should appear.

In order to be perfectly sure, the hematoporphyrin test should be added. A minute drop of blood or a small quantity of blood dissolved in a drop of water is allowed to dry on a glass slide. After the preparation is thoroughly dry, it is placed under the ultra-violet rays and a drop of concentrated sulfuric acid is added. If the stain consists of blood there will gradually develop a beautiful brick-red luminescence due to hematoporphyrin.

Laboratory Tests—Of the methods used in the laboratory, the microchemical tests of Teichmann and Strzyzowski are here mentioned.

In the method of Teichmann a thread of fabric from the stain or some scratchings are dissolved in a drop of distilled water on a glass slide. The fluid is then evaporated by holding the glass slide over a flame. The temperature should not be higher than 140 degrees Fahrenheit. A cover glass is put on the preparation and a drop of glacial acetic acid is allowed to run along the side of the cover glass. This will then seep under it by capillarity. The slide is then carefully heated again until the acid has evaporated. Another drop of acid is added and evaporated. A third drop of acid is added, and the preparation is then examined under the medium power of the microscope.

If blood is present, one will then find the characteristic coffee-brown hemin crystals. If the reaction is not successful, the process can be repeated, using more blood or fabric. It is sometimes difficult to obtain the crystals, and if the result is negative, it should be confirmed by performing a few more tests. The method of Teichmann can be regarded as specific for blood. It gives, however, the same crystals with indigo dyes, and when the presence of indigo is suspected, tests should be made on other parts of the fabric. Lime, sand and iron rust also interfere with the formation of hemin.

Another method is that of Strzyzowski, altho this has one inconvenience: the reagent does not keep very long. It must be prepared fresh each time before using. The reagent has the following formula:

Alcohol .... 1 cc.
Distilled water .... 1 cc.
Glacial acetic acid .... 1 cc.
Hydriodic acid .... 3 to 5 drops

The hydriodic acid is difficult to buy and should be prepared in the laboratory. In doing this, one treats a concentrated solution of iodid of potassium with a concentrated solution of tartaric acid, when insoluble tartrate of potassium and iodhydric acid will be formed. If one, for instance, wishes to make 10 cc. of hydriodic acid one puts in a test-tube 5 cc. concentrated iodid of potassium and adds 5 cc. tartaric acid solution. This solution is filtered into a test-tube, which is sealed by means of a paraffined cork.[2]

The spectroscopic examination is made with the aid of a microspectroscope. Only a very small amount of blood is needed. The blood is dissolved in a 30 per cent potassium hydroxid solution, a drop of sulfhydrate of ammonia is added, and the preparation is examined with the microspectroscope. In the presence of blood, the spectrum of the hemochromogen is seen.

C. Is the Origin of Blood Human or Animal?

An early method used to determine the origin of blood was a microscopical examination of the shape of the red blood corpuscles. With this method it is, however, only possible to differentiate between mammal and saurian blood, and this usually only if one deals with fresh bloodstains.

Numerous methods have been invented for the determination of the origin of the blood. The commonly used one is the precipitin reaction of Uhlenhut. By this method some blood from a stain is scraped off and dissolved in saline solution for a few hours, filtered so as to obtain a crystal-clear liquid and then carefully mixed with the so-called human anti-serum obtained from a rabbit previously injected with human blood.

Technique: Capillary Tube Method—A clean capillary tube is examined against a dark background to determine its cleanness. Its lower end is brought in contact with the crystal-clear saline extract of the bloodstain and a column of approximately ½ inch is drawn into the tube by capillarity. This amount represents

---

[2] Edmond Locard, *Manuel de Technique Policière*, Paris, 1934.

about ⅛ of a drop of the unknown blood extract. The lower end of the tube is next allowed to draw up about the same amount of the anti-serum without shaking the tube. If the bloodstain is due to human blood, at the junction of the two liquids a white ring will appear within two to five minutes. This gradually becomes more dense and at the end of twenty minutes a white precipitate forms. The reading should be taken against a dark background.

If this precipitin reaction is not obtained the stain is not due to human blood. Of course, control tests must be carried out to demonstrate (1) that the anti-human serum will produce the white ring and the precipitate when mixed with known human serum; (2) that the extract of the stain will not give the reaction with known normal rabbit serum; (3) that both anti-serum and stain extract will not react with normal saline solution.

It is imperative that the anti-human serum should be powerful enough to give a distinct reaction within the specified time (titre of 1:1000, amount of serum, 1 cc.).

This test is highly specific, and it is only between closely related animals such as the horse and the mule, the dog and the fox, the hare and the rabbit, the hen and the pigeon, the goat, the sheep and the cow, that any doubt can arise. Tho the reaction may be positive with blood of a chimpanzee, gorilla or orang-outang, it will not be had with high dilutions as is the case when dealing with human blood.

It must also be remembered that if blood has undergone putrefaction or has been heated or altered chemically by soaps, peroxid of hydrogen or tannic acid from leather, the reaction will not be obtained.

D. From Which Part of the Body Does the Blood Originate?

A murderer will often try to explain the presence of bloodstains on his body or his clothing by telling a tale about the blood originating, for example, from the nose, from shaving, or from various accidental causes. In cases where blood grouping does not give results, it is important to verify such a tale. It may be verified if the form and the position of the stains correspond with the tale. On the other hand, it is difficult to believe that bloodstains on the rear of a coat or under an apron can come from the nose.

A microscopic examination of the blood may sometimes disclose the origin of the blood through the presence of foreign particles. In the blood from the nose, one may find mucus from the nose or hairs from the nostrils. In the blood by rape semen and hairs from the genitals may be found. In blood from menstruations, epithelial cells from the vagina are found.

Questions of this kind arise often. In a trunk murder case, for example, where a woman was killed, bloody linen was found after a search of the suspect's home. The woman had lived with him. He denied any knowledge of her fate and explained that the bloodstains were menstruation blood. This was corroborated by the result of the examination.

The presence of such elements or particles in the blood may lead to a definite conclusion about the origin of the blood, but their absence does not prove that the blood does not originate from the part of the body from which it was said to come.

E. Does the Blood Come from a Certain Individual?

This problem can only be solved in a negative way.

One can determine that the blood *does not* originate, but not that it *does* originate, from a certain individual. It should not, however, be forgotten that negative proofs are just as valuable from the viewpoint of the investigation as positive ones.

For this examination, the so-called "blood-grouping tests" are used.

Human blood of all races can be divided into definite groups because of the ability of the blood serum of one person to clump, or agglutinate, or bring together the red blood cells of certain other individuals. Landsteiner recognized this phenomenon, which is due to certain properties in the blood corpuscles and serums of the various bloods. The properties contained in the red blood cells were called *agglutinogens,* and those contained in the serums (liquid portion of the blood after it has clotted) were called *agglutinins.*

The agglutinogens have been known as *A* and *B* and the agglutinins as *a* and *b*. The *A* and *B* substances may occur separately, that is, *A* alone or *B* alone, or they may be found together, that is, *AB,* or they may be entirely absent, that is, *O,* in the blood of an individual. The very same applies to the agglutinin content in the serum of an individual. According to the absence or presence of both agglutinogens and agglutinins we have the formulæ indicating the various blood groups, of which there are four.

CLASSIFICATION AND COMPOSITION OF BLOOD GROUPS

Group	Red Blood Cells (Agglutinogen)	Serum (Agglutinin)
O	—	a and b
A	A	b
B	B	a
AB	A and B	—

Cells of Group *O* do not contain agglutinogen but the serum contains both agglutinins. Owing to the fact that the agglutinogen is absent, the red cells of this group cannot be clumped by any blood with which it may be mixed. On the other hand, as *a* and *b* are found in this serum, when it is brought in contact with another blood there will be clumping of the opposite red cells as the result of the action of *a* and *b* on the agglutinogen therein contained. Consequently we must conclude that the red blood cells of a person belonging to Group *O* cannot be agglutinated by the bloods of the remaining three groups, while its serum will agglutinate the red cells of all groups.

Red cells of Group *Ab* are agglutinated by Groups *Oab* and *Ba* bloods.

Red cells of Group *Ba* are agglutinated by Groups *Oab* and *Ab* bloods.

Red cells of Group *AB* are agglutinated by bloods from all

CHEMISTRY AND BALLISTICS SECTION, BUREAU OF IDENTIFICATION, DETROIT POLICE DEPARTMENT.

[PLATE 14]

Courtesy of St. Louis Police Dept.

MICROSCOPIC IDENTIFICATION OF BULLETS IN THE
VALASCO CASE (Page 190)

Institute of Police Science, Univ. of Stockholm

EXAMPLE OF BLOOD TEST WITH THE TEICHMANN
CRYSTALS (Page 228)

[PLATE 15]

groups, while its serum, lacking agglutinin, is unable to clump the cells of the other groups. Bloods of corresponding groups cannot agglutinate each other, *i.e.*, Group *Ab* or *Ba* cannot agglutinate Group *Ab* or *Ba*, respectively. Landsteiner formulated the following law: "In a given blood containing a given ag-

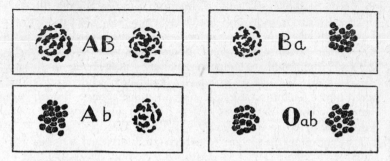

Fig. 66
Blood-grouping

Capital letters = Agglutinogen in   Small letters = Agglutinins in
    red blood cells   serum

glutinogen, the serum will also contain agglutinins which are incapable of acting on the said agglutinogen and thus bring about agglutination."

The following table will elucidate further:

Red Blood Cells	Oab	Ab	Ba	AB
Oab	—	—	—	—
Ab	+	—	+	—
Ba	+	+	—	—
AB	+	+	+	—

Serum heading spans Oab, Ab, Ba, AB columns.

The plus sign indicates agglutination.
The minus sign indicates no agglutination.

Group *Oab* corpuscles are not agglutinated by any of the serums, while its serum agglutinates corpuscles of all other groups. Group *Ab* corpuscles are agglutinated by serums *Oab* and *Ba*, while its serum agglutinates corpuscles *Ba* and *AB*.

Group *Ba* corpuscles are agglutinated by serums *Oab* and *Ab,* while its serum agglutinates corpuscles *Ab* and *AB*. Group *AB* corpuscles are agglutinated by all serums, while its serum does not act upon the red cells of the other groups. Notice that no red cells are agglutinated by the serum of its own group.

The agglutinogens *A* and *B,* besides being present in the red blood cells, are found in all the cells of the body, and in various body fluids, such as saliva,[3] urine, semen, tears, nasal discharge, etc. Their presence or absence determines the group to which the individual will permanently belong throughout life.[4] In other words, the blood group is hereditary, and since it is hereditary it is immutable. It can no more change during life than the color of one's eyes or the form of one's physiognomy. An individual born in Group *O* will die in Group *O,* etc.

To determine the group to which an individual belongs we must have serum *Ab* and serum *Ba* at our disposal. These serums must be prepared by experts in the laboratory and must be powerful enough (high titer) to agglutinate susceptible blood corpuscles within a very short period of time and in an unmistakable manner. The technique is the following:[5]

A small drop of serum *Ab* is placed on the left extremity of a glass slide and a drop of serum *Ba* is placed on the opposite extremity of the same slide. A finger of the person to be tested is pricked with a needle, and with its eye some of the blood is transferred from the finger to the serum *Ab* and intimately mixed with it. With the eye of another clean needle the same procedure is carried out with serum *Ba*. The slide is then agitated from side to side for a few minutes until the presence of agglutination, if there be any, is detected. The clumps of red cells may be seen either with the naked eye or microscopically. The reading of the reaction should not be taken until one-half hour has elapsed. The reaction should be interpreted in the following manner (see Figure 66):

---

[3] Cuboni, *Boll. Ist. Sierot.,* 1928, 7, 1.

[4] De Biasi, B., *Studies on Iso-Agglutinins in the Blood of the New-Born,* J.A.M.A., 1923, 81, 1776.

[5] De Biasi, B., "Transfusion of Blood," paper read before Assn. of Italian Physicians in A., 1921.

1. Agglutination in both serums *Ab* and *Ba*—Group *AB*.
2. Agglutination in serum *Ab* only—Group *Ba*.
3. Agglutination in serum *Ba* only—Group *Ab*.
4. No agglutination in either drop of serum *Ab* and *Ba*—Group *O*.

The above technique is carried out only in cases where the liquid fresh blood may be obtained from the individual to be tested, and with fresh bloodstains represented by large quantities of blood soaked into the fabric (cotton, linen, gauze, towels, cloth, etc.). In these cases the red blood cells, still intact and retaining their normal contour, may be extracted from the soaked stain with minute amounts of normal saline solution, examined under the microscope to become certain of their presence, and finally tested against the known serums *Ab* and *Ba*, as described above. On the other hand, when we are dealing with old bloodstains (weeks and months old) we find that the red cells have been destroyed and can no longer be seen under the microscope. In other words, they have been broken up or hemolyzed, and in that condition they are unable to be agglutinated if the grouping test is carried out. What we find in the stain is the liberated hemoglobin (red coloring matter previously contained in the intact red blood cells). Nevertheless, the stain still contains the properties *Ab* or *Ba* or *Ab* or *Oab*, as the case may be, unless they have been destroyed by age, prolonged exposure to the sun or heat, putrefaction, or by other chemical and physical agents. Experiments have demonstrated that the agglutinogens are more resistant to extraneous influences than the agglutinins.

In cases of old bloodstains or clots, therefore, to establish the "individual diagnosis" we may follow two courses:

1. Extraction of agglutinins and determination of the group by testing directly against red cells *A* and *B*, or
2. Determination of the agglutinogen present in the dried blood by the absorption method.

In the first case, if the blood is in the form of crusts, it should be scraped and weighed on a sensitive balance. If we are dealing with soaked fabric the weight of the blood is calculated by weighing the stain and an equal surface of unstained material. Equal amounts of distilled water and saline should be added (about 4 times the weight of the blood) and the mixture allowed to remain in the refrigerator overnight. The extract is then tested with the known cells A and B. The test depends upon the ability to extract agglutinins from the stain, which, if present, will agglutinate its antiagglutinogen present in the test red blood cells.

The method described by Lattes [6] is applied in the second case. We search for the agglutinogens A and B. This method requires delicate technique and knowledge of immunology. The blood-stain is treated with a serum containing agglutinins a and b in about equal proportions (determined by titration methods). After 12 hours the supernatant serum is withdrawn and tested against suspensions of A and B red cells and its titer or power to agglutinate re-tested. If at this second titration we find that the a or b substances previously present in the serum have been absorbed together or separately, or if we detect diminishing agglutinating power of the serum, we may conclude that the substances A and B are present in the bloodstain. The correct grouping of the stain in question depends on the reactions obtained. This test is more reliable than the method of agglutinin extraction, owing, as mentioned elsewhere, to the greater resistance of the agglutinogens as compared to that of the agglutinins, which are easily destroyed.

The result of the blood grouping, however, depends entirely on the ability of the expert. One can say that the value of the method as evidence stands or falls with the expert. Through too popular introduction of the method, the public is of the mistaken opinion that blood-group determinations are easily carried out. On the contrary, they require extensive practise and experience; they have so many sources of error that control tests, a thorough knowledge of the properties of the serums used, and, above all, a deep knowledge of all reactions which may be confused with true agglutination (false agglutination, self-agglutination, rouleaux

[6] Lattes, L. *Boll. Sez. Ital. Soc. Int. Microbiol.*, 1932, 4, 585.

formation, cold agglutination) are absolutely necessary. It goes without saying that accurate knowledge of the mechanism involved is a prerequisite, if scientific as well as practical deductions are to be drawn in work as delicate as this.

In the white race, the blood groups A and O are most common, the former occurring in 40% and the latter in 45% of the individuals examined. Group B is found in 10% and Group AB in the remaining 5%.

As above stated, a positive conclusion can be drawn only if an extract of a human bloodstain is found to agglutinate the cells of a given suspected individual. In this case the stain cannot be due to this person's blood. If no agglutination occurs there is always the possibility that the blood may come from the suspect, but nothing can be proven because there are millions of individuals belonging to the same group. In the latter case there are, however, probabilities which grow stronger if the blood belongs to Group B, or to the still rarer Group Ab.[7]

The recently discovered and heritable agglutinogens M and N by Landsteiner and Levine,[8] which are put in evidence by delicate technique and by using serum obtained from rabbits previously injected with human red-blood cells, give promise of valuable aid in the "individual diagnosis" of bloodstains. According to the discoverers, besides the four classic groups mentioned, individuals may belong to any one of three groups—M, N, or MN —and bloods lacking either one of these agglutinogens do not exist. There is no doubt that when examining bloodstains the combined search for A, B, and M and N will facilitate matters a great deal.

Determination of Non-Paternity by Blood-Grouping Tests— During the past few years the problem of determining fatherhood from blood grouping has been greatly debated, but there is absolutely no doubt that by examination of the blood a negative proof is obtained, *i.e.,* it may in certain cases be possible to show

[7] See Lattes, *Die Individualität des Blutes,* trans. from the Italian, Berlin, 1925; Schiff, *Die Technik der Blutgruppenuntersuchung,* Berlin, 1929, and Bohmer, "Die Blutgruppen als Beweismittel," in *Kriminal Monatsh.,* v. 7 and 8, 1929.
[8] Landsteiner, K., and Levine, P., *J. Exp. Med.,* 1928, 47, 757.

that the man *is not* the father of a certain child, but one can never prove that *he is* the father of a given child. This fact is of importance and interest to the police and legal authorities, and its possibilities will be briefly brought out. In order fully to understand the problem, one must be familiar with Mendel's Law of Heredity, on which the entire structure of blood-group transmission is based. This law is described in any comprehensive encyclopedia.

The agglutinogens *A* and *B* are dominant properties, and the absence of agglutinogen, *i.e.,* the property *O,* is said to be recessive. The fundamental law is that the properties cannot occur in a child unless at least one of the parents has them. Innumerable experiments [9] and extensive work have definitely shown that unions of:

Parents			Offspring				Offspring
OXO	give only	O	but cannot give				A,B,AB
OXA	"	"	O,A	"	"	"	B,AB
OXB	"	"	O,B	"	"	"	A,AB
OXAB	"	"	A,B	"	"	"	O,AB
AXA	"	"	O,A	"	"	"	B,AB
AXB	"	"	O,A,B,AB				
AXAB	"	"	A,B,AB	"	"	"	O
BXB	"	"	O,B	"	"	"	A,AB
BXAB	"	"	A,B,AB	"	"	"	O
ABXAB	"	"	A,B,AB	"	"	"	O

Exceptions have been reported, but they are said to be due to faulty technique, to incorrect interpretation of the tests, or to illegitimacy.

While it is true that blood-grouping reactions cannot determine paternity, a man accused of being the father of a child will be able to establish his innocence, according to Hooker and Boyd,[10] once out of six times. But the work of Landsteiner and Levine on the new agglutinogens *M* and *N* has made it possible to help

9 Hektoen, L., *J. Inf. Dis.,* 1907, 4, 297; Ottenberg, R., and Epstein, A. A., *Proc. N. Y. Path. Soc.,* 1908, 8, 187; v. Dungern, E., and Hirschfeld, L., *Ztschr. f. Immunitats u. exp. Therap.,* 1910, 6, 284; Mino, P., *Policlinico Sez. med.,* 1924, 211, 1; Bernstein, F., *Klin Wchnschr.,* 1924, 23, 1495; De Biasi, B., *Heredity of Human Blood Groups,* in publication.

10 Hooker, S. B., and Boyd, W. C., *J. Immuhol.,* 1929, 16, 451.

to establish innocence in one-third of the cases if all the known factors are studied.

F. Stains of Semen

Stains of semen may occur in rape, sex murders, and sex offenses of different kinds, as illicit intercourse with children, bestial acts, etc.

The seizure of wearing apparel that has relations to sex offenses must be made as soon as possible, because it has often happened that an important trace has been destroyed by the washing of the clothes. The most common parts of wearing apparel carrying semen stains are chemises and shirts, trousers and drawers, stockings, corsets and garters. The location of the stains is easily determined under the light of the ultra-violet rays because of their characteristic and strong luminescence.

When the location of a suspect's stain has been determined, the stain is marked with a pencil. Stains of semen on fabrics have the form of a geographical map and the area looks as if it had been starched.

Dried semen has no smell, but fresh semen has a very characteristic odor.

The packing of wearing apparel or objects carrying stains of semen must be made in such a manner that there is no friction whatsoever against the stains. When in dry condition these are very brittle and will break in small particles, which can be lost. The friction may also cause the breaking of the spermatozoa. It should be absolutely forbidden, for instance, to roll a piece of clothing for transport.

The suspected pieces of clothing should be gently laid between two sheets of cardboard or similar material which are tied together with a string so that friction is avoided. Smaller objects, as, for instance, hairs, should be put in a test-tube and corked.

If fluid semen is found, it should be put in a test-tube, altho it is preferable in cases where it is nearly dry to let it dry thoroughly before it is transported. In the summer, when there is danger of putrefaction, fluid semen may be safeguarded by some drops of toluol or of a 10% solution of formalin.

The semen contains small "animals," spermatozoa, consisting of an egg-shaped head and a long fine tail, and having the length of about 0.05 millimeter (approximately ⅟₅₀₀ part of an inch). The spermatozoa die when the semen dries, but preserve their shape indefinitely if they are not destroyed.

The examination has two stages. The first consists of a preliminary test called the Florence reaction, and the second stage is the microscopical determination of the presence of spermatozoa.

In the Florence reaction, a minimum part of the suspected stain is dissolved in a drop of iodo-potassium iodid solution under the microscope. The solution is prepared in the following manner:

> Iodid of potassium .... 1.56 grams
> Pure crystalline iodin .... 2.54 grams
> Distilled water 30   c.c.
>
> The iodid of potassium is first dissolved in the smallest possible quantity of water, and the iodin is added. The rest of the water is added after the iodin crystals have lost their form.

If semen is present, the so-called Florence semen crystals, brown and of rhombic shape, can be seen. This reaction is very sensitive and gives results also with old, putrefied semen and semen that has been subjected to heat. On the other hand, unfortunately, the reaction is not specific for semen alone, but gives crystals also of other human secretions and certain vegetables. Both mucus and saliva will give similar crystals. A positive result of Florence reaction, therefore, means only a probability of the presence of semen. A negative result does not justify certain conclusions in any direction. Foreign elements, as, for instance, excrement, pus, blood, urine, and chemicals, may prevent the reaction.

Only the determination of the presence of intact spermatozoa with head and tail allows a conclusion with absolute certainty. The absence of the spermatozoa, on the contrary, does not constitute a negative proof, as they may have been destroyed by putrefaction or friction.

The inexperienced examiner may be tempted to mistake the trichomonads, which are occasionally found in the secretion of the female vagina, for spermatozoa. The trichomonads differ, however, distinctly in form from the spermatozoa, and for an expert such a mistake should not be possible.

The differentiation between human and animal semen is difficult. There is no relation between the size of the animal and the size of the spermatozoon. Certain insects have spermatozoa that are larger than the human ones, and, on the contrary, the whale has smaller spermatozoa than humans.

Generally speaking, the spermatozoa of the common domestic animals are larger than those of the human being, and the heads have a slightly different shape. There is also a certain difference in the form of the Florence crystals between human and animal semen, altho this difference too is very slight.

There have been numerous attempts to determine the origin of semen in a biological way, similar to the formerly described precipitin test and the blood grouping.

G. Other Stains of Interest

Obstetrical and Gynecological Stains—Examination of the scene of abortion, infanticide and sex offenses may lead to the discovery of bed linen, towels, chemises, shirts, mattresses, blankets, etc., which have stains. It is many times important to determine the composition of the stains. The medical examiner or a skilled physician should be employed for these examinations.

Excrements—Excrements may be found at the scene, on paper as stains, or together with obstetrical stains in the investigation of sex offenses. Especially in cases of burglary it is not unusual to find excrements at the scene, which may have been left there on account of superstition or revengeful desire, or more often on account of real need due to the nervousness of the perpetrator.

Excrements of adults are normally yellowish brown and solid. The excrement of infants is greenish yellow, contains undigested cheesy lumps, and shows microscopically lumps of milk and fine needles of fatty acid. A thorough analysis of excrements is very difficult and seldom carried out for the purposes of police science. Generally, a miscroscopic diagnosis of the components is sufficient. For this purpose the excrement should preferably be washed in a special apparatus constructed by Professor van Ledden Hulsebosch of Amsterdam—the so-called "coprolysator."

Many times characteristic parts of the excrement, as, for instance, fruit cores, parasites, etc., have led to the apprehension and conviction of a criminal.

Paint Stains—The perpetrator, in committing a crime, may have brushed against a newly painted wall, or a wall with loose whitewash, and may carry some of the paint or lime on his clothing. Or the tools used by the perpetrator may carry small adherent particles of paint from the scene. Microscopic diagnosis and microchemical analysis may lead to identification of the paint, as even extraordinarily small quantities of paint can be analyzed. The possibilities of such identification should never be overlooked.

Other Stains—Naturally numerous other stains may play a rôle in criminal investigation, altho in many cases the most important step is the differentiation from stains of blood and semen. Among other stains which may be of interest in criminal investigation one can mention those of meat, vegetables, fat and sugar; stains of oils, candles, rust, mud, etc.

QUESTIONS

1. Describe briefly where one should look for bloodstains in a room in an ordinary homicide case.
2. What is meant by the leuco malachite test?
3. Tell how to determine whether a bloodstain is of human or animal origin.
4. Is there any possibility of determining from what part of the body the blood originated?
5. What is meant by blood grouping?
6. Describe the precautions to be taken when transporting stains of semen.
7. Are there any other stains than those of blood and semen which may be of importance in criminal investigation?

XVI

VARIOUS TRACES

ALMOST everything imaginable may constitute a clue in a criminal investigation. In the following pages we shall describe briefly some traces which are not treated in the other chapters, but which have frequently been found of value.

Traces of Cloth—The perpetrator of a crime may at times leave negative prints of his knee or his forearm in clay, soft earth, dust, etc. If the fabric has a characteristic pattern or has been repaired the traces can be of importance. They are photographed and, if possible, a cast is made of them. In order to get comparison prints the same method is used as that used in taking fingerprints. The fabric is inked with the fingerprint roller and fingerprint ink and pressed against white paper.

Feathers—The question of examination of feathers arises in illegal hunting, theft, unnatural acts against animals, etc. The feathers may be divided into down and contour feathers.

Contour feathers are characteristic in shape and color. They grow out of the feather sacks, and their lower part, which is hollow and hard, is called the quill. The quill is continuous with the shaft, which generally has a square cross-section and is composed of a porous horn-like material. Barbs protrude from both sides of the shaft. The barbs are supplied with two rows of barbules carrying fine hooklets which serve to connect the barbs and make it possible for the contour feathers to offer resistance to the air during flight. The shape and number of these barbules are different in different classes of birds and serve for identification of the feathers along with the color and general form of the feather.

Birds of the Gallina order (hen, turkey, partridge, etc.) have hooklets which are short and close together. The latter usually number from four to six. Pigeons have a similar arrangement. Feathers of marine birds and wading birds have long, fine hooklets which are covered with hair up to the tips. Sparrows and song birds have fine, haired hooklets which end in fine, fork-shaped tips.

The down differs from the contour feather because of the fine soft shaft, with round cross-section. The barbules have no hooklets and consist of small joints with knot-like projections at their junctions. The form and position of these knots are very characteristic in the various orders of birds and aid in the differentiation of the orders.

In the order of the Gallinæ and in the wading birds we find conical, pointed knots, varying in number from four to six. The barbules are hard and haired.

In the order of pigeons the feathers have long knots, consisting of several protruding tips.

The aquatic birds have strong knots with dull points.

The climbing birds have strongly protruding knots with four tips.

In the sparrows the knots are conical and close to each other. They have a darker pigment than the barbules, which are covered with very fine hairs.

The down of birds of prey has nothing characteristic.

In each case comparison feathers from the suspected order of birds should be used. It is strongly recommended to have a collection of common feathers and down at the police laboratory for comparison purposes.

The examination of feathers is very simple. The feathers are placed in hot soapy water for a short time, washed in running water, then in alcohol, and examined microscopically. If one wishes to make a regular microscopic preparation to photograph them, they should be dyed.[1]

Tracks of Skis—Identification of the tracks of skis is of very little importance because almost all skis are of standard type, of

[1] Kockel, *Viertelj. f. gerichtl. Med.*, Bd. XXXVII, 1909, II Suppl.

the same size and pattern, and are used by the thousands. A study of the tracks can, however, answer a few questions, as, for instance, if the ski runner has gone up or down hill, if one or more persons have run in the same tracks, if the tracks have been made by a man or a woman, and finally, if they are old or new.

If the two tracks do not show straight, fleeting lines but often draw closer together, and if it is seen that they have slid backwards, the runner has gone upwards. The traces are quite different if he has gone down hill. The lines are then straight and fleeting if the slope has not been so steep that the runner has been forced to break the momentum by pointing the skis inwards. This movement gives the tracks quite another appearance than that caused by the regular position of the skis used when going upwards.

The appearance of the traces of the ski pole suggests immediately the direction in which the runner has traveled when on level ground. Through those traces it is also possible to determine how many persons have run in one track. Good runners leave even and uninterrupted ski tracks, and the traces of the ski poles succeed one another at fairly even intervals. The inexperienced ski runner often runs with legs spread apart, avoids steep slopes and makes bad turns. He may also leave traces of many falls.

It is more difficult to determine whether a man or woman has made the tracks. Women, however, take very short steps when going up hill and the tracks of the skis follow each other at short intervals. Going down hill men are generally bolder than women.

Old tracks are recognized by the fact that the edges are never sharp but are rounded by the wind and sun. The small heaps of loose snow produced around the tracks when running are never seen in old tracks. If new traces of wild animals cross the tracks the latter are likely to be old. If the traces of animals break before the tracks of the skis, the tracks still carry the human odor and must have been made recently.

Ear-Wax—If a person has been subjected for some time to dusty environments the dust will find its way into the interior of his ears and be deposited on the wax. This dust will remain attached to the wax even after the most careful cleanliness. The question has been especially studied by Severine and Jean Maurel; [2] they obtained some remarkable results by examining longshoremen who had worked at unloading coal about one year previously. In spite of this lapse of time small particles of coal were still present mixed with the wax. Other laborers had coffee-bean particles in the ear-wax (coffee roasters), hairs (barbers), flour (bakers), sawdust (laborers in sawmills), particles of copper (workers in copper), etc.

The finding of insignificant quantities of dust is of no great importance. In order to arrive at certain conclusions, fairly large quantities of the dust in question must be found. If the particles are abundant and originate from rare substances, important conclusions may be drawn.

A small quantity of the ear-wax is put on a glass slide and examined microscopically. If foreign matter is found, a microchemical analysis may be necessary.

Traces of Animals—In some rare cases it may be necessary to examine traces of animals—horses, donkeys, dogs, cats, monkeys. The animals may leave traces of their feet, teeth, hair and excrement.

Certain animals leave traces of their friction ridges, as the monkeys and some dogs. The shape of the feet will permit identification of the animal in question.[3]

Dust—Dust and dirt which are in or on the suspect's apparel, shoes, hair, under the nails or in fissures, or on weapons or tools, may give some clue as to where the suspect has previously been or what he has done. The possibilities of dust analysis are not sufficiently exploited by detectives. By such examinations the presence of what is called professional dust may be determined, as glue and sawdust (carpenters and laborers in sawmills), lime (bricklayers), etc., and also dust from places where

[2] In *La Nature*, No. 2457, May 7, 1924; also Edmond Locard in *Manuel de Technique Policière*, Paris, 1934.
[3] Goddefroy, "Les Empreintes de pattes de chiens comme moyen d'identification," in *Revue Intern. de Criminalistique*, 1929.

the suspect has made a brief visit, as, for instance, flour (flour mill), fibers or parts of vegetables (from a barn). Shoes and cuffs of the trousers should also be examined for the presence of certain dirt or soil.

Such examinations sometimes play a helpful rôle in an investigation, and yet they are still regarded by many investigators as too imaginary and romantic to be considered.

Dust is generally characterized as being composed of micro-

Fig. 67
Trace of a dog's right fore foot (E. Goddefroy, Brussels, Belgium)

Fig. 68
Part of Fig. 67 enlarged

scopic particles so small that they can float in the air. From the viewpoint of police science the collective name "dust" may also include other particles of importance, which are either too small to be collected in the usual manner or are later discovered accidentally by collecting the dust to be examined. These particles (splinters, sawdust, hair, feathers, seeds, etc.), especially if they have settled on the surface of the fabric, may be collected by very simple methods, as, for example, with a magnifying glass and forceps, or by beating the article of clothing in question. In the latter case the article of clothing is put in a large, clean paper bag and beaten forcefully for five minutes, whereupon the dust which falls to the bottom of the sack is collected. Dust from the pockets should be collected and kept in envelops labeled as to their origin.

If the dust clings to the surface of the fabric or the dust in the interior of the fabric is to be examined, a special vacuum cleaner must be used. The vacuum cleaner collects the dust on filter paper, on which it may be examined microscopically.[4]

A complete analysis of dust is very complicated and needs some experience, altho the determination, for instance, of certain

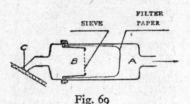

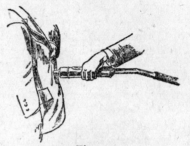

Fig. 69

Söderman-Heuberger Filter, to be attached to a vacuum cleaner

Fig. 70

Gathering dust with the special filter attached to the vacuum-cleaner

metals is fairly easy and can be made in any police laboratory. The analysis of dust has been especially studied by Locard in his excellent *Traité de Criminalistique* which gives a thorough description of the methods used.[5]

Wood Particles—Small particles of wood and sawdust often have importance in investigations. When doors, windows, locks or drawers have been forced, particles of wood may be found on wearing apparel or on the tools used by the criminal.

In one case, for example, microscopic examination showed that sawdust from a handsaw had not originated from a cherry tree

[4] See Söderman, "En ny apparat för uppsamling av damm i forbrytares kläder" and "Ett bidrag till fragan on den kriminaltekniska dammsugningens teknik" in *Nordisk Kriminalteknisk Tidskrift*, 1931.

[5] For a treatment of the technique of microscopy and the methods of examining dust, see also Else and Garrow, *The Detection of Crime*, London, 1934.

but from a pine tree. This proved to be of great importance in the investigation. In another case, the wife of a barber was found murdered, and the husband was suspected of having committed the crime. A particle of wood was found in one of the fissures of his pocket knife. The prosecuting attorney showed, with the aid of expert evidence, that the barber had carved away all traces of blood from the hammer he had used to kill his wife.

The determination of the origin of particles of wood may sometimes be very difficult when the question of related trees arises. It is, however, easy even for the amateur to differentiate evergreen from leafy trees.[6]

Tobacco and Tobacco Ash—Since the days of Sherlock Holmes the examination of cigaret and cigar ashes has been regarded, at least by the layman, as having some value for investigation. As a matter of fact, however, the differential diagnosis of tobacco ashes gives very meager results.

Microscopic examination of tobacco shows dark, almost black, particles which by high-power magnification are revealed to be cells filled with small crystals of oxalate of calcium. Those so-called crystal sand cells are found in all sorts of tobacco, with the exception of snuff.

Cigar and cigaret ashes are differentiated by the presence of paper ash in cases where cigarets have been used. The paper ash is easily recognized under the microscope.

Brain Substance—When a skull has been smashed, part of the brain substance may be found not only in the immediate vicinity of the body, but also in other places not suspected during the first few moments after the discovery of the crime. The brain substance may be mistaken for numerous other substances, and the detective should have a certain amount of knowledge of its appearance. A preliminary examination may be made with the aid of strong magnifying glasses.

The brain is composed of two different substances, white and gray matter. The white seldom plays a rôle in murder cases. It gets its color from the nerve filaments which run through it and

[6] Further information may be obtained in *An Introduction to Plant Anatomy,* by Eames and McDaniels, New York, 1925.

are kept together by connective tissue. The gray substance, which may have all kinds of colors, yellow, red, blue, and even dark brown, consists of small quantities of fine-grained connective tissue and nerve filament.

The gray matter represents the outer layer or cortex. It encloses the white matter, or inner portion, and covers the entire brain proper at the surface, dipping down even into the depths of the many convolutions of which the brain is composed.

QUESTIONS

1. What information may be obtained from the ear wax of a person?
2. What information may be obtained from dust in a suspect's wearing apparel?
3. How is the dust gathered?
4. Has the analysis of tobacco or tobacco ash any importance in criminal investigation? Give reasons.
5. What part of the brain substance is of importance in criminal investigation?

XVII

INVESTIGATION OF HOMICIDE

A. General Rules and Schedule of Investigation

THE methods of investigation in murder cases have been greatly improved during the last score of years. In training schools for detectives conducted by Federal, State and large municipal police departments and in the so-called zone schools conducted in many States under various auspices for smaller municipalities, young detectives have been given the benefit of the experience of older men and of experts in related fields. In most of the large departments a special squad has been organized, known as the homicide squad, composed of detectives who have shown special ability in murder cases. Such steps supplant the old system of assigning to a murder case any detective who happened to be on duty, regardless of his ability and knowledge of this type of crime.

Among improvements in methods of operation have been (a) speed in getting to the scene of a crime, (b) arriving at the scene with all necessary appliances, and (c) conducting the necessary preliminary investigation with system and planning.

The specialists of the homicide squads are on duty every hour of the day and night, together with a stenographer, a photographer, a fingerprint expert and a technician particularly qualified to develop traces and clues at the scene of the crime.[1] High-powered automobiles transport them rapidly to the scene.

The necessity for having proper appliances resulted in the establishment of a "homicide kit" containing every conceivable

---

[1] These technicians in the homicide squads should be specially-trained detectives who have worked for some time in the police laboratory. They can be regarded as the "tentacles" of the laboratory.

article which experience had shown might be helpful.[2]   A powerful portable light is carried to illuminate a cellar, areaway, or any other large space.

In New York City and other metropolitan centers the medical examiner or his deputy or assistant, with a toxicologist, if necessary, speeds to the scene as well as the experts from the police laboratory, to investigate and to secure every possible scintilla of evidence.   They make and preserve an accurate report of the scene of the crime, proceeding in an orderly and businesslike way throughout.   This is essential, as the evidence obtained must afterward stand a legal test.   With a dominating mind in authority, the delicate work of photographing, sketching, sifting out the material witnesses, obtaining statements, and searching for fingerprints and other traces and clues of evidential value, proceeds without confusion from a temporary headquarters in an orderly and authoritative fashion.

In examining the scene one should not only look for the usual, standard traces—fingerprints, footprints, etc.—but should also have eyes open for details which at the first glance may not seem to have any connection with the crime.   A few examples will illustrate this.

On a highway in France a woman had been violated and slain.   The only thing found on the scene was a piece of bread.   By questioning the workers in the neighboring bakery it was found that this piece of bread had been given to a tramp who had asked for it.   The bread was recognized by the fact that it was burnt.   A stone was missing in the oven of the bakery and the portion of the loaf nearest to this particular place had been burnt.   The murderer was arrested on the description furnished by the baker.

Some years ago a homicide was committed in the neighborhood of Oslo, Norway.   No traces were found at the scene, but the chief of detectives ordered a combing of the surrounding terrain.   A piece of paper, part of a printed blank issued by prisons, was found along the banks of a stream.   This paper gave the information that a certain man had been released from a prison on a certain day.   The man was arrested and admitted his guilt.

A servant girl was found murdered in an apartment in a town in Germany.   The murderer had left his own clothing in the apartment and had

2 See pages 427-429.

donned new clothing found there.   An examination of his clothes furnished very good descriptive material.   A red blond mustache hair was found on the lapel of the coat, blond head hairs were deposited on the collar, and particles of tobacco, crumbs of white bread, débris of vegetables, some fish scales and two phosphorus matches with blue tips were found in the pockets.   The much-worn and rather filthy clothing had been repaired in several places and apparently by expert hands.

With the aid of the above-described findings the following description of the murderer was developed: he had blond hair and a reddish mustache; smoked strong tobacco; the repairing of the clothing showed that he was familiar with the handling of needle and thread, but not to such a degree as to classify himself as a skilled tailor; he had probably learned the trade in some prison; the remains of the fish, bread and vegetables showed that the man was a tramp who carried his food in his pocket.

The description was very accurate.   Blue-tipped matches were rather rare, and were found in two municipal lodging houses in Cologne.   After two days the murderer was arrested.

It cannot be sufficiently stressed that the suspect and his clothing must be thoroughly searched.   Some examples of investigations where such examinations have had great success are the following:

A woman had been murdered in the neighborhood of Lyons, France. An examination of the body and the scene revealed no clues.   A few days later some tramps were arrested for other reasons and subjected to a close search.   Some seeds were found on the clothing of one of them.   Examination by an expert botanist showed that these seeds were those of a plant of rare occurrence in the neighborhood.   Such plants were found on the scene of the crime, and the arrested man finally confessed.

In a burglary the burglar had forced his way into a cellar through a narrow corridor.   Some electric cables were suspended on the walls of this corridor.   The perpetrator must have touched them, because the under surface of his fingernails was filled with the same pitch with which the cables were covered.

In another case [3] the shoes of a man suspected of having burglarized a flour mill were examined.   The shoes were covered with dirt consisting of three layers, first earth, then a thin layer of flour, and finally another layer of earth.   The arrangement of these layers disclosed that the man had walked through a muddy road leading to the mill and had returned on the same road.

In still another case a person was suspected of having hidden stolen

[3] Tage-Jensen, "Undersökelser paa gerningssteder," in *Tidskrift for Strafferet*, 1923.

money in the neighborhood of a small stream. Sand from the banks of the stream, found on his shoes, gave him away.

It is almost impossible to visualize and comprehend the manifold duties devolving upon a police officer or detective investigating a homicide. Many detectives are peculiarly qualified to perform the mechanics of an investigation in a homicide case, but if asked to enumerate the steps taken they would be at a loss to do so. It is deemed advisable to list in an orderly fashion here the complex duties devolving upon the investigator at the scene of a murder. Such a schedule naturally cannot cover the whole field. Crime is ever changing in its aspect, and each case will present its individual sides, to which the successful detective must adapt himself.

Upon arrival at the scene:

Ascertain who the perpetrator is and arrest immediately if possible.
Note time of arrival.
Expose shield and hold everyone at scene for questioning.
Notify station or headquarters, giving a brief outline of case.
Prevent anyone from touching body or disturbing anything, pending arrival of medical examiner or coroner, homicide squad, and technicians from police laboratory.
Prevent unauthorized persons from entering upon the scene.
Take names and addresses of all persons present and endeavor to ascertain name of perpetrator or perpetrators and a detailed identifiable description for immediate alarm.
Prevent destruction of evidence such as fingerprints, footprints, etc.[4]
Clear room and immediate area of all but authorized persons present upon official business or detained on case.
Keep witnesses separate to prevent conversation.
Assign specific task to each detective—proceeding in a systematic manner. Keep record of all assignments and detail of work.

Examination of scene:

The position of the body is examined.
The clothing and its position are noted.
Traces on the body and on the clothing are noted, photographed and sketched.

---

[4] One cannot sufficiently stress the importance of instructing patrolmen in the elements of police science and criminal investigation so that they may avoid the destruction of traces.

(*Only after the above facts have been ascertained, should the body be allowed to be moved and its position altered.*)

The wounds are examined by the medical examiner. The back of the body is examined, and the ground under it.

(If something has been altered before the arrival of the homicide squad, the original position of objects sketched and photographed should be established with the aid of witnesses.)

The weather (a) when the crime is discovered and (b) when the homicide squad arrives should be noticed, especially in rural crimes. (Position of sun and moon, rain, snow, frost, thaw, visibility, direction of wind, force of wind.)

Examination of doors and windows, furniture, etc., will disclose the probable direction of entry and exit of the perpetrator. Note position and whether doors are open, closed, or have been moved.

Bullet holes, empty shells and bloodstains. Note and mark location.

Search for visible and latent fingerprints, plastic and surface footprints, traces of tools, cut telephone wires, traces of teeth, strands of hair, cloth, buttons, cigaret butts, etc.

Other traces and clues.

Determine if traces come from victim, murderer or third party.

Search terrain about premises or vacant lot, noting vegetation, condition of soil, footprints, etc. Determine movements of victim and murderer.

Take photographs to show body in original condition with relation to stationary objects, the route of the murderer, etc. The photography should be carefully planned (see Chapter VI).

Make diagram of scene (see Chapter V).

Officer in charge should dictate to stenographer complete and detailed description of scene.

Try to visualize what has taken place, with the aid of the position of the victim, traces of violence, position of bloodstains and weapon, etc.

Search for clues. Follow to the end. Investigate every theory.

Preserve evidence.

Record findings in memorandum book.

Determining perpetrator:

Statements of eye-witnesses. Information.

Motive.

Number of murderers.

Weapons.

Route of murderer. Search for traces along the road. Reconstruction of the movements of the murderer is all-important.

Was the murderer wounded or his clothes soiled?

If suspect is arrested, search clothing, fingernails, etc., for blood. If scene had peculiar dust, soil, or other substances, search suspect's clothing, fingernails, shoes, etc.

Diaries, journals, letters, addresses, telephone numbers, photographs.
Associates, relatives, sweetheart, friends, enemies, etc.
Places frequented; hangouts.
Habits.
Wearing apparel; laundry marks thereon, etc.
Traces and clues found on the scene or elsewhere, linking the suspect with the crime.
Description of vehicle, if any used.
Stolen property. Secure complete list and description.
Poisons (search for container on suspect or in his dwelling; seize suspicious glasses, bottles, etc., on scene; gather vomited substances and excrement of deceased; never allow family or friends to aid in the search).
Unguarded statements of witnesses or bystanders.
Fingerprints found and photographed at scene compared with those on file.
(Unless impractical or not expedient, question witnesses at station house. It may be necessary to take witnesses to bureau of identification to view photos on file.)

Direction of escape of perpetrator:

Inquiries should be made concerning means and direction of escape.
Detective should familiarize himself with roads, streets, routes of public conveyances for alarm and other purposes. Notify desk officer at station or headquarters.
If outside of State or city limits, headquarters will give alarm.
If direction is to a distant point, headquarters will telephone and telegraph.

Notification:

A. Ordinary homicides:
  (a) Chief of Police.
  (b) Commander of detective division or bureau.
  (c) Borough (New York City) and district commander, detective division or bureau.
  (d) Squad or precinct commanding officer.
  (e) Medical examiner (or coroner).
  (f) District attorney.
  (g) Telegraph or telephone bureau at headquarters.
  (h) Homicide squad, specialists.
  (i) Technical police laboratory.
  (j) Photographers.
  (k) Stenographers.
B. Homicides caused by explosions; in addition to above, notify special squad of detectives concerned.

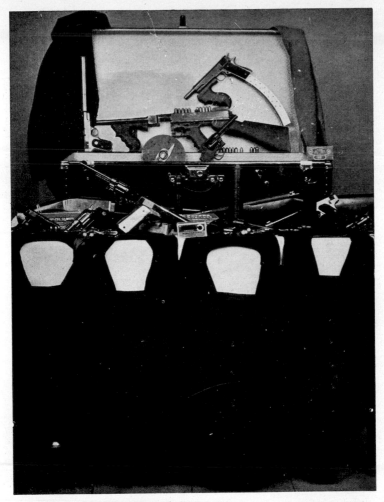

WEAPONS USED BY PROFESSIONAL CRIMINALS AND GANGSTERS,
WITH FOUR SO-CALLED BULLET-PROOF VESTS

[PLATE 16]

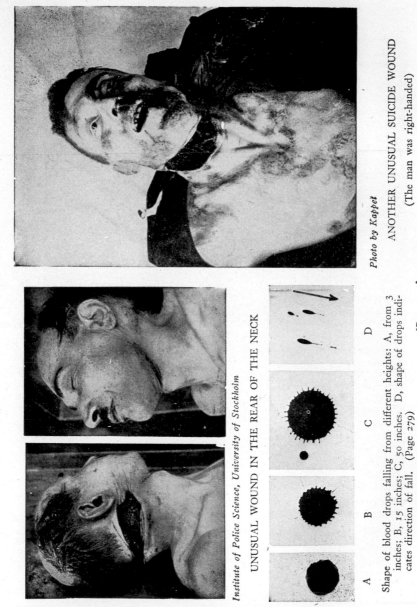

Photo by Kappel

ANOTHER UNUSUAL SUICIDE WOUND

(The man was right-handed)

Institute of Police Science, University of Stockholm

UNUSUAL WOUND IN THE REAR OF THE NECK

A   B   C   D

Shape of blood drops falling from different heights: A, from 3 inches; B, 15 inches; C, 50 inches. D, shape of drops indicates direction of fall. (Page 279)

[PLATE 17]

C. In other cases such as accidents on railroads, elevated transit lines etc., notify Transit Commission, Building Department or Public Service Commission or other public authority having jurisdiction.

Treatment of evidence:

Articles requiring analysis are delivered to the proper experts (medical examiner or coroner, police laboratory, and ballistic expert).

Preserve and transport the articles carefully. (See for treatment the different chapters on traces.)

Mark for future identification, secure against tampering, label, wrap, and forward evidence to property clerk.

Tag and wrapper should be marked:

Date of arrest and marking.

Charge.

Nature of evidence or sample.

Name of prosecuting authority (State or national).

Name and address of deceased person.

Name and address of the defendant.

Rank, name, shield number and command of the officer.

Time and place of court examination.

Res Gestæ:

(a) Circumstances and things said at the instant of the homicide are the res gestæ.

(b) Wearing apparel worn by deceased and weapon or instrument showing marks of violence are res gestæ evidence.

Motives (facts showing):

Revenge.

Feud.

Jealousy.

Crank.

Gain.

Civil suit.

Sadism.

Sex motives other than sadism.

Moral turpitude.

Insane person.

Self-defense.

Preparation before committing homicide:

Attempt to determine whether defendant or fugitive wanted was armed shortly before crime, or had in his possession means for its commission.

Try to determine if defendant or fugitive wanted was near the scene of the crime under suspicious circumstances such as disguised, armed, uttering threats, etc.

Dying declaration:

Questions to be asked (statement signed in presence of witnesses, if possible):

What is your name?

Where do you live?

Do you now believe that you are about to die?

Have you no hope of recovery from the effects of the injury you have received?

Are you willing to make a true statement of how you received the injury from which you are now suffering? (Dying declaration is competent evidence. Admitted only when person has no hope of recovery.)

Identity of deceased:

Complete and correct name of deceased.

Complete and correct name of witnesses and memorandum as to what is expected to be proven by each.

First member of the force to arrive at scene must identify body of deceased to medical examiner or coroner as body of the person found at scene of homicide.

Officer must produce witnesses (preferably relatives of deceased) at autopsy to identify the deceased in presence of medical examiner or coroner as body of person whom they knew during life.

Officer should record in his memorandum book a record of identification for future use.

Clothing, letters, photographs, moles, birthmarks, conformation of teeth, are aids in identification (see Chapters II and IV).

Conduct of accused subsequent to crime:

Study actions and demeanor carefully. Flight, attempt to commit suicide, false statements, concealment, are considered indications of guilt.

Question him at opportune time.

Steps to arrest:

If perpetrator is known, forward alarm, giving name, address, description, also peculiarities, habits, associates and places where he might be found.

Determine movements of perpetrator for days prior to crime.

Keep home and place of employment under surveillance.

Supervision over all channels of communication.

Trail associates, sweetheart, and family.

Look for information at hospitals and doctors' offices (if circumstances warrant).

If indicted, mail a circular with picture to principal cities.

(See Chapter III for further steps.)

Alibi:

Question prisoner as to his whereabouts at the time of the crime. Check up immediately.

Determine movements of perpetrator for days prior to crime and on day of crime.

Disposal of body:

Medical examiner or coroner determines cause of death, pending autopsy at morgue.

Tag placed on all dead bodies in homicide cases.

Remove body to morgue.

Fingerprint deceased. If circumstances warrant, have samples of head-hair and beard taken from the body. In sex murder also hair samples from the torso. Examine clothing.

In the case of a female, notify Policewomen's Bureau. Assigned member will assist.

Clothing must be removed from body and taken care of by detective. Mark each article and place in sealed package as per regulations.

Deliver to property clerk.

Forward valuable property to desk officer.

Do not remove body without permission of medical examiner.

Send body to morgue.

Burial cannot take place until district attorney and medical examiner release body.

Autopsy:

Only the medical examiner or coroner is qualified to testify as to cause of death.

The medical examiner or coroner aids investigation by disclosing types of wounds and manner of infliction.

Officer should know location of the wounds, condition of clothing, and surrounding property in order to give accurate description.

Expert and non-expert evidence as to bloodstains (see Chapter XV):

Stains found upon person or clothing of accused.

Stains found upon person or clothing of deceased.

Expert's opinion competent evidence.

Non-expert may testify as to existence and color of stain.

Practical suggestions:

Question thoroughly those concerned.

Obtain complete descriptions.

Search pawnshops, second-hand jewelry stores and other likely places (robbery motive).

Be careful in questioning an individual. He may turn out to be a principal in the crime.

Call upon experienced detectives to assist.

Confer with your co-workers.

Listen in on open wire.

Cover place where suspect is expected sufficient time before the appointed hour.

Separate witnesses.

Handle witnesses courteously and tactfully.

Make inquiries of neighbors and bystanders.

Cooperate with fellow officers.

Give constant attention to general alarms.

Do not disclose valuable information.

B. Suicide or Homicide?

In the investigation of homicides, the boundary line between the work of the criminologist and the medical examiner, or coroner, is difficult to draw so far as concerns the exterior examination of the body. Theoretically, the criminologist should confine himself to traces of the murderer while the medical examiner or coroner should give the exterior description of the body and perform the autopsy. Experience shows, however, that such a strict limitation of duties gives very limited results. Sometimes the medical examiner or coroner, as a pathologist, may, aside from the autopsy, confine himself to a formal description of the exterior of the body. The report is often made out in such a professional manner that the average detective has very little use for it. On the other hand, if the coroner or medical examiner happens to be personally interested in the detectives' side of the question—and in many localities he is—he can, as experience shows, be of enormous service to the investigator. The latter must, however, know something of legal medicine and its possibilities, so that he can meet the medical examiner or coroner on the same ground, at least as far as the exterior examination is concerned. It is here, in the exterior examination, that we meet the vague boundary line between police science and legal medicine. It is also here that many of the most difficult problems in homicide investigations will be encountered, as, for example, the determination of whether it is a case of homicide or suicide. Intelligent cooperation between the medical examiner or coroner and the skilled investigator is the best means of solving such problems.

Shooting—In shooting cases the wound caused by a bullet fired from a short distance must have a typical appearance—and so must the immediate surroundings—to lead to a conclusion of suicide. One cannot fire a shot against oneself at a greater distance than about 20 inches. Generally, the suicide will press the muzzle of the firearm directly against the skin, or at least keep it very close to make the result certain. The entrance to the wound in such cases is always larger than the diameter of the bullet. Hairs surrounding the hole are singed and the skin around the hole is burnt to a reddish brown or gray-brown color. The skin around the hole will be covered with unburnt powder grains, and if the shot has been fired from less than 8 inches, a smeary, black coat of powder residue will be found. This is especially abundant if black powder has been used, and less apparent if the smokeless type has been employed. All these signs are missing when the shot has been fired from a long distance.

If the direction of the canal in the body seems plausible and the wounded part of the body (heart, forehead, temple, mouth) is so situated that the suicide may have fired the shot from a comfortable position, a conclusion of suicide may be well founded, especially when the wounded part of the body has been uncovered. There are a few cases where suicides have shot themselves by firing through their clothing. This is somewhat characteristic of persons who are familiar with firearms, as, for example, hunters, soldiers, etc., altho women have been known to shoot themselves through their furs.

Naturally attention should always be paid to fingerprints, footprints, traces of violence, etc., which may indicate murder. If several bullet wounds are found in a dead man a conclusion of homicide may be reasonably drawn, but it should be kept in mind that suicides may and sometimes do shoot themselves several times. There is a case on record where a man inflicted upon himself five wounds in the head. A case of this sort will naturally supply the investigator with plenty of food for thought.

In normal suicides the entrance to the wound will be smaller than its exit. This is natural, because the bullet on its way through the body encounters resistance which alters its form. The margins at the entrance are as a rule turned inwards and those at the exit outwards. There are, however, exceptions to this rule. The wounds of entrance and of exit may look quite alike, especially if the shot has been fired from a fairly long distance and the bullet has traveled at high speed. Putrefaction and drying may also completely alter the original appearance of the wound.

Suicides by means of dynamite or other explosives occur among miners, road workers, etc. The explosive may be placed either on top of the head or in the mouth. In the first case only the head, or parts of it, will be blown away. In the second case, as a rule, the whole neck and part of the breast will also suffer. A similar result may be achieved by using a shotgun whose barrel is filled with water. The suicide puts the end of the barrel in his mouth, pulls the trigger, and a blank cartridge is discharged. The column of water produces enormous damage to the head.

Hanging—Strangulation is one of the most common methods of suicide, owing to the ease with which the act is performed. Ropes of all kinds, towels, handkerchiefs, suspenders, aprons, belts, gauze bandages, electric wires, can be used. Furthermore, it is not necessary that the body should swing free to bring about the desired result. During the act of strangulation, the arteries of the neck which carry blood from the heart to the brain are pressed upon. This immediately shuts off the blood supply, causing almost instantaneous unconsciousness because of the resulting anemia of the brain. The effect on the brain is further aggravated by the fact that the return flow of blood—through the veins to the heart—is also interfered with by pressure on these

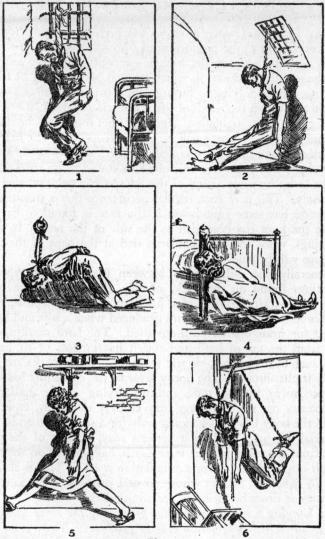

Fig. 71

Some cases of suicide illustrating the fact that the body does not need to swing free. No. 6 is, of course, an unusual case, but the presence and position of the chair indicate suicide

veins. This interference increases the pressure within the skull and contributes to the production of unconsciousness. Comparatively little pressure on the neck is necessary, and this accounts for the peculiar positions in which hanged persons may be found (sitting, standing, lying). Strangulation proper—asphyxia—then sets in and causes the death of the unconscious person.

In cases of strangulation, signs of the rope will be found around the neck. There will be an interruption in the mark at the place where the knot was tied. If the knot was made at one side of the neck, the face will often be found to be red because of the complete compression of the arteries and veins on that one side only. This is of such regular occurrence that a suspicion of homicide has some foundation if the face is found to be pale while the knot has been tied at the side of the neck. In most hangings, when the knot has been tied at the nape of the neck the face will be pale.

Generally one differentiates between two different types of markings found on the neck, namely, the soft and the hard. The soft marking consists of a pale groove with purplish, swollen borders. Such markings are produced when a soft and broad object for strangulation has been used. The hard markings result from the use of hard and rough instruments of strangulation, such as hard ropes, electric wires, etc. Such marks are generally leather-brown. The horny layer of the epidermis has been scraped away by the rope, causing drying of the epidermis. Sometimes the soft markings may entirely disappear, especially when the body has been hanging only for a short time and a soft material has been used. Fat persons may, because of the pressure from the collar or shirt after death, have marks on the neck which can be mistaken for strangulation marks. This is also the case in new-born infants whose normal furrows of the fatty tissue may at times be mistaken for strangulation marks.

By hanging a murdered person practically the same marks as those caused by strangulation may be produced. There is no sure way, either by autopsy or by microscopic examination of the marks, of determining whether a person was hanged after death or not. Hanging of a living body by murderers does not occur very frequently, altho a few cases are on record. In such a case traces of violence almost always will be found if the hanged person is an adult. On the other hand, outer signs of violence on children and drunk or aged persons may not be found at all. In most cases strangulation will be used to simulate suicide, altho poisoning and especially choking may have caused death. In such cases not only the scene must be carefully studied, but also the probabilities of voluntary strangulation. If the body, for example, hangs free, there must have been a place from which the person could have jumped—a chair, a table, a ladder, etc. Such objects should be carefully examined for traces of the suicide's feet and in more doubtful cases, reconstructions should be attempted.

Fig. 72

Schematic drawing of Goddefroy's method to determine if a person found hanged was pulled up or not

The examination of the rope used may reveal most important information. This question has been studied by the Belgian detective, E. Goddefroy, and such examinations have led, in the last few years, to the solution of quite a few crimes on the Continent. The fibers of the rope will lie in the opposite direction of that of the pulling. If a person slides down a rope the fibers will be directed downwards. If what appears to be a voluntary strangulation is in fact murder and the murderer has pulled the body up, the fibers will be directed upwards on that part of the rope which was pulled by the murderer, because of the contact of the rope with the substructure. A dead person is a very heavy and limp mass, hence it is difficult to raise the body and put the head in the noose. Experience shows that the murderer will in some cases pass the rope over, for instance, the branch of a tree, put the sling over the head of the body and proceed to pull it up (see Figure 72). On the other hand, if the fibers of the rope maintain their normal direction this is no proof of suicide, because the murderer may have raised the body and put the head in the sling. The knots on the rope may give valuable information and should not be untied when removing the body. The rope should be cut with great care instead (Figure 72 will show what parts of the rope must be protected against friction in an examination). It is advisable to get a long, strong, wooden box for the transportation of the rope, which should be in the center and held there by a string arrangement to avoid friction. It goes without saying that the part of the rope which has been in contact with the substructure as well as the ends of the rope (in case the rope has been cut) should be marked in some manner; for example, with labels fastened to the rope with strings.

Choking—In choking, the markings on the neck have a different appearance from that produced by hanging. They run almost horizontally around the neck, and there is no such interruption in their continuity as may occur in hangings, where this interruption is due to the knot of the rope used. An interruption may, however, be found if a collar or something similar has prevented the formation of the markings. Self-choking with the hands is obviously impossible because the hands gradually become powerless as unconsciousness develops. The markings by choking are generally deeper than those found in hangings. Traces of violence found on other parts of the body and not brought about by previous, unsuccessful attempts at suicide indicate homicide.

Slit Wounds—Slit wounds in suicides generally occur only on certain parts of the body and have a certain direction, since the intention of the suicide is to bleed to death as quickly as possible from some main artery. The wounds, either one or more, are then found on parts of the body which can be reached with comfort by the arm, *i.e.,* on the front part of the neck, the middle of the upper arm, the elbow, wrists or thighs. Wounds on the abdomen are seldom found in suicides. Persons mentally deranged, however, sometimes have self-inflicted wounds on parts of the body more difficult to reach. Very often one finds, besides the deadly incision of an artery, superficial wounds, the result of the first unsuccessful attempts.

In normal cases the direction of the wounds in suicide should indicate that the left-handed or the right-handed individual has been able to make them himself with enough pressure and in normal positions. If, for instance, we assume that a right-handed person has cut his own neck, the wound should begin on the left side behind or under the left ear and run obliquely over the front of the neck to the right. If the line of incision runs in the opposite direction and the suicide is known not to be left-handed, strong reasons for a suspicion of homicide must be entertained. This is especially the case when the bloodstains are found mostly on the posterior portions of the body, i.e., the nape of the neck, the back of the head, the shoulders and back. In authentic suicides the bloodstains are generally found on the anterior part of the body, on the front part of the neck, on the breast and abdomen. Several incisions on the neck will often be found, and some may be very deep. On the other hand, if the wound extends to the vertebræ of the neck, this is a sign of homicide. Sometimes, in suicides, besides the fatal wounds, typical wounds running across the fingertips and the nails will be found. These arise from the fact that the suicide, in stretching the skin with the finger of one hand over the area which he has selected to incise, involuntarily cuts them with the knife carried across by the other hand. These finger wounds may also be due to the grasping of the knife-blade with both hands so as to exert more power during the performance of the act. These wounds are not to be mistaken for the "defense wounds" found in the palm of the hand, which are signs of homicide.

Suicides will almost always uncover the part of the body intended to be sacrificed. This is the case in slit wounds as well as in stab wounds and shootings. If the clothing of the person has been cut through, a suspicion of homicide is justified, especially if the injured area has been uncovered later to make the crime appear one of suicide.

So much for the appearance of the cuts in typical cases. It may be extremely difficult to arrive at definite conclusions as to whether we are dealing with a suicide or homicide merely by the

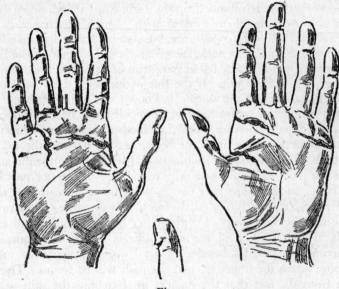

Fig. 73
Typical defense wounds in homicide

appearance of the cuts. One cannot with absolute certainty determine whether a weapon has been used from right to left or from left to right. Experience shows that the area where the weapon has been inserted may be identical with the place where it has been withdrawn. There is also no possibility of drawing conclusions on the basis of the number of cuts on the neck, because in both homicides and suicides one or several cuts may be found. Neither from the depth of the wounds nor from their direction may any certain conclusions be drawn. Suicides in many cases inflict wounds upon themselves which appear totally different from the above-described classical types.

In conclusion it may be said that it is not possible to arrive at definite conclusions on the question of homicide or suicide solely from the appearance of the cuts.   There are, however, certain things, besides the fatal wounds, which allow one to differentiate to a certain extent.   A sign of suicide is the presence of one or more parallel cuts over the temples, wrists, elbows or thighs—often superficial ones.   Signs of homicide are several irregular, deep cuts, especially if accompanied by bruises, contusions, abrasions, scratches.   The "defense wounds" on hands and under side of the arms, as already stated, are almost sure signs of homicide.[5]

Chop Wounds—Chop wounds are seldom found in suicides. They are almost always on the forehead or on the scalp, and are of varying depth, parallel and close together.   In homicides chop wounds on the head run in different directions and are larger. This type of wound is very seldom found on the limbs of suicides.

Stab Wounds—Stab wounds in suicides are as a rule close together on the anterior part of the body.   Typical of suicides are small superficial holes in the vicinity of the deep wounds, as the result of the first attempts.   Scattered wounds indicate homicide. The above description of slit wounds applies to the stab wounds also.

Death Due to Traffic Accidents and to Leaps from Great Heights—Such deaths may result from homicide as well as from suicide, a fact which renders it very difficult to determine whether the death was voluntary or not.   Signs of homicide are impressions on the skin, which, because of their shape and position, may indicate that they originate from another person, *e.g.*, impressions of nails, of kicks, of cane blows, etc.   Suicides often previously disclose orally or in writing their intention of committing the act.

Occasionally it may happen that the murderer attempts to

[5] See Rehfeldt, *Zum Selbstmordsproblem*, Berlin, 1929, and Kippel, "Zur Beurteilung von Halsschnittwunden" in *Arch. für Kriminologie*, B. 79, h. 2/3.

hide the nature of his act by making it appear a traffic accident or a death resulting from a leap. An interesting case was reported a few years ago in France. A contractor and two of his engineers were motoring at night on a highway running parallel with the railroad tracks. They traveled at high speed in spite of the fact that the headlights of the car were in a bad condition, only lighting the road for a few yards ahead. As a result they ran over a farm hand of Polish extraction who was walking along the side of the highway. In order to hide the accident the motorists put the victim across the rails and continued their journey. A fast train which passed soon afterwards beheaded the Pole and mutilated his body. During the examination of the body, traces of motor car tires were found on the leg of the dead man and an investigation resulted in the discovery of the motorists and their car. They unanimously denied their guilt, but the police found traces of human blood on one of the mudguards of the car. This fact brought about a confession.

Drowning—Drowning is the most common form of suicide. Direct homicide by drowning is unusual and can hardly be accomplished on a male adult in possession of his full powers and knowing how to swim. It is often extremely difficult to determine whether an apparent case of death by drowning is the result of suicide or of a disguised, previous homicide, since even the most unusual bruises and mutilations present may be due to the body colliding with different objects in the water—for instance, propellers, etc. Of common occurrence, however, is the hiding of homicides by throwing the body in the water after the crime.

Poisoning—Poisoning is often a means of committing suicide. The investigator ought to be familiar with the more common poisons and their action. As a rule the murderer will not use poisons which, because of their color, smell or taste, may awaken suspicion. On the other hand, the suicide may take any evil-tasting and evil-smelling poisonous substance. In homicide or suicide by poisoning special attention should be paid to the appearance of the skin, to the smell, and to changes in or around the mouth, the genitals and anus.

When there is a suspicion of poisoning, all bottles and drugs in the house must be seized. Food which the poisoned person has eaten, glasses, cups, dishes, vomitus, excrements and urine are collected and sent for examination. The collecting and transportation of these substances and objects should not under any pretext be taken care of by the family or neighbors of the dead person, because death from poisoning is often a family affair. It is of greatest importance to act speedily, because the evidence is perishable and easily destroyed.

The most common poisons, their action on humans, and their antidotes will here be briefly described.[6]

Special circumstances which may cause one to suspect poisoning are:

1. Quick death without special symptoms (prussic acid and cyanid of potassium).
2. Vomiting of coffee-brown substances with odor of onions or garlic (phosphorus).
3. Black vomitus (sulfuric acid).
4. Greenish-brown vomitus (hydrochloric acid).
5. Yellow vomitus (nitric and chromic acid).
6. White vomitus which turns black in daylight (silver salts).
7. Vomiting of substances with a sharp smell (strong vinegar or ammonia).
8. Bluish-green vomitus (sulfate of copper).
9. Colic and pronounced diarrhea (arsenic, sublimate and lead salts).
10. Cramps, paralysis, unconsciousness (carbolic acid, lysol, strychnin, nicotin).
11. Drowsiness (morphin and opium).
12. Excitation and delusions (belladonna and atropin).

Arsenic plays an important rôle in the process of oxidation in the human body. Normally, traces of arsenic are found in the urine, milk, menstrual blood, nails, hair, skin, etc. This fact must be considered when examining a dead body if poisoning is suspected. Quantities of arsenic less than 0.1 milligram may be regarded as originating from the body itself.

The symptoms of arsenic poisoning as a rule do not appear immediately but usually after half an hour or an hour. The

[6] For a study of this subject see: *Detection of Poisons*, by Autenrieth, Philadelphia, 1928, and *Legal Medicine and Toxicology*, by Webster, Philadelphia, 1930.

person poisoned has a burning sensation in the throat, vomits substances which are either colorless or have the color of the arsenic preparation, complains of acute pains in the abdomen, accompanied by diarrhea; this last, however, may not occur in very severe arsenic poisoning. The urine is bloody and diminished in quantity and the agony is extreme. Death almost always occurs during the first twenty-four hours. When large quantities of arsenic have been administered, death, preceded by vomiting, may follow within a few hours.

Arsenic has always played an important rôle in the history of poisonings because of its odorless and almost tasteless qualities. Chronic arsenic poisoning is not uncommon in certain metallurgical plants and in glass factories. Some horse dealers feed arsenic to horses in order to improve their appearance. Arsenic is also an ingredient of many medicinal preparations for anemia and nervousness. The lethal dose varies from 0.1 to 0.5 grams.

It is very important to determine in what part of the body the arsenic is found; the organs to be examined are therefore divided into three categories. The first consists of the stomach with its contents, the second of the intestines, and the third of the liver, the kidneys, the spleen, the lungs and the heart. Poisons are seldom found in the brain—except ether, alcohol, strychnine, atropine and prussic acid. In arsenic poisoning the examination of the hair, nails and skin may be important, because they may also contain arsenic.

The separate examination of the different organs of the body will show whether the whole system was impregnated with arsenic in chronic poisonings resulting from excessive and prolonged use of medicines, etc. (such as subcutaneous injections of arsenical preparations), or whether the greatest amount of the arsenic was found in the stomach and intestines. This latter fact indicates that death resulted from the oral ingestion of the poison.

Arsenic remains in the body unbelievably long: its presence may be determined several years after burial. It has even been possible to show the presence of arsenic in the ashes of cremated bodies. In a case reported by Jeserich [7] a school teacher took more than 1 gram of arsenic in order to commit suicide, but she survived. Three months afterwards 0.1 gram of the arsenic could still be recovered from the urine and hairs; and about one year later the hair still contained arsenic. During anti-syphilitic treatment arsenic is found in the hair of the patient two weeks after the beginning of the cure.

In exhuming for the purpose of determining the presence of arsenic, the soil around the body should always be analyzed, as well as all objects in the coffin or in its surroundings which may contain arsenic, as, for instance, artificial flowers, paint on the coffin, etc. When large quantities of arsenic are present in the body, some of the arsenic may, during the process of putrefaction, reach the soil under the coffin. The soil around the coffin must therefore be tested in different places.

Antidotes for acute arsenic poisoning are washings of the stomach and the intestines with water, milk, and oil and limewater mixed, magnesium hydroxid, and magnesium oxid mixed with ferric hydroxid.

Phosphorus occurs in two forms, the colorless and red varieties. The red phosphorus is not poisonous. On the other hand, the colorless phosphorus is such a powerful poison that 0.1 to 0.3 grams will cause death. The symptoms of phosphorus poisoning vary. In most cases there is a burning feeling of thirst, pain in the abdomen, belching, vomiting, etc., and toward the end bleeding from the intestines, muscular twitchings, etc. The time elapsing between the ingestion of the poison and death depends on the quantity administered and on the individual resistance to its action; but death usually supervenes in from two to seven days, and in rare cases it takes place in only a few hours.

Phosphorus is decomposed relatively soon in the dead body. However, it is still possible to show its presence there after three months—in the form of phosphoric acid. Here, as in all cases of poisoning, the composition of the soil surrounding the coffin

---

[7] Dr. Rudolf Jeserich, *Chemie und Photographie im Dienste der Verbrechensaufklärung.*

plays a large part in determining the presence of the poison in the dead body.

Antidotes for phosphorus poisoning are stomach lavages and sulfate of copper, 1 gram in 500 cc. of water. The administering of milk and fatty foods should be avoided, as the phosphorus will be dissolved and the condition aggravated.

Antimony salts have sometimes been used in poisonings, especially in the form of emetic wine. The presence of antimony in the body can easily be determined chemically. The antidote is tannic acid aided by the stomach tube.

Lead salts are nowadays very seldom used for criminal purposes. In medieval times, however, they were one of the chief ingredients of the so-called "heritage powders." The antidote for acute lead poisoning is sulfate of sodium or sulfate of magnesium, either of which turns the lead into insoluble lead sulfate. Milk and purgatives are also given.

Mercury salts, especially corrosive sublimate and calomel, are used in suicides and homicides. The symptoms are rather individual. In most cases there is abundant salivary secretion, a burning sensation in the mouth, vomiting, ulcers of the mouth, abdominal pains, delirium, etc. Sometimes there will be delusions simulating alcohol poisoning: persons poisoned by sublimate have been arrested for drunkenness. The time of death generally depends on the dose taken, varying from a few hours to several days.

The presence of mercury in the organs is difficult of detection, owing to the fact that usually only small quantities have been ingested; but in almost all cases the detection is possible.

Antidotes are of little value, and persons who have already taken the fatal dose (0.2 to 0.4 gram) may be regarded as lost. Toxicologists recommend the stomach tube, eggs, milk, castor oil, camphor, iodate of potassium, and other antidotes.

Strong acids, such as sulfuric, nitric, and hydrochloric, have been used for suicidal purposes. The victim lingers for several hours or even days in the most extreme agony, because of the burning of the internal organs. The use of acids for such a purpose can only be attributed to ignorance. The most common antidotes are magnesium oxid, lime water, and milk of magnesia.

Strong alkalies, such as hydroxid of potassium and sodium, produce extensive burns, agony and death after quite a while.

The most common antidotes are tepid water containing citric, tartaric or diluted vinegar to neutralize the hydroxids. The citrous fruits, such as lemons, oranges and grapefruit, are often used. Milk, oil, camphor, and ether have also been recommended.

Prussic acid is a colorless liquid having a strong odor of bitter almond. *Cyanid of potassium* comes in small white sticks, also with this characteristic odor. Prussic acid is formed when the cyanid of potassium is brought into contact with any weak acid, as for instance the acid of the stomach. Its action is extremely rapid. Death within a few minutes will follow the administration of only 0.1 gram. The lethal dose of pure cyanid of potassium is about 0.15 gram.

The swift action of the poison usually precludes the use of an antidote. Toxicologists recommend a 3-per-cent solution of peroxid of hydrogen, which transforms the prussic acid into a harmless compound.

Organic Poisons—To this large group of poisons belong opium and its alkaloids, morphin, heroin and codein, cocain, strychnin, brucin, the South American curare, atropin, digitalis, and the "sleeping powders" such as veronal and luminal.

We do not need to describe here the tragically common use of some of the above by the drug addict. All these drugs have played their parts in homicides and suicides.

Acute poisoning by *opium* and *morphin* is followed by urinary urge and suppression, perspiration, drowsiness, slow rate of respiration and pin-point pupils. The victim becomes cold and clammy, the temperature of the body is diminished, coma supervenes, and death soon follows because of respiratory paralysis. The lethal dose is from 0.2 to 0.5 gram, altho drug addicts are known to have taken as much as 5 grams every twenty-four hours without fatal effects. Antidotes are strychnin in small doses and atropin.

Cocain poisoning produces heart and respiratory embarrassment, thirst, paleness, dilated pupils, headaches, delirium, etc. The lethal dose is highly individual and ranges from 0.04 gram upwards. Death may follow within a few minutes, or be delayed for hours.

Strychnin shows very characteristic symptoms. The limbs and muscular system in general are subject to jerking movements, twitchings, convulsions of tetanic nature, and generalized rigidity. The victim is generally conscious throughout, and suffers terrible pain, which may cause him to scream. Death usually follows in from one to three hours, but may occur sooner or later.

Strychnin is one of the most powerful poisons known, altho the quantities an individual can stand are varying; 0.03 gram is considered a lethal dose for an adult.

Antidotes are tannic acid, emetics, potassium permanganate, and inhalation of chloroform to control convulsive seizures.

Strychnin is a very stable substance and will remain in the dead body for a long time. Its presence may be determined several months after burial.

Atropin poisoning results in sensations of constriction around the throat, vomiting, thirst, dilated pupils, double vision, sometimes blindness, later convulsions, unconsciousness and death.

The fatal dose is generally 0.1 gram. Antidotes are emetic substances.

Digitalis poisoning symptoms are headaches, abundant salivary secretion, abdominal pains and slow heart rate. There may also be chills, dilated pupils, diminution of vision, etc. The symptoms may occur within one to four hours, but in some cases only after a few days. Death occurs in five to thirteen days, and cases are known where it has followed without any previous sign. The fatal dose varies greatly.

Veronal is used frequently as a suicidal agent. Large quantities will produce sleep in about half an hour and death may take place after several hours or days. Antidotes are stomach tube, laxatives and preparations used to stimulate the action of the kidneys.

Luminal is much more poisonous than veronal. Large quantities produce death in about twenty-four hours.

All the above-described poisons are complex chemical compounds. Their detection in a dead body is almost always possible, altho difficult. Owing to the fact that from a dead body weighing 120 to 160 pounds only a few organs weighing a few pounds are obtainable, the presence of the poison must be determined from as pure and concentrated an extract of the organs as possible. An examination of the dead organs, especially for unknown alkaloids, generally takes three to four weeks if it is carefully made.

C. At What Time Did Death Occur?

This question will be answered by the medical examiner after observing the temperature of the body, the rigor mortis, the post-mortem lividity, and the degree of decomposition.

In some rare cases, as for instance in typhoid fever, cholera, and deaths caused by certain poisons, the temperature after death may rise for two or three hours and then drop. Normally, however, the temperature becomes gradually lower until it approaches the temperature of the surroundings within six to eight hours. It is then possible to determine approximately the time elapsed since death by measuring the fall in temperature with a thermometer inserted in the rectum.[3] The temperature is said to drop one degree Centigrade for each hour after death. This, however, depends very much upon the conditions of the individual case and the assumption is always hazardous. It is dependent on whether the body is obese or thin, whether clad or nude, whether the exterior temperature is exceedingly low or high, etc.

The rigor mortis generally occurs two to six hours after death. The stiffening usually begins from the head and gradually spreads down over the whole body. After a time which varies from eight to twenty hours (in most cases ten to twelve) the rigor is

[3] A special thermometer has been constructed for this purpose by Professor van Ledden Hulsebosch in Amsterdam.

complete. It disappears after two to three days, altho in some cases it may last until the fifth day. The time for the appearance and disappearance of the rigor mortis is dependent upon many factors, especially the temperature and the strength of the muscles. In cold weather it appears sooner and the stiffness is more pronounced than in hot weather. Poorly developed individuals and children do not show as pronounced rigor mortis as strong persons.

The post-mortem lividity occurs three or four hours after death, altho it may sometimes occur earlier or later. It occurs sooner in cases of instantaneous death, as for instance in strangulation, and later in arsenic poisoning. Post-mortem lividity is due to the action of gravity, which causes blood to sink to the lowest level of the body. When the position of the body is altered during the first few hours after death, the lividity appears in other places if the blood is still liquid. This may be very important in homicide investigations, hence the necessity of always carefully noting the position of the lividity.

The first signs of decomposition are seen twenty-four to forty-eight hours after death and consist of a greenish-blue coloration of the veins in the skin and a diffused greenish-blue coloration of the abdomen. The presence of insects on the body will also give indications. In summer, on a body lying in the open, after a few hours there will already be eggs of insects in the corners of the eyes and of the mouth and nostrils; larvæ will form after forty-eight hours, the pupæ after eight days, and a new generation of flies after two weeks. If empty pupæ are found on the body the person must have been dead at least three weeks. In summer, maggots may completely eat away the soft tissues in four to six weeks.

In "floaters" the "washerwoman's skin" will appear on the fingers after a few hours and on the entire hand after forty-eight hours. The skin does not begin to loosen from the flesh before six to eight days.

The rare adipocere formation, in which the fat of the body is turned into a whitish, waxy substance, does not occur before six to eight weeks, and a complete transformation of the whole body into wax requires at least half a year.

The condition of the stomach noticed during the autopsy may cause one to draw conclusions about the time when death took place. These conclusions are, however, only approximate, because the stomach continues to digest food for twenty-four hours after death. If death takes place immediately after a meal the post-mortem digestion will be found to be very slight. If the amount of the stomach content is small it may signify that the person has been dead for a considerable time. The stomach of a living person empties in two to six hours. An empty stomach then indicates that death has occurred at least two to six hours after the last meal.

When skeletons are found the degree of the decomposition of the clothing may give certain information. Cotton fabrics fall to pieces after four to five years, woolens after eight to ten years, and silk and leather after twenty years or more.

D. What the Shape and Position of Bloodstains Will Tell

The appearance of bloodstains can often give important imformation concerning the circumstances of the murder. Blood drops and blood sprinkles will have a different appearance according to the height from which they have fallen. If the distance is short they appear as round drops, provided the surface on which they fall is not rough. If the height of the fall is greater, the blood drops have jagged edges, the jaggedness having relation to the height. The greater the height the more jagged the blood drops will appear. (See Plate 17.) If the drops fall from a considerable height, say two or three yards, the contents of the drop will be sprinkled in many small drops.

The above applies only to blood drops which fall at right angles from a stationary object. If the drops fall from a person who is moving, their form will be quite different. The movement of the drop in this case consists of two components:

(1) A vertical movement due to gravitation.

(2) A horizontal movement due to the forward progress of the person.

When the first part of the drop touches the floor, the remaining portion is still moving in a horizontal direction and splatters over the first part, thereby forming toothlike projections. The direction of these teeth denotes the direction toward which the person is moving. The more rapid the walking the longer and narrower are the blood drops and their teeth. It should, however, be pointed out that such an appearance may also be had under other conditions. If, for instance, while a murder is being committed, an ax smeared with blood is raised during the act of delivering a second blow, drops of blood may fall from this weapon which assume the characteristics described above. It is then necessary to examine all bloodstains on the scene, because the position of the different stains in relation to one another may throw light on such an occurrence.

One should not arrive at hasty conclusions concerning the direction taken by the person from the appearance of the blood drops. The person walking may have moved the blood-smeared or wounded hand in a direction opposite to the one in which he was walking. He may also have remained quiet and moved only the limb. In such cases the blood drops with their teeth will extend in the opposite direction. In most cases, however, such drops are characterized by small teeth.

If a blood drop is quickly spouted at an angle against an object, blood sprinkles will form. As a result of the rapidity of the movement of the drops in touching the object, the last portion of the drop will continue over the first part with such speed that a stain resembling an exclamation point will be formed. The pointed end of this exclamation mark will reveal the direction of the movement. The more obtuse the angle at which the blood spout meets the object, the thicker the exclamation point; the more acute the angle the longer and narrower is the shape of the exclamation point.

If a blood spurt from a long distance touches a vertical wall obliquely, the direction of the exclamation point may lead to false conclusions. What has been said above concerning the thickened part of the exclamation point representing the source and the point representing the direction of the movement, holds good only for sprinkles originating from a short distance. If the distance is great the individual drops will very soon gravitate towards the floor. Then even if the blood spurt had, originally, an absolutely horizontal direction the stain on the wall may show these exclamation points at an opposite direction to that of the movement.

The source of blood sprinkles may vary. They may originate from injured arteries, giving highly characteristic sprinkles, altho this occurrence is rather rare. More often the sprinkles occur when a bleeding wound is struck with violence or when blood drops fall from the quickly-moved bloodstained weapon of the murderer. The number, relative position, and appearance of the individual stains will in many cases allow conclusions as to their origin. It has many times been possible to tell the position of the murderer and the manner in which the weapon was handled by simply examining the bloodstains.[9]

When examining the appearance of bloodstains a reconstruction with the aid of ox blood is recommended.

The material upon which the bloodstain rests is important, inasmuch as it may alter the original shape of the stain. If the substructure is smooth metal, tile, smooth or hard wood, glass, porcelain, leather or a similar material, the bloodstain will keep its original form. On the contrary, if the material is porous, as, for instance, cotton, wool, blotting paper, hairs, porous bricks, soft wood, etc., the original form will be altered by absorption of the blood in the substructure.

No bloodstain is so characteristic that it can have originated only in one way. Wide experience is needed to draw correct conclusions. The position and shape of the stains are to be carefully recorded by photographs and sketches.

The shape of the bloodstains on the clothing is also important, since it affords a means of testing the explanations of the defendant as to the presence of the stains on his clothing. When,

---

[9] See also Jeserich, *Chemie und Photographie im Dienste der Verbrechensaufklärung*, Berlin, 1930, where the shape of bloodstains is fully described.

for instance, a defendant claims that the presence of blood-sprinkles on his clothing is due to the fact that he has touched such clothing with bloody hands, one can immediately conclude that he is lying

In Chapter XV we deal with the search for bloodstains and how carefully the weapons, clothing and body of the murderer must be searched for very minute traces. It should be added that an important part of the clothing to be searched is the opening of the trousers, because the murderer after the crime will often urinate involuntarily.

E. Problems of Locked Doors

If a door is found locked from the inside, this is looked upon as a sure sign that no one has left the room by the door. Many times in suicide investigations detectives have looked upon this sign as infallible, and if no special circumstances suggest homicide, the result of the investigation is inevitably a conclusion of suicide. A door with a common lock, however, is easily locked from the outside after leaving the key on the inside. A patented lock, however, cannot possibly be manipulated in this way, because the key is outside and the door is locked from the inside.

The criminal who closes a door from the outside, leaving the key on the inside, will use one of two methods. He will either use a tool, known to international hotel thieves by the French slang name *oustiti,* or he may use a simple device consisting of a string and a small piece of wood. In many cases the piece of wood is superfluous.

The *oustiti* may change in form, but in principle it is always the same. A pair of thin semi-lunar tongs, rifled to prevent sliding, is inserted into the lock, and the tip of the key is grasped and turned in any direction. The *oustiti* may have the shape of a common pair of pliers, but closer examination will show that the tongs are unusually thin, round, and have a semi-lunar shape on the inside (see Figure 79, page 325). Some thieves use pliers with detachable tongs to fit the different sizes of keys.

Originally this tool was used to open doors of hotel rooms at night for the purpose of robbing the sleeping guests. Many careful persons who live in hotels lock their doors at night with two turns of the key, and then leave the bit in a cross position

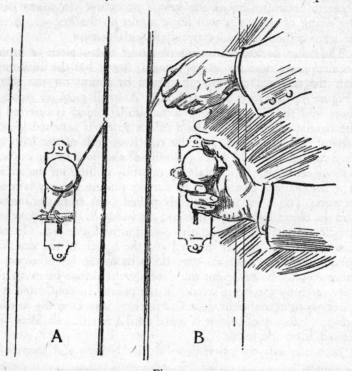

Fig. 74

How a door is locked from the outside with the key inside: A shows the door inside with a lead pencil and a string applied to the key. B shows how the key is turned from the outside

to prevent the pushing out of the key and the opening of the door with a skeleton key. These precautions are, however, so far as the *oustiti* is concerned, not only useless but even helpful to the thief. It is more difficult for him to use a skeleton key than to turn the original key with the aid of the *oustiti*. The *oustiti* may also be used to lock a door from the outside with the key inside. This has the advantage that one can lock the door with two turns. In order to determine if the *oustiti* has been used, a careful examination of the key is necessary. In many cases the rifling of the tongs will leave marks on the key which can be seen without difficulty by slight enlargement.

The other device, consisting of string and a piece of wood, requires more time for its application; but it has the advantage that the material can almost always be found on the scene. (Figure 74 illustrates this method.) A small piece of wood, a short lead pencil, a match or some similar object is inserted in the handle of the key. A loop of the string is fastened loosely around the object used, and the two long ends of the loop are then carried along the line of closure of the door to the outside. The object is kept in its place by carefully pulling on the string. The door is now closed, and by further pulling the key is made to turn. The string is completely pulled away from the outside and the object falls on the floor on the inside of the room, where it will in most cases attract the attention of the expert. In certain cases when the lock is oiled and the handle of the key is of special shape the criminal may do without the bit of wood or other object. In any event the door should always be examined very carefully for string marks in the paint. In conclusion it is necessary to examine the door and the lock very carefully in cases where the theory of suicide is based on the fact that the door was locked from the inside.

Both methods were first described by Nelken and Jeserich of Germany.[10]

F. Investigations in Special Cases

Fatal Motor-Vehicle Accidents—The large number of fatal motor-vehicle accidents render necessary the organization of special units in the police department to cope with the technical problems encountered in such investigations. New York City

[10] Jeserich, *Chemie und Photographie im Dienste der Verbrechensaufklärung*, Berlin, 1930.

has had a motor-vehicle homicide squad since 1928. Numerous other cities in the United States have also "accident investigation squads."

Investigations of this nature have only one goal: to determine the question of guilt. As in no other investigation, the result of the work instituted has an enormous bearing on the decision of the court. Owing to the well-known fact that witnesses in motor-vehicle accidents as a rule are often very unreliable, the judge and jury welcome any technical evidence that can be offered.

The field is too large to be entirely covered in this book. The

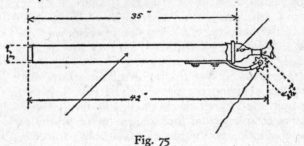

Fig. 75

Chaulmontet's device for marking skid marks in photographing motor-vehicle accidents

ideal interrogator in motor-vehicle homicide cases must have a thorough knowledge of motor vehicles and their mechanism and should be a qualified brake expert.

The scene of major accidents should be photographed from different angles, if possible before the removal of the vehicles. The skid marks of the vehicles showing the efforts of the application of the brakes should appear on the photograph. As these generally last for quite a while even on hard surfaces, such as asphalt and concrete, this is not difficult. However, these marks should be colored so that they may appear clear in the photographs. For this purpose plaster of Paris is spread over the trace with a special spreader.[11] The spreader consists of a brass tube

[11] Invented by André Chaulmontet, head of the laboratory of the Police Department, Geneva, Switzerland.

with a lid at one end and a rubber hose with brass mouthpiece and a cogwheel on the other end. This spreader leaves a thin even line of plaster on the trace. Sometimes it is advisable to differentiate between the traces of two vehicles. The method of Ernst Fontell,[12] consisting of the use of two coloring materials, such as plaster and red lead, may be employed.

If necessary and possible, reconstructions of the accident should be made on the scene. Such reconstructions may be of immense value to the investigator.

The scene must always be sketched. A good sketch throws light on many important facts, as, for instance, the length of the skid marks, the position of the vehicles at the moment of collision, their dimensions, etc. Any one of these items may decide the case. A bad and inaccurate sketch may lead to a miscarriage of justice.

Skid Marks—The skid marks reveal the efforts made by the driver when applying the brakes. The real skid marks originating from the locked wheels should not be confused with the tire marks resulting from the progress made by the car following the application of the brakes. Generally, however, the real skid marks are so characteristic that no mistakes are possible.

The entire distance covered from the moment the motorist observed the danger until the car came to a stop consists of two separate divisions. The first embraces the distance traveled in the so-called "reaction time," *i.e.*, the time that elapsed from the moment he discovered the danger until he applied the brakes. The reaction time shows a slight difference in different individuals, altho in normal circumstances it is fairly constant. As a rule the reaction time is one-half of a second.

The second division consists of the skid marks. The speed at which the car had been traveling immediately preceding the accident may be at least approximately calculated by measuring the length of the skid marks. The action of the brakes on different roads and for different tires varies. Two-wheel brakes, four-wheel brakes, dry, wet, slippery and icy roads influence the

[12] Fontell is Commissioner of Police in Gothenburg, Sweden, and is a well-known Scandinavian criminologist.

distance a great deal. It is then advisable to make tests with the incriminated car on the scene, using an instrument called the decelerometer, which will show the actual distance which the car travels before coming to a full stop. If the length of the skid marks experimentally produced is known, it is easy to determine the speed of the incriminated car by comparing the results shown by the decelerometer with the distance of the skid marks found on the scene.

If, however, the incriminated car has been smashed and cannot be used for the experiments, the speed of the incriminated car from the skid marks must be calculated. For this purpose there are brake tables showing the average distances for two-wheel and four-wheel brakes on dry and wet roads.

The problem is very much simplified in places where police regulations fix the required efficiency of the brakes. In New York City, for instance, every motor vehicle capable of a speed in excess of 10 m.p.h. must have a service brake capable of decelerating the vehicle when traveling at the rate of 20 m.p.h. so that it will stop within 43.3 feet if equipped with two-wheel brakes and 22.2 feet if equipped with four-wheel brakes, from the location where the brakes are applied.

Fig. 76

The decelerometer mounted on the running-board

The emergency brake operating independently of the service-brake mechanism should be capable of decelerating the vehicle when moving at the rate of 20 m.p.h. so that it will come to a stop within 50 feet from where the brake was applied.

The brake test, if not carried out on the scene, is made on an asphalt roadway, which should be level, dry, clean and free from loose material and holes. In testing a roadway, we may assume it to be level when a car remains stationary with all brakes released and its transmission control in neutral position. The brake test is made with the above-mentioned decelerometer, the accuracy of which is checked frequently with the master decelerometer certified by the United States Bureau of Standards.

The decelerometer is mounted or clamped on the right running-board of the automobile. If it is found that the vibrations of the car are so pronounced as to interfere with the proper functioning of the decelerometer, it may be placed on the front bumper or other part of the car where the minimum amount of vibration is found.

With the small lever on the face of the meter set at "free," the instrument is mounted face upwards so that an imaginary line connecting the point of the two arrows on the dial face would be exactly at right angles with the direction in which the car will move. The instrument is leveled by tilting the head forward or backward until the mark "set level" on the scale comes exactly opposite the pointer. The meter should now be tapped gently to insure final settlement of the scale. When the instrument is set to "level" the head is locked by fastening the two thumbscrews. The car will then be in readiness for the actual road test. The small adjusting lever on the face of the clock is now set to "test" and the vehicle driven at any speed between 10 and 20 miles per hour. The brake to be tested—either foot brake or emergency brake—is now applied with full force until the vehicle comes to a full stop. The testing should be done with the clutch disengaged. If the test discloses a defect in the brakes, another test should be made with the clutch engaged. Where a motor vehicle is not provided with a clutch, as in the case of electrically driven vehicles, the test should be conducted without any motive power being supplied to the driving wheels.

The reading under caption "feet to stop" on the decelerometer dial will indicate the maximum deceleration during the stop in "feet to stop from 20 m.p.h."

It goes without saying that when a mechanical defect in the vehicle concerned has been found, the detective investigating must be prepared to say whether, (a) the mechanical defect existed before the accident, or (b) the defect was caused by the collision incidental to the accident, or (c) the defect developed subsequent to the accident.

Calculations of Space and Time—It is often necessary in the investigation of motor-vehicle accidents to determine the *speed* of a car on a certain distance and in a certain time; or what *distance* the car traveled in a certain time and at a certain speed; or the *time* taken by the car to travel a certain distance at a certain speed. The formula for calculating these three quantities is as follows:

$$\frac{T}{3600} = \frac{D}{M}$$

3600 is a constant and indicates an hour expressed in seconds.
T is the time in seconds.
D is the distance which the car travels.
M is the miles per hour.

The formula may naturally be expressed in three different ways:

$$D = \frac{M \times T}{3600} \quad \text{or} \quad T = \frac{3600 \times D}{M} \quad \text{or} \quad M = \frac{3600 \times D}{T}$$

In order to have those three formulas always handy, the following method [13] may be used. The three quantities are expressed by the above-mentioned letters and the constant 3600 is expressed by C. We then have the letters C, M, D, T. The letters are placed in this order in a circle divided into four sections as follows:

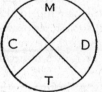

If the circle is rotated so that one letter is always at the top, two letters will always be at the sides and one at the bottom. The letter at the top expresses the quantity to be calculated, the two

[13] Kleinschmidt and Schneikerling in *Der Verkehrs-Unfall*, Berlin, 1930.

letters at the sides are the numerator, and the letter below is the denominator.

This circle may be drawn on a small piece of cardboard which is kept for reference. The following examples explain how the formulas are used:

Ex. 1. What is the distance traveled by a motor-car in ten seconds, at a speed of 40 m.p.h.?

$$D = \frac{M \times T}{C}$$

$$D = \frac{40 \times 10}{3600} = \frac{400}{3600} = \frac{1}{9} \text{ Mile}$$

Ex. 2. How long will it take a car to travel .2 of a mile at the rate of 30 m.p.h.?

$$T = \frac{D \times C}{M}$$

$$T = \frac{.2 \times 3600}{30} = \frac{720}{30} = 24 \text{ sec.}$$

Ex. 3. If a car travels .4 of a mile in 25 seconds at what speed has it been going?

$$M = \frac{C \times D}{T}$$

$$M = \frac{3600 \times .4}{25} = \frac{1440}{25} = 57 \text{ m.p.h.}$$

"Hit-and-Run" Cases—In recent years the hit-and-run cases have increased enormously, owing to the increase in automobile traffic. The offenders in such cases present peculiar psychological phenomena. In most instances they are hitherto perfectly honest persons, but if they kill or injure someone with their car and see the chance of escaping they will do so, because they are either panic-stricken or too cowardly to face the result of their actions, or even because they are of a latent criminal type.

The technical part of the investigation in such cases must be concentrated on identifying the car, as in most instances there are no witnesses. Even if witnesses are present, they seldom have enough time and presence of mind to ascertain the license of the fugitive car. As a rule the investigator must be satisfied with the clues which he can unearth on the scene.

The description of the car must be obtained by a study of the tire patterns. As stated in Chapter IX, a car is seldom supplied with the same make of tire on all four wheels. A careful search should be made to ascertain the tire patterns of the incriminated vehicle, as well as individual scars which may be present on the tires. The following case, reported by Robert Heindl,[14] illustrates how tire patterns can be of use in tracking down the hit-and-run car.

Police found the body of a young man on the highway. The car which caused the accident was unknown. No witnesses were at hand. Only the traces left by the car could lead to its identification. The body, which was lying face down, showed, after having been undressed, traces of a tire pattern on the skin of the back. These traces were, however, too faint and blurred to be used. In addition there was a very clear pattern left on the inner surface of the coat worn by the dead man. It showed a diamond-shaped pattern with the formula $A\frac{6}{6}$ after the tire-pattern classification described in Chapter IX. An impression of a tire with the same formula $A\frac{6}{6}$ was also found on the road at that place. At a distance of 1.56 meters there was a second trace of the tire pattern made by the other rear tire of the missing car. This trace had three rows of squares and had a formula $A\frac{4}{1}$.

The classification of tire patterns kept by the police showed that $A\frac{6}{6}$ was a "Goodyear" and $A\frac{4}{1}$ was a "Dunlop." The missing car, therefore, had a Goodyear on the left rear wheel and a Dunlop on the right rear wheel. The direction in which it was traveling was also found out by the fact that the tail of the coat of the victim was flapped over his back so that the pattern of the

[14] *Archiv für Kriminologie.*

tire was printed on the inner side of the coat. The car must then have traveled from the feet to the head of the victim.

Had it been possible to follow the tracks to where the car had made a sharp turn, one would also have obtained the patterns of the front wheels.

The description of the car obtained through the traces led to a positive identification.

The scene must be photographed, sketched and examined as described on pages 285-288. When the fugitive car has been tracked down, all the details of the accident can be reconstructed and presented to the prosecutor.

The vehicle itself may leave marks on the victim, or the victim on the vehicle. The most common marks are here described:

1. *Marks on the Victim:*

(a) *Glass*—Very often the lamps of the car will break as the result of a collision. Pieces of glass may be found on the victim's clothing or in his skin and scattered about the scene of the accident. Every piece must be collected carefully, and attempts to put the pieces together should be made. Often the patterns of the glass will give a clue to the make of the car.

(b) *Radiator*—The pattern of the radiator may sometimes leave clear marks on the victim. As the radiators are characteristic of a certain make, they constitute a good clue as well as serve in the reconstruction of the accident.[15]

(c) *Tire Marks*—As stated above, the tire patterns may leave very distinctive marks on the clothing and on the skin of the victim. Such traces should be photographed.

2. *Marks of the Victim on the Car:*

(a) *Glass*—We have already described how broken lamps may be identified. If very small quantities of glass are found on the scene and the lamps have already been repaired, a chemical and physical analysis of the glass should be performed. The chemical analysis determines the amount of silicon, iron, aluminum and calcium. The physical test embraces thickness, color and grinding of the glass.

(b) *Blood*—The incriminated car should be examined for bloodstains with the utmost care. If the car is dirty the stains may be covered by a layer of dirt. The front parts of the car must then be carefully cleaned by scraping with a knife. Should the car have been washed, minute stains

---

[15] These marks have been especially studied by Professor Einar Sjövall, of Lund, Sweden. See Sjövall, "Om formade märken och vissa säregna skador vid bilolyckor" in *Nord. Kriminaltekn. tidskr.*, 1932.

of blood may still be present. The leuco-malachite reaction is recommended for the detection of blood.

(c) *Clothing*—In quite a few cases fibers from the victim's clothing, cloth gloves, etc., have been found adhering to the paint on the mudguards of the incriminated car. Other valuable evidence has been obtained through the markings of the pattern of the fabric of the victim's clothing present on the mudguards, This may give marks clear enough to be photographed.

Railroad Accidents—In railroad accidents where strong forces of nature, as fire, water, steam, etc., play a rôle, many valuable traces and clues will be destroyed during or after the catastrophe.[16] A derailed, rapidly-moving locomotive, for example, will destroy everything in its path. The cause of the derailment does not have to be negligence on the part of the railroad employees; in many cases it is purely an accident. It is, however, very difficult to determine if the accident is the result of criminal intention, negligence or otherwise, because of the scarcity of evidence. The investigator must then possess the ability to draw conclusions from the scanty clues at his disposal. His sources of information should be the employees of the division in question, the train-crew, the track-walkers and foremen as well as other employees of the railroad company. Since the search for traces is hindered by the necessity, in the interest of traffic, of clearing the line as soon as possible, the investigator must be able to gather all traces and clues in a very short time. The overlooking of this fact may later hinder court proceedings.

Fairly long distances surrounding the tracks on both sides of the scene should be examined. The position of the switches at the critical moment should be ascertained, as well as the position of the steam regulator, the slide regulator, the brake handles, etc., on the locomotive.

Furthermore, several other questions are to be answered: How many cars have been derailed? At which side has the derailment occurred? Are the derailed cars upright or overturned? Were the wheels worn out? Who is dead or injured? What

---

[16] The engineer in many cases is killed. Should he escape, experience shows that often he is in such a mental state that no accurate information can be obtained for a considerable time.

prominent persons were on the train? Was the mail car robbed? What is the condition of the roadbed?

During the examination of the roadbed only actual damages are described. Damages may also result from the derailment. When examining the condition of the roadbed it is advisable to mark the different sleepers with crayon. If tools used to derail the train are found, they should not be touched before examination by an expert. The broken stone of the roadbed is examined as to displacements. The displacements may be shown by the fact that the blackened upper surface is turned downward. Footprints may be found on the slope of the roadbed in the broken stone or in the grass. A criminal may also leave other traces. He may, for instance, lose or throw away things. It has often been proved that too little attention is paid to the necessity of searching all terrain within the range of vision. In many cases the criminal will encamp a hundred yards or more away from the tracks in order to view them before or after the accident has taken place. Here he may leave pieces of paper, wrappings, cigaret packages, etc. Fingerprints and other traces may be found on all these articles.

During the examination of the scene the position of all objects should be noted and marked on the sketch. One never knows what rôle they may play later. The position of the articles found on the roadbed and scratches on the rails should also be noted. Photographs of the scene and its surroundings should be made.

If an obstacle has been caught by the train and has been dragged along it should be ascertained, if possible, where it could have been caught.

Abortion and Infanticide—Investigations of abortion and infanticide often arise in detective work. Abortion is by far the more common of the two, even tho it rather seldom comes to the attention of the police.

The investigation of abortion can be divided into two categories: the first embraces the cases in which women are suspected of having provoked abortion with their own hands or with the aid of a second party. Direct evidence is represented only by the remaining portion of poisons which may have been used, injuries on the miscarried embryo, or injuries on the woman's genitals. In most cases there is only circumstantial proof. One of the strongest signs of abortion is high fever in relation to the miscarriage. In many cases, however, the fever will drop immediately after the expulsion of the infected egg, so that the physician who later examines the woman is unable to detect any rise of temperature. High temperature and chills before and during the miscarriage constitute a very important sign of abortion. Another proof is the possession of a sound. It should be pointed out that a soft catheter may be made rigid by the introduction of iron wire in its cavity.

A woman who denies being pregnant when she actually is should always be suspected.

The second category embraces the cases where professional abortionists are concerned. Here, only direct confession by the woman on whom the abortion has been performed is of any value.

Naturally all the investigations and examinations above described should be made in close collaboration with the proper medical authority, such as the medical examiner or the coroner.

In infanticides the mother will almost always try to get rid of the dead infant by throwing it away in a sewer, river, forest, etc. The remains and especially the wrappings should be carefully examined as to fingerprints on the paper, laundry marks on lingerie, etc. Wounds found on the body may have been inflicted before or after death and may also have originated from natural causes. The solution of these problems should be effected by the autopsy.

QUESTIONS

1. Give some examples out of your own or others' experience where seemingly insignificant details have played a part in the tracking down of a murderer.
2. If you arrived at the scene of a homicide, and the position of the body as well as of several pieces of furniture had been altered, what would you do?
3. If you arrived at the scene of a homicide together with two fellow

officers, enumerate briefly the duties which would devolve upon the three of you, and describe especially how you would organize the investigation and divide the duties among you.

4. If you arrested a suspect what would you look for upon his body and wearing apparel?
5. Describe the steps to be taken in a poison case to gather evidence.
6. What authorities should you notify in case of a homicide?
7. Build up and describe an alarm system in your community to be used in case of an escape of the perpetrator. Make a map of your community with all adjoining roads and put in the names of the gasoline station attendants, bridge tenders, ferry captains, railroad-crossing attendants, station agents, bus drivers, etc., whom you would have to instruct and immediately notify by an alarm. (Such a plan of general alarm should be built up as soon as possible if it does not exist.)
8. What is meant by *res gestæ* evidence?
9. Indicate what questions should be asked in order to obtain a dying declaration.
10. How is the identity of the deceased proven?
11. Describe how you would remove and dispose of the body in a homicide case in your community.
12. Outline the rôle of the medical examiner or coroner in a homicide case.
13. Describe the typical appearance of the wound of a suicide by shooting.
14. Describe the examination to be made of the rope in a case of strangulation.
15. In case of a slit wound, is there any possibility of determining whether it was caused by suicide or by homicide?
16. Describe some occurrences in connection with the death of a person which would make you suspicious of poisoning.
17. State briefly the means of determining at what time death occurred.
18. Tell briefly what information may be gained from the appearance of bloodstains.
19. Describe the methods of locking a door from the outside with the key on the inside.
20. What information can be gained from the skid marks in fatal motor-vehicle accidents?
21. What is meant by the decelerometer?
22. How long will it take a car to travel two miles at the rate of 45 miles per hour?
23. Enumerate the steps of investigation to be taken in hit-and-run cases.
24. Enumerate briefly the steps to be taken in the investigation of a railroad accident.
25. Describe briefly a case of abortion in which a conviction was obtained, giving special attention to the evidence offered.

A TYPICAL KIT OF BURGLARS' TOOLS

[PLATE 18]

A RIPPING JOB AND THE "CAN OPENER" AND OTHER TOOLS USED
ON IT (Page 300)

A "BLOW JOB" IN WHICH NITROGLYCERIN WAS USED

[PLATE 19]

XVIII

INVESTIGATION OF BURGLARY

A. Technique of Burglary

A THOROUGH knowledge of the technique or *modus operandi* employed by burglars is essential in order to conduct a successful investigation. Of great aid is the perseverance of the criminal, *i.e.*, his unbelievable adherence to a certain method or technique. The ingenious and wise criminal is rarer than he is believed to be. Instead, the common burglar shows a marked narrowness of thought and a peculiar disability to vary his actions. Having once invented or learned a method, he believes it will do. He is a specialist who seldom goes out of his field. If he has started to enter houses by the roof, he will in all probability follow the same course throughout his career. If he has found it convenient to become familiar with the premises by making the acquaintance of servants, he will probably continue to do it as long as he is at liberty to follow a career of crime. The types of headings under "Burglary" in the *Crime Index* of the criminal investigation department of the London metropolitan police [1] will show clearly how far this perseverance persists:

Burglary—Armed
    "   —Bank (false key)
    "   —Bogus message
    "   —Boring hole through window catch
    "   —Breaking out
    "   —Breaking glass panel of door
    "   —Climbing

---

[1] *Crime Index*, printed by the Receiver for the Metropolitan Police District, New Scotland Yard. See also M. O. in *Criminal Investigation and Detection*, by L. W. Atcherley.

Burglary—Country mansion
"   —Cutting bell wires
"   —Cutting out lock or panel of door
"   —Cutting out panes of glass
"   —Cutting through party wall
"   —Early morning
"   —False key
"   —Fanlight or skylight
"   —Flats or chambers
"   —Forcing cellar grid
"   —Forcing door
"   —Forcing window or window bars
"   —Front window
"   —Horse and vehicle or motor car, with
"   —House abutting on railway
"   —Insecurely fastened window
"   —Jeweler's and pawnbroker's shops (see also
               under shopbreaking)
"   —Killing dog
"   —Making acquaintance of servant
"   —Operating at rear of premises from river
"   —Operating at rear of premises
"   —Post office
"   —Public house
"   —Public house fanlight or skylight
"   —Suburban
"   —Through adjoining premises or grounds
"   —Through roof
"   —Traveling
"   —Unattended premises
"   —Using adhesive substance
"   —Using bodily pressure
"   —Using cycle
"   —Using ladder or rope
"   —Wearing gloves, mask, etc.
"   —Violence.

In the following pages the *modus operandi* of different American burglars will be described.

Safe Burglars—There was a time when almost every safe burglary was committed by some "yegg" or "safe cracker" fairly well known to the police, but today this type exists only in fiction. The modern safe man—or rather men, for they always work in groups of two or more called "mobs"—may be of any race, creed, color or occupation, and of any age between eighteen and sixty.

As in every successful business, each member of the criminal partnership has his own particular duties. The "finder"—often an employee of the victim, or some person having access to the building—locates the job and reports on the details. This information includes the size and make of the safe, when the cash is left in it, method of entrance and escape, habits of neighbors, of patrolman and watchmen, and countless other items of knowledge necessary for the undisturbed completion of the theft.

With the plans carefully laid, the first positive action is taken. If the "mob" members fear to be caught with burglars' tools in their possession, they will have them "planted" or hidden in a definite spot in or near the building during the late afternoon or early evening preceding the night set for the commission of the crime. This will be done by some person whose underworld connections would never be suspected—a woman, an old man, or a boy.

Some time between midnight and daybreak, depending upon the type of building and character of the neighborhood, the mob will enter the office and begin their attack on the safe or "can," as it is called. The word "attack" is used advisedly, for it well describes the methods used by modern safe men. Gone is the phantom of the novel, sensitive-fingered "Jimmy Valentine," famous in romance and song—and probably only there. He, together with his more mortal companion, the gentleman who with a well-placed charge of "soup," called nitroglycerin, could unhinge the doors of the strongest safe, has almost vanished.

His successors now rip the bottom or back out of a safe with the aid of brute strength and a giant can-opener, or a sectional jimmy, or a fair amount of skill and the cumbersome equipment of an acetylene torch. Or they bludgeon the dial from the front of the safe with a heavy copper or leaden hammer used for the sake of quiet, and are then free to punch out the combination and open the doors.

The loot or "swag" consists of money, jewelry, precious stones, negotiable bonds or other property easily disposed of through a "fence" and difficult to trace and identify.

A recent case, tho not sensational, well illustrates the methods used by detectives in apprehending safe burglars. An observant patrolman's suspicion was aroused by the presence on his post of three men whose lavish spending belied their lives of leisure. Upon investigation he discovered that two of his "lilies of the field" had police records for burglary.

When a report was made to the detective bureau, the patrolman was interviewed and pointed out the individuals in question to three of the detectives, who immediately placed them under close observation. After two weeks of tedious shadowing or "tailing" the suspects entered an office building late one evening.

The detectives waited outside, intending to catch the men with the stolen property in their possession. When the latter attempted to make their exit they were held by one of the officers while the remaining two went through the building looking for signs of forced doors or other means of ingress to the office. A cursory examination revealed nothing. Upon making a minute inspection of the doors in the building the detectives discovered that one glass panel had been carefully removed and replaced. The office contained a safe from which the bottom had been ripped and the contents removed.

To connect the suspects more thoroughly with the crime, the fingerprints on the door were photographed, and when the photo was enlarged and compared with the prints in the records of the former convicts of the trio, they were found to match perfectly. When faced with this evidence all three men confessed and are now serving prison sentences.

The technique used today by safe burglars may be any one of the following methods:

Ripping Jobs—Equipment used by criminals includes a sectional jimmy, a can-opener, brace and bits, a flashlight. There are many kinds of sectional jimmies, among them a one-piece type with one of its ends chiseled, and the two- or three-section type with one of its ends like the point of a pencil and the other end chiseled.

The safe burglar makes a hole in the upper left-hand corner of the door—or one of the doors—with an electric drill, inserts the pencil point of the jimmy into the aperture, and rips in an upward or downward direction until the front steel plate is off (see Plate 19, page 297).

Punch or Knob-Knocking Jobs—This is a type of safe job frequently perpetrated today. The dial is knocked off with a sledge hammer, and the spindle or dog is punched back with a center punch and mallet and the small sockets broken, allowing the release of the lock (see Plate 20).

Chopping Jobs—In these cases the safe is turned upside down and the bottom chopped out.

Drag Job—The upper half of Plate 23 shows how the drag works as it tightens on the dial, and forces and breaks the dial and spindle. This method is considered obsolete since the "punch" method was created.

Blowing Open a Safe with Explosives—The criminal who uses this method must know the proper amount of explosive to employ. A hole is drilled in the door of the safe a little to the left and over the dial and a piece of cotton saturated in nitroglycerin is wrapped around a fulminating cap, which is inserted in the hole. All crevices are covered with ordinary kitchen soap. A connecting wire is run from the fulminating cap a distance of about fifteen feet to a battery or electrical outlet and the detonator is set off. Equipment carried by the blowers includes brace and bits, flashlight, nitroglycerin, and a jimmy or tools to effect entrance into the premises (see Plate 19, lower half).

Torch Jobs—In jobs of this kind one of the criminals is a mechanic who knows the proper amount of air and acetylene gas that has to be applied to heat and burn steel on the safe. It is necessary to transport an oxygen and gas tank, a burner, and adequate footage of hose, and to hide them in the selected premises. As the risk of detection is greater than when using the method of ripping, blowing or punching, this method can be regarded as almost obsolete (see Plate 20).

When the investigator of a safe burglary finds that the safe has been opened by the combination, it is evident that the safe was not locked properly or that someone knew the combination or had gained access to where it was kept, and committed the crime. While such a case calls for a check of the movements of employees of the concern and of the building in which the concern reporting the crime is located, the probability of a professional sneak gaining and otherwise searching drawers of desks in offices and obtaining the combination from written memoranda pasted to the side or bottom of a drawer or otherwise left exposed to view must not be overlooked.

Tools of Safe Burglars—Following is a list of paraphernalia used by safe burglars. It must not be supposed that all these things are carried to any one job.

Flashlight; the battery is used to set off the fulminating cap in blow cases.
Jimmy.
Bolt cutter.
Small saws, hack-saw, compass-saw.
Brace.
Bits. For drilling holes in wood and steel.
Percussion cap.
Sectional jimmy.
Can-opener.
Copper or lead hammer.
Chisel.
Electric drill.
Nitroglycerin.
Keys.
Acetylene torch.
Dynamite.

When dynamite is used generally a quantity filling the thumb of a glove is placed in the hole made in the safe that is to be blown. The technique is similar to that employed when nitroglycerin is used.

Various methods are used to carry tools to the job. They may be carried in a suit-case or in a case used to carry a musical instrument, such as a violin, saxophone, and so forth. One of the mob may carry one part of a sectional jimmy and another the other part. Or the sectional jimmy may be hung on a rope or cord from the neck and concealed by the clothing. A neat merchandise package may be simulated at times to transport the tools. On the other hand, they may be hidden under the seat or in the tool-box of an automobile or taxicab, or a shipment is made to the premises or adjoining premises for a firm which had already closed for the day, the superintendent or other person receiving them.

Loft Burglars—While the safe burglar can ply his trade the year around, the loft man is more seasonal in his activities, since only at certain periods of the year is a substantial amount of valuable merchandise stored in lofts.

This type of criminal is, for some unknown reason, usually of foreign extraction. In the Middle Atlantic States for the last few years many thefts have been committed by negroes who were formerly employed in loft buildings, or who, having received their early training as small-store thieves, were led to the newer field of endeavor by glittering accounts of the profits in looting lofts. Their jobs, however, are distinguishable by the fact that they usually take a large quantity of finished goods without distinction as to quality.

As in the case of safe burglars, the loft men work in "mobs" of from two to six members, depending upon the type of job and the bulk of the merchandise. They are active between seven o'clock in the evening and daylight, while the loot may be transported from the scene at any time during the succeeding day and night.

Because of the precautions taken by business houses which store furs, silk, or other valuables, a loft mob must carefully plan the crime. Information may come to them through employees of a firm or building, from salesmen who have had access to the loft, or from numerous other sources. These "finders," as they are called, receive a percentage of the haul for their services. A member of the gang, an expert, is then sent to examine the premises. He discovers the best method of gaining an entrance, and of carrying off the "swag"; whether the loft is wired or "bugged" by a protective agency or some other company, and if so, whether there are any unwired spots in the doors, walls, floors or ceiling through which an opening can be cut.

With the plans before them, the thieves may take any one of several methods of action. A member of the mob may secrete himself in the loft or building before closing time and make a careful selection of the desirable goods. When his confederates arrive they pack his choice in specially prepared "swag bags" and carry them to the street. Here a truck, cab or private car receives the loot for transportation to the "drop" or hiding place. If there is danger in this rather open method, the "swag" is hidden sometimes in a vacant loft in a neighboring building or in the very building in which the burglarized loft is located, in the cellar, on the roof, in the tank house or motor house, or in another loft with the permission of its tenant.

But all jobs are not done so easily. More often it is necessary to force an entrance into the loft. If there is no electric alarm system—few loft buildings lack this protection—a door or window is broken open. A "bugged" or protected storeroom presents greater difficulty. To attack it, the mob obtains permission from a neighbor who is not very particular as to his source of income, to use a loft above, below or adjoining the one containing the property about to change hands. After some drilling and excavating, an aperture approximately eighteen inches square appears in the lightly constructed ceiling, floor or wall of the treasure-house. This hole must be carefully drilled, so that no alarm wires are met and broken.

Another class is known as the "kick-in" mob. Usually it consists of three or four men operating late in the evening, about midnight, or shortly before or after the opening hour of the business day. It is immaterial if the place is wired for protection. They drive up in a high-powered car to the curb in front of the premises, or adjacent thereto, the driver accomplice keeps the motor running, and his confederates force or jimmy the street door if locked, step into the vestibule or hallway, and there force or jimmy the inner door or crash a window, enter and grab armfuls of valuable furs, ladies' coats or garments, and take flight in the waiting automobile. Generally the premises selected for attack are on the ground floor.

A lone "kick-in" burglar may operate on any floor, and if there is commotion will hide in the same building until the alarm subsides, and sneak down the stairway to the street, hail a taxi-cab and leave with the loot.

The colored burglars usually enter lofts or shops where finished garments are made or sold. They are not as expert as their white colleagues.

Tools used by loft burglars depend on the kind of job to be done. If entrance is to be gained through a door, a goose-neck

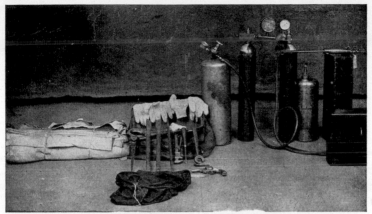

TOOLS FOR A "TORCH JOB"

"PUNCH JOB" WITH THE DIAL PUNCHED OUT

[PLATE 20]

SAFE BURGLARY—A "PUNCH JOB"

[PLATE 21]

jimmy from eighteen to thirty-six inches in length, purchased at a hardware store for about $1.25, is used. The trade name is a case-opener or ripping bar (see Plate 18, opposite page 296, for exhibit of tools).

If entrance is to be gained through a wall or through a floor or ceiling, the tools consist of a sectional jimmy with a sharp point on one end for knocking or chipping out concrete in floors or ceilings; a brace and wood bit; or an electric drill for boring several holes in the wooden floor. An opening of sufficient size is made to gain entrance and to pass the merchandise through.

Other paraphernalia may include candles, flashlight, canvas or cloth gloves to protect hands from injury and to avoid leaving fingerprint impressions, and black cloth or burlap bags in which to carry away plunder. Sometimes a chisel—with the aid of a copper hammer or a gut or leather mallet—is used to cut away concrete. Sound is lessened when the chisel is struck by a leather or gut mallet.

The sectional jimmy and can-opener are made in blacksmith shops. The burglar makes a sketch of the tool he desires and brings it to a blacksmith whose respect for law and order is nil. The unscrupulous blacksmith knows he is making a burglar's tool and charges accordingly. Several years ago it cost $10 for a two-piece sectional jimmy. A can-opener and a three-piece sectional jimmy cost $25; the price today is about $10. A small hook jimmy, brace and bits and other tools may be purchased in any hardware store. The need for thorough investigation at such stores is obvious.

Window Smashers—Window smashers are usually young men of daring or men addicted to the use of narcotic drugs. These criminals may have a car, with motor running and an accomplice driver on the seat, parked around the corner from the store selected. In jewelry-store cases the job is done during business hours, while the jewelry is on window display. The criminal, carrying a brick or stone wrapped up in a paper or cloth, approaches the window, knocks or throws the missile against the glass, breaks a hole in it, inserts his hand, grabs a tray of jewelry or its contents, runs to a waiting automobile and flees. Success depends upon suddenness and surprize of attack and boldness of action.

Another type operates in mobs of three or four. They also use a car. Their speciality is fur shops, department stores and dress shops where valuable merchandise is on display. The hour of attack selected is when stores are closed and not many persons are about. Midnight is a favored time, when patrolmen on post are walking or riding in to the station-house or waiting near relieving points, with their thoughts concentrated on going off duty. Other favored times are when street lights are extinguished in early morning, or when a policeman leaves post on duty or otherwise; when elevated railway trains are passing, and during winter nights when it is raining or snowing. Throwing a brick or other missile—or a milk can—through the window, the thieves grab the merchandise and take flight in an automobile.

The lone window smasher operates as a rule in the winter season during late night or early morning hours. While some lone workers might be classified as mental defectives, the urge for sustenance and shelter has furnished motive for some normal men to commit this type of crime in recent years.

Store Burglars—Store burglaries are usually committed by youths of fourteen years or more, and by men up to fifty years. Generally two or four work together. The amateur store burglars are young men usually residing in or near the area in which they operate. Stolen goods are disposed of locally to unscrupulous dealers, or pawned.

The regular or professional store burglar uses great care in planning and executing jobs. Finders are sometimes employed to locate jobs, or tipsters furnish information. This type of burglar is usually an ex-convict who gets together a mob of younger men with less experience than himself. He inspects places to be burglarized, plans the job, secures tools and arranges for sale of stolen merchandise to a fence. When the job is done he is usually in the vicinity to make sure he is not double-crossed. The place selected to be burglarized is observed and inspected during business and closing hours for one or more days prior to the crime, which is committed during late night or early morning hours. Habits of owner, employees, persons in the neighborhood, policemen on post, private watchmen, and passers-by are noted. Opening and closing time of store is observed, and it is determined whether the premises are wired for burglary protection or not.

When the crime is completed the loot is placed in the yard or the hallway, or near the front door. A lookout signals when the way is clear; another accomplice in an automobile then draws up to the premises, and the loot is taken away in the car. The other criminals follow in another car or leave the scene afoot.

Tools selected depend on the entry to be effected. Eighteen- to thirty-six-inch jimmies are used for doors and windows. If there are bars on windows, a Stillson wrench, a setting pipe cutter or a hack-saw may be used to cut the bars. To enter through the floor or ceiling, or through a side wall from the hallway or an empty adjoining store, braces and wood bits are employed. Tinsmith's snips are used to cut sheet-iron ceilings.

Residence Burglars—Types of residence burglaries may be said to include those committed in flats or apartment houses, those committed in private residences, those committed in vacant houses, and—a type prevalent in recent years—those committed in penthouses.

Flat and Apartment-House Burglars—The day burglar usually operates between 9 A.M. and 11 A.M. and from 2 P.M. to 7 P.M. The night burglar operates between 7 P.M. and 9 P.M. and from midnight to daybreak.

Many burglaries are committed by youths ranging in age from fourteen to twenty-three years, who are without funds to satisfy their desire for pleasure or recreation. Youths of this class usually frequent candy stores and cheap pool parlors; sometimes they fly kites and pigeons from roofs. Their criminal operations are, as a rule, confined to their neighborhood, seldom going more than a mile distant from their rendezvous. Loot is often bought by the owner of the store which they use as a hangout, or is pledged, pawned or sold at a pawnshop or second-hand dealer's

establishment by the owner of their hangout or by one of the
burglars, or by an older boy who frequents the store.

This type of burglar will also break locks on quarter-dollar gas
meters and steal the money deposited therein.

Another class of youths committing flat burglaries in the daytime are those not residing at home but living in cheap furnished-room houses. They range between the ages of seventeen
and twenty-three, and may be found lounging in pool parlors,
coffee restaurants, bakeries, parks, or around cheap moving-
picture theaters. They start out about 9 A.M. from their rendezvous or hangout.

Different methods are used to ascertain if the occupant of a
flat or apartment is not at home. The inexperienced thief may
be observed looking up at the front windows of the house selected, from the opposite side of the street. When an apartment
is spotted where the shades are down full length, the vestibule
of the building is entered and the bell of the flat or apartment
rung. If there is no answer, he either uses a pass key or rings
another tenant's bell to gain entrance. Proceeding to the apartment he intends to burglarize, a knock is given on the door, or
the buzzer or bell is pushed. If there is no answer, the door may
be opened with a pass key if it has a common lock. If the door
has a patent lock, a jimmy is used to effect entrance, or a panel
of the door is cut out and a hand inserted to unlock it. Contents
of bureau drawers, sideboards, and other pieces of furniture are
dumped on beds, on dining-room and other tables, or on the
floor. Everything of value is sorted and placed in a suit-case,
hand-grip or pillow-case. Escape is made by way of the roof or
by walking boldly out at the front door. If a pillow-case is used
to carry the loot, it is swung over a shoulder to simulate a laundry collector. There have been cases where flat burglars had a
laundry cart or wagon on the street to remove the proceeds.

House Mob—Sometimes a flat burglar works with two or
three accomplices. They compose what is known as a "house
mob." One is a lookout. A faked letter is placed in the letter-
box of the apartment selected. Persons entering the hall are
checked by the lookout. If the letter is removed, the lookout

signals by ringing the bell of the apartment as the tenant starts upstairs. The burglars either escape by way of the roof or walk downstairs past their victim, being careful to conceal the face by tipping the hat in such a way as to cover it or by using a hand-kerchief. Gaining the street, they proceed to the nearest subway, elevated railway, or street-car line or bus, or may use a "Drive your own car" and return to their hangout or rooms.

Jewelry, silverware and wearing apparel are usually pawned or sold late in the morning or afternoon. Clothing may also be disposed of by pledge or sale to a dishonest proprietor of a second-hand clothing store, who immediately removes labels and other marks of identification. Attention to such suspected or known places should be given by police and detectives during business hours.

There have been cases where burglars of this type have kept clothing and wearing apparel in their rooms until a quantity was secured and then sold to a cast-off-clothes man.

In criminal argot, the burglar who has not a place set to bur-glarize when he starts out, but chances to find one, is referred to as "going on the blind" or "peddling a flat."

The burglar who works on tips has advance information about the flat or apartment to be burglarized, and knows where valu-ables are kept. Such tips may be given by a laundry, grocery, hall or telephone boy, janitor, possibly by a son or daughter of the janitor, or by a relative of the victim. In cases of the last type the person who gave the tip may make it convenient to be present in the apartment burglarized when the police or detective is called to investigate. The tipster listens to what is said as to efforts that will be made to solve the crime and observes the offi-cer examining articles for fingerprints. The tipster thereupon is likely to undertake to smudge every fingerprint impression.

Supper Burglar—The supper-time burglar uses methods sim-ilar to those of the day burglar to determine if occupants of an apartment are at home. He ascends the stairs and opens or forces the door. Sometimes he uses the fire-escape, enters through a window, and places a chair under the knob of the door leading from the room he is in to other rooms in the apartment or to the hall—to afford time to leave by way of the fire-escape should the occupant discover his presence.

The Night Burglar—This type usually ranges in age from twenty to thirty-six years. A night-time burglar of one class, in residential sections comprised of apartment houses, works between the hours of 7 and 11 o'clock, alone or with a partner, while owners are away from home. Such criminals are shrewd and artful, and will visit a residential section making observations to select likely places to burglarize. These observations may be made from adjoining or adjacent houses, occupied or in course of construction, or from areaways or roofs of occupied houses. Some may even inspect the victim's house during the daytime to plan approach and getaway. Suitable pretexts are assumed by them in such instances; they often pose as canvassers, salesmen, inspectors, or pretend to be looking for a relative or friend. Should there be an empty apartment in the house, the burglar may secrete himself there until nightfall. If not, he returns later, stopping before entering the house to make sure he is not being shadowed or observed. To effect entrance to the selected apartment, he may use a skeleton key, a pick-lock or a jimmy. Or he may ascend or descend by way of the fire-escape to a window leading into the apartment. Gaining entrance, he places chairs across doorways and in the private hall of the apartment, so that warning will be given him if the absent occupants return, and the latter will be impeded in any attempt at pursuit.

This type of night burglar at times operates on tips and may park an automobile in the same street in which he operates, or in the next street thereto.

The after-midnight burglar uses a technique in many ways similar to his colleague who commits burglaries during the hours before midnight. Gaining the roof, he may remove his shoes there, or remove them on the fire-escape, from which he may also alight in the areaway or yard. He enters the selected apartment by way of a window leading to the fire-escape, by a rope ladder dropped from the roof, or by means of any available physical abutment or contrivance which is attached to the building.

He listens to hear the breathing of occupants asleep. Cautiously stepping into the bedroom, he removes trousers, coat, vest, purses and bags found there to the dining-room, kitchen or other room or to the fire-escape, roof, yard, areaway or cellar, and extracts money and jewelry therefrom. He may also place chairs across doorways or in the private hall of the apartment so that if the occupant or occupants awake and attempt pursuit they will trip and fall and afford time for escape. Seldom does he reach the street by way of the house entered. Exit generally is by way of an adjoining house, or the next street is reached by climbing over a fence. Generally an automobile is parked at a convenient location. In instances where an automobile is not used, operations are usually confined to localities adjacent to transportation systems.

Some after-midnight burglars operate by inserting a mechanical contraption through the window from the fire-escape which will pick up trousers and wearing apparel placed on chairs, etc., near windows. Others immediately cut the telephone wire upon entry. After-midnight burglars may be classified as the most dangerous type. They have been known to be armed with pistols, to wear masks, and to carry lethal and non-lethal agents or substances to assist them in their operations.

Paraphernalia used by night burglars comprises flashlight, jackknife, small jimmy, screw-driver, glass-cutter, nail-clipper, large safety pin or a piece of wire, false keys and picklocks.

Miscellaneous Burglars—Dishonest hall boys, elevator operators, telephone boys and janitors form another group. They know when the occupant is out and when return can be expected. Sometimes the keys to the apartment have been left in their care. Keys are easily duplicated. They either commit the burglary or have an accomplice commit it. Loot may be secreted in a storeroom or locker on the premises to be removed when work is finished.

Private-Dwelling Burglars: (a) *Town and City Type*—While private dwellings in towns and cities are often entered by day and night burglars using a criminal technique along the lines used by flat and apartment-house burglars, attention should also be given to the professional private-dwelling burglar in the urban area who operates while the occupants are away on vacation, abroad, or absent for a protracted period. Information may be secured by use of the telephone, by tips from delivery boys, from gossipy tradesmen, or from an artizan or servant employed on the premises. In instances where a tip is furnished, details of where jewelry, money, bonds, and other valuables are kept are also supplied. False keys are used, or entrance is gained by breaking through a window or door, generally in the basement, areaway or yard.

(b) *Private-Dwelling Supper Men*—Then there is the supper man, who robs private dwellings exclusively between 7 P.M. and 9 P.M., while the occupants are in the dining-room. Search is made in rooms only on upper floors. Money, jewelry, furs and valuable coats comprise the plunder taken. This type climbs to the roof of the private dwelling from the roof of an adjoining house and enters by way of skylight or scuttle, or by climbing up or down a drain pipe to an open window. Before going to work he arranges a getaway, perhaps by placing a ladder or table under the skylight. In investigating such cases the detective should carefully examine walls around scuttle or skylight entrances for fingerprint impressions or for articles or memoranda which may be dropped by the burglar in making entrance or getaway. Search roof for clues. Cases are on record where the burglars lost memoranda and left other clues which led to apprehension. (See Plate 18 and Plate 22 for display of burglars' paraphernalia.)

(c) *Suburban Private Dwelling*—The amateur and the professional criminal operate against this type of residences in the suburban or sparsely-built-up sections of a city, town or village. While the burglar generally works during the absence of the home owner and his family in the day and evening hours, in recent years entrance has been effected after midnight and up until daylight. Entrance at any time may be effected by forcing a cellar window or a window on the first floor, usually from the rear yard; by climbing up porch or extension and forcing an upper window, or by false keys.

This class of burglar nowadays steals only such property,

money, jewelry, silverware, and fur coats as may be concealed on his person or carried away in a suit-case or grip found handy for the purpose.

Some such burglars also steal radios, particularly when there is a market for their purchase. Often the suburban burglar operating after midnight cuts telephone wires as soon as he gains entrance and may be classed as a very dangerous type who will shoot to effect escape and prevent capture.

Police officers and detectives should be suspicious of the movements of strangers on the streets in suburban sections, especially after midnight.

(d) *Penthouse Burglars*—With the advent of the penthouse, the field of activity for the professional residence burglar grew larger. Fair and warm weather also helps him. Dwellers in penthouses generally like plenty of fresh air and are accustomed to have windows and doorways open but screened. The technique used by the penthouse burglar is similar to that of the night burglar. Generally only money and jewelry are stolen.

In investigating such cases it is important to determine when and where other penthouses have been burglarized, and plans accordingly laid and followed to effect a capture.

No matter what the type of the professional burglar, he will be shrewd enough to take almost all precautions to prevent stolen property being found on him, and may resort to its transfer by express or its checking in a self-service or a service checking station for a period of time.

B. Criminal Receivers

A person who earns a livelihood by criminally receiving and disposing of stolen goods is a malignant enemy of society. It has been said truthfully time and again that if there were no receivers of stolen goods there would be very little crime against property and against persons who are attacked and robbed of property. Criminal receivers are responsible for most of the dishonesty and unethical practises in business, for youths committing crime, and for professional criminals continuing in crime. Operating ostensibly as a business man in a manner to keep away from the arm of the law, the criminal receiver or fence does business only with one man. As a rule that man has a criminal record. Often, however, the fence will operate through a third person designated by him as his lieutenant. Goods purchased are paid for in cash and rarely is a record made or kept of the purchase.

The finder locates a desirable haul and takes notice of the quality and quantity of the merchandise. This information is given by the finder to the criminal band of burglars or thieves. One of the thieves then locates a receiver and informs him of the amount and quality of the merchandise. The best offer is accepted, and the drop or location of delivery is named. The drop may be a warehouse, a garage, a stable, loft or store, occupied or unoccupied. The lieutenant sees to it that the drop is set to receive the delivery. The stolen goods are delivered to the drop by one or two of the thieves while others in the band precede the load to the drop to make certain that the way is clear.

With delivery made, the merchandise is examined by the lieutenant. Upon being found satisfactory, identification marks are removed. These marks include selvage markings, stamped numbers or letters, trademarks, tags, wrappings, stencils, or sewed-on marks.

When this task is completed the receiver is notified, arrives, pays cash for the loot, and removes it in a truck to his place of business, which has the appearance of a legitimate establishment. Weekly visits are made to the receiver's place by small retail merchants who come from various parts of a city or from suburban towns to purchase marketable merchandise. So it is that goods stolen are scattered about. The small retail merchant is not the only buyer. Jobbers and merchants doing business on a larger scale are contacted and told of exceptional buys below market quotations, and avail themselves thereof, thus making a quick turnover by underselling reliable competitors.

Again criminal receivers get control over thieves and burglars by lending money to carry them along while awaiting favorable criminal opportunities, and engaging attorneys to defend them in court after arrest. The receiver also busies himself to make advantageous contacts to "fix a case."

In order successfully to prosecute and convict a receiver it is necessary to prove he knew the goods purchased to have been stolen. This may be brought about by interrogation leading to his admission of the fact, or by discovery of the stolen goods, concealed, re-marked or relabeled. In making investigations of receivers, intelligent interrogation, check and search play important rôles. Conversations are voluble: denials, lies, evasive answers, misstatements are made; false labels and bills or a lack thereof appear; unethical and furtive buying methods appear in combination with a very low price paid.

Criminal receivers may be found in the field occupied by reliable pawnbrokers, second-hand dealers, junk dealers, auctioneers, jewelry merchants, and the like. To the layman the successful prosecution of a man for criminally receiving stolen goods therefore seems a difficult task. It is not. To illustrate with a case:

Several months ago a truck load of silk valued at $20,000 was reported by the driver to have been stolen. It afterwards developed that the truck had been turned over by the driver to a thief. The latter drove it to a drop, an unoccupied loft, where the lieutenant for the receiver examined the goods and bought them. Stencil marks on the cases were removed and the goods were taken out and—after removing the marks thereon—shipped to the receiver. Detectives located the thief and the loft in which the goods were dropped. The thief did not know the receiver nor his place of business, as the only person with whom he had come in contact had been the lieutenant for the receiver. A careful search of the building in which the loft was located was made. In a coal pit of the fire room, parts of the wooden cases, some of which had been burned, were found. It was later determined that the superintendent of the building had received a sum of money for destroying the wooden cases and tags. Continuing the investigation, detectives located the porter in the building, who had helped to carry some of the goods out of the express wagon. A description of the expressman and of the wagon was obtained. The expressman was located, and he revealed the address of the premises to which he had delivered the goods. Here the cases were found on tables ostensibly in process of manufacture.

The receiver produced a lease showing that he had sublet the loft to a man a week previously. The reason for the sublease was because he had received a telegram from a relative in California requesting him to come to California. He produced the telegram to substantiate his story. A check-up of associates, home conditions, and his movements before and after receiving the stolen merchandise disclosed that the receiver had slept in a friend's house while the goods were in his loft and that he had informed his friend of anticipated trouble in his loft. The lease and the telegram were proved to be false. It was also ascertained that he told his friend he wanted to stay for two weeks longer in the loft, as he anticipated trouble. This was sufficient to show that the receiver had knowledge that the goods were stolen.

Criminal receivers of stolen goods resort to all sorts of tricks for the purpose of secreting these goods. One trick is to have a trapdoor through which the stolen merchandise is thrown into a secret compartment. The trapdoor is then closed, and simulated packages, all wrapped in the same fashion, are placed on the floor over it. Criminal receivers may visit the homes of thieves for the purpose of inspecting and buying stolen loot, and if found satisfactory a taxicab or closed automobile is driven up to the premises and the loot removed.

In cases where jewelry comprises the stolen plunder, the burglars or thieves are apt to hire a room in the neighborhood a week or more in advance of the job, and continue to occupy the room for a few weeks after the job has been committed, the purpose being to have a ready and safe place to hide the stolen goods and keep under cover. Contact is subsequently made with the criminal receiver. The receiver and one of the thieves then may proceed to a bank in which the receiver has a safe-deposit box into which the thief puts the stolen jewelry. Subsequently the receiver returns to the vault, examines the jewelry, places a value thereon and pays the thief. Shortly thereafter the jewelry is removed to another bank and safe-deposit box.

In one case a merchant was robbed systematically of over 100 cases of woolen yarn. A check-up of the employees disclosed a shipping clerk visiting a shady place and conversing with a criminal receiver. The receiver was covered. A few days later, he was seen talking to a truckman, and the truckman and his vehicle proceeded to within half a block of the merchant's store. There he was met by the shipping clerk during his lunch hour, and four large cases were taken from the freight elevator of the premises and placed on the truck. Delivery was made to a factory some miles away. Here it was found that the criminal receiver had made many purchases of goods stolen from the same merchant. On the premises were found over fifty cases of merchandise bearing the merchant's name. The criminal receiver could only account for the purchase of ten and refused to explain whence the others came. The shipping clerk was arrested. The truckman and the elevator man in the factory of the receiver told of their work in connection with the stolen cases. This, supplemented by the books of record containing no record of the merchandise, as well as by evasive answers and denials of the receiver, led to successful prosecution and conviction.

C. Search for Stolen Property

When property has been stolen a thorough search should be made of the building from which it has been taken. Many times the plunder has been recovered on back stairways, in empty rooms or apartments of residences, in empty or occupied lofts in the building in which the crime was committed, or in adjacent buildings, garages, pieces of furniture, candy boxes, match boxes, bird cages, electric-light fixtures, etc.

Many police departments today have a card system in which to record stolen property, and the cards from this file will often match the cards sent in by pawnbrokers and dealers compelled by law to report pledges and purchases and by banks and honest merchants ready to cooperate with the police. The efficient detective also personally visits and inspects the premises of licensed brokers, accompanied by the victim or complainant; he likewise visits known or suspected fences and drops, in his quest of stolen goods. Never should the room, apartment or residence of a prisoner whose arrest is concerned with stolen property or extorted money be overlooked in such a search. Immediate visit should be made thereto. A systematic and thorough search should follow, conducted with patience, skill and perseverance. Automobiles owned or hired by the defendant should also be searched, as well as any garage or outhouse he may use. Among the agencies of assistance in locating stolen goods, the Furriers' Alliance in metropolitan cities is very cooperative. The Fur Dressers' Association maintains a record of all marks placed on raw furs. In the case of silks, the Silk Association is also cooperative.

Secret marks known as "scratch marks" are placed on pieces of valuable jewelry by many jewelry manufacturers, and are of importance to secure when valuable jewelry is stolen. The Jewelers' Alliance is helpful in such cases.

D. Description of Property

It is essential for the police investigator or detective to secure a complete description of the property that is wanted. The following covers, in the main, general articles that are subject to theft or loss:

Watches:

Kind of metal; description of case and movement, and numbers of each; tell whether lady's or gentleman's; use abbreviations "h.c." for hunting case, and "o.f." for open face; initials; monograms or inscriptions; value.

Rings:

Kind of metal; lady's or gentleman's; style; setting; kind and number of stones; weight; maker's name; initials or other marks; value.

Chains:

Kind of metal; lady's or gentleman's; length and weight; kind of link; style; value.

Earrings or Studs:

Kind of metal; style; whether screw, coil or drop; kind, size and number of stones; value.

Jewelry, Miscellaneous:

Name of articles; kind of metal or material; kind and number of stones; design; initials; inscriptions or monograms; maker's name; value.

Table Silverware:

Name of articles; solid silver or plated; heavy or lightweights; maker's name; design, such as plain, beaded or flower, formal, animal, etc.; initials, inscriptions, monograms; value.

Miscellaneous Gold and Silver Goods:

Name of article; kind of material; plated or solid; size; maker's name; design; number of pieces if set; initials; inscriptions or monograms; plain, chased, etched or engraved; open or solid pattern; value.

Bric-a-Brac or Antiques:

Name of articles; material or materials; design; size; shape; carved, engraved, enameled or inlaid; age; value.

Pocketbooks, Handbags, Suit-cases, etc.:

Name of article; material; size; color; shape; initials or other marks; value; contents.

Clothing:

Name of articles; material; style; size; color; maker's name; initials or other marks; value.

Fur:

Name of article; coat; muff; collar. etc.; kind; size; color; value.

Animals:

Kind; size; distinctive color or distinguishing marks; age.

Trucks and Wagons:

Type; shape; color of wagon and running gear; name or other distinctive marks; contents.

Motor Vehicles:

See separate heading.

Motorcycles:

Make; year of model; number of cylinders; manufacturer's number;

make of saddle; make and condition of tires; position of speedometer; horn; front and rear lights; distinctive marks; license number.

Bicycles:

Make; color; number; kind of brakes and saddle.

Typewriters:

Kind; serial and model numbers.

AUTOMOBILES

License Number:

Make:

Year of Model:

Whether Rebuilt:

To what extent. If original lines have been changed, a full description of the appearance is necessary.

Kind of Body:

Whether Body has been Rebuilt:

To what extent.

Body Number or Trademark (if any):

Location of number or trademark.

Motor Number:

Factory Number:

Changes or Repairs:

Made on interior construction.

Exterior Injuries:

Such as dents.

Changes Made:

On instrument board, new instruments added.

Wheels:

Wood, wire, or disk.

Tires:

Size; make and conditions.

Precautions Taken:

What was done to prevent theft of the car, such as having the switch locked?

ESCAPING AUTOMOBILE

License Number:

Make of Car:

Number of Passengers:

With description of them.

Direction Going:

Kind of Body:

Note if body has cowl or dash; number of doors.

Steering Wheel:

On right or left side.

Color:

Size of Car:

Heavy, medium or light.

Radiator Hood:

Location and general shape.

Hood:

Shape, location of ventilators, if any.

Mudguards:

Shape.

Lights:

Type; shape; location.

Tail Light:

Exact location (important), whether shining on license plate from above or from the side.

Rear View:

Note presence of anything such as tire carrier, tool box, gas tank, type of rear springs, baggage rack, bumper, or shock absorbers.

Hub Caps:
  (Important) material (brass, nickel or painted), shape.

Wheels:
  Wire, wooden or disk.

Injuries:
  Such as broken lamp; hub cap missing; mudguard bent; dents.

E. Simulated Burglaries

Altho not always susceptible of proof, many burglaries, robberies and larcenies are prearranged and fraudulent; in character of motive they are in the same category as numerous cases of arson to which recourse is had for the purpose of concealing insolvency and theft. There is a vast difference, however, between fraudulent claims for indemnification due to alleged burglary or theft, and those based on losses by fire. In the former there has been no real loss to the policyholder, whereas in the latter there is a tangible obvious loss of property which leaves little to be determined but the criminal participation—if there is reason to suspect it of the person insured.

In either instance the possibilities for fraud are unlimited. The property, for instance, alleged to have been stolen or burned may never have been in the possession of the insured, or he may have sold it, or, having guilty knowledge of what was about to transpire, had it transferred elsewhere. The loft districts of metropolitan cities have always been the scene of activity for depredations of the dishonest merchant, endeavoring to realize on an insurance policy through burglary, larceny or arson. So the importance of a careful investigation of the phases referred to in the first chapter is obvious.

Fig. 77

These screws have been pulled away by force. The splinters of wood located in the pitch show the fact very clearly

In investigating various types of burglaries too much emphasis cannot be laid on an exhaustive search for fingerprint impressions on doors, doorknobs, lights of glass in doors and windows, window frames and sills leading to and in the premises burglarized, and a thorough and systematic search of the building burglarized and the building adjoining it. Record a full description and secure all identifying marks of the stolen merchandise or property. A preconceived notion that the goods have been removed should never be held. Cases are on record where parallel investigations conducted by detectives specializing in the apprehension of safe, loft, and residence burglars have by diligent search located the stolen property in a vacant apartment, office or loft, and have traced the criminals through a trunk which they purchased to transfer the loot, or through information given by owners or lessees of nearby apartments or furnished-room houses from which the approach to the scene was made by the criminals.

A careful investigation of the way of the perpetrator on the scene and of his *modus operandi* will often give information regarding faked burglaries. The owner of a store who is going to simulate a burglary seldom has a correct idea of a burglar's methods; hence he often fails to avoid logical pitfalls; broken windows will be found smashed from the inside, holes in walls will be too small to allow the entrance of an individual, etc.

In one of the authors' cases [2] a jeweler reported to the police that a burglary had been committed in his shop and that goods valued at $40,000 had been stolen. An examination of the scene indicated that the perpetrator had entered through the basement, forced the door of the cellar, and there made a hole in the brick ceiling, which was more than a yard thick. The floor of the shop was occupied by counters and other paraphernalia, but the burglar had been lucky enough to penetrate the open floor space. There were no traces, such as fingerprints. A careful investigation was made, with the following results:

1. The cellar door showed evidence of jimmy marks and evidently had been forced open from the outside. The lock on the inside of the cellar

[2] Söderman, *Brottets Värld*, Stockholm, 1927.

door had been held in place by four screws. Two of the old and rusty screws showed fresh marks of a screw-driver. Small pieces of wood were found attached to the threads of the two remaining screws, a sure sign that the screws had been torn away by force (Figure 77). Two of the screws had been removed from the inside with a screw-driver and only two forced away.

2. Along the edges of the hole in the ceiling loose pieces of brick and concrete were hanging. Ordinarily they should have fallen down if anyone had tried to go up through the hole.

3. The floor of the shop was covered with encaustic tiles. When examined with a magnifying glass, it was discovered that the slabs had been chiseled from above.

Facing these overwhelming technical evidences, the jeweler finally admitted that he had committed the burglary to collect insurance. At first he had tried to break open the cellar door, but had failed. Then he proceeded to unscrew two of the screws that held the lock from the inside, and had succeeded in breaking the door open. He had begun to pierce the ceiling from the cellar, but found this operation too tiresome with pieces of brick and concrete constantly falling on his face. Finally he went up to the shop and proceeded to make the hole from above.

F. Burglars' Tools and Their Traces

On April 28, 1930, the Supreme Court of the State of Washington, in an opinion written by Justice Millard and concurred in by Chief Justice Mitchell and Justices Parker, Beals and Tolman, stated:

Courts are no longer skeptical that by the aid of scientific appliances, the identity of a person may be established by fingerprints. There is no difference in principle in the utilization of the photomicrograph to determine that the tool that made an impression is the same instrument that made another impression. The edge of one blade differs as greatly as the lines of one human hand differ from the lines of another. This is a progressive age. The scientific means afforded should be used to apprehend the criminal. (Case of Washington *vs.* Clark.)

On pages 160-163 we deal with burglars' tools and how to make casts and photographs of the traces they leave. The possibility of such identification should never be overlooked.

Some other methods of burglars may also leave traces, as, for instance, that of making a wax cast of a key. Sometimes this is done by dipping a blank key in molten wax or other substance. This leaves a thin coating on the blank, which is then introduced into the keyhole and turned so that it touches the mechanism of the lock. The points of contact will leave marks on the wax, making it easy to file the blank to the desired shape. This operation leaves traces of wax in the interior of the lock and can easily be discovered.

The use of a skeleton key can also be determined by examination of the lock. As a rule the mechanism of the lock is covered with a coat of oil and grease, and only the spots which are regularly touched by the key

Fig. 78

The interior of the lock can be examined by this device, described below.

are shiny. The irregular and searching movements of the skeleton key leave traces in the grease and in other spots.

In order to avoid the removal of the lock, one can with advantage use a small apparatus which consists of a tiny tube with a

Fig. 79

The "oustiti," with which keys are turned from the outside

minute bulb and mirror at its end (Fig. 78). The bulb is lighted by a battery. With this instrument all cavities may be searched. In larger size it may be used for searching houses, when articles are supposedly hidden in the interior of walls, etc. Instead of breaking down the walls or destroying the furniture, a hole is opened in the suspected place and the interior explored with the instrument.

The *oustiti*, shown in Figure 79—and already described on page 282—also leaves characteristic marks when it is used by a burglar to turn a key from the outside of the door.

When a burglar breaks a windowpane he may use a handkerchief with soft soap, a paper having sticky tar on it, adhesive tape or a similar material, placing it over the pane so that the pieces of the broken glass by adhering to the substance used are prevented from falling and thus causing noise. Windowpanes that have been handled in such a manner should be carefully searched for fingerprints.

QUESTIONS

1. What rôle does the perseverance of a criminal play in the investigation of burglary?
2. Enumerate the methods commonly used by safe burglars.
3. What are the most common ways used by burglars to dispose of their loot?
4. Enumerate briefly the steps to be taken in searching for stolen property.
5. How would you describe your own watch, your own motor-car, and your own clothing?
6. If you suspected a simulated burglary, what would you especially look for in the way of technical evidence?

XIX

INVESTIGATION OF LARCENY

A. Modus Operandi of Common Larcenies

THE perseverance of the criminal, described in Chapter XVIII, applies to the same degree, if not even more, to all kinds of larceny. Thus it is obvious that the investigator in larceny cases must be thoroughly familiar with the technique employed by the criminal. We shall therefore describe the *modus operandi* used in the most common larcenies, as well as the methods of a technical nature employed to set traps for thieves and to examine evidence where mail is concerned. It is true that most investigations concerning mail in the United States are carried out by post-office inspectors; but questions about opened letters, forged seals, etc., frequently arise in ordinary detective work, and a modern all-round investigator ought to be familiar with the technical aspects of these questions.

Automobile Thievery—Persons who engage in stealing automobiles vary greatly in type and are often shrewd and skilful in this line of crime. The types arrested most frequently are:

(a) Youths who steal an automobile for joy-riding and when through abandon the car.

(b) Men who are stranded a considerable distance from their homes and are without carfare or a conveyance.

(c) Persons under the influence of alcohol.

(d) Bandits who steal cars for use in committing other crimes, usually holdups.

(e) Lastly, the out-and-out automobile thief who steals and sells automobiles as his sole means of livelihood.

As a rule, the genuine automobile thief is an experienced chauffeur. This experience enables him to operate any type of

327

car and to start a locked car more readily than an inexperienced person could do it. Thieves always have certain spots from which they prefer to steal cars. The scenes of their activity are usually in congested portions of the city, such as theater districts, baseball parks, race-tracks, etc. The cars are so closely parked together in these places that it is a comparatively easy matter for the thief to steal one without being discovered.

In stealing a car the door is generally forced open with a piece of pipe which is put over the handle and used as a lever to break the lock. If the ignition system is locked the thief uses a so-called "ignition jumper"—a high-tension coil concealed in a small box. One wire is removed from the distributor and replaced with a wire from the jumper. The car will then start even if locked. It is said that an experienced mechanic needs only about 45 seconds to start a locked car with this method.

In the investigation the numbers on the motor and other parts of the car should be especially ascertained. In many cases the thieves will file away the numbers and replace them with new numbers. They then have to resort to a die-maker who makes the necessary dies in the same form as the original numbers. Sometimes a car may be identified by examining the inner tubes where the repair men occasionally write their initials or those of the owner.

The thief will often repaint the car and change accessories, front wheels, headlights, trunks, and sometimes the whole body.

Automobile thieves usually operate in twos or threes, and average between seventeen and twenty-five years of age. If three youths are working together, one watches the patrolman on the beat, one follows the owner to guard against his return before the theft has been accomplished, and the third actually puts the car in motion and makes away with it. A vigilant police officer can often prevent such thefts by observing the nervous and suspicious appearance of these groups of thieves.

Occasionally the automobile thief adopts more subtle methods. Two detectives patrolling a zone noticed that a man accompanied by a woman carrying a baby were often seen within the zone boundary and that after their appearance there was always a report of another automobile theft. The detectives finally brought this trio to headquarters, where questioning developed that the man was a veteran automobile thief who used the woman and baby as a shield for his operations and an alibi in the event of detection. This man's method was as follows:

He would buy at second-hand a moderate-priced automobile of a popular make. Thousands of these cars are sold daily and they are all identical in equipment and other characteristics. The thief would have his car properly licensed and then commence operations.

He would drive about with the woman and baby until he came upon a new car of the same make as his own. He would then park immediately in front or back of the new car and all three would alight, enter a building close by and promptly emerge. But when they returned they entered the new car, which the man opened by the use of other keys or by forcing the lock. Then, accompanied by the woman and baby, he would drive off.

The thief's next move was to drive to an automobile auction sales room, where he would find someone who wished to purchase the particular type of car he had just stolen. He would tell the prospective buyer a hard-luck story about his wife and baby being ill, and say that for this reason he would sell his car at a greatly reduced price, as he was very much in need of cash. The thief would then bring the buyer out to the car where the "sick" baby and wife would be sitting. The sight of them nearly always allayed any suspicion the buyer might have, and he would close the deal, never suspecting that he was purchasing a stolen car. The thief, of course, was clever enough to provide himself with fictitious registration papers and bills of sale.

Experience has shown that thieves steal cars in front of residences shortly after their delivery by a garage employee where the car is garaged with service. Delivery service requires the keys to be left at the garage. Opportunity is thus presented to a dishonest employee to arrange for the keys to be duplicated. The automobile is delivered in front of or adjoining the owner's home. The original key may be left in the car. In that event the duplicate is not used by the thief. If, however, the original key is delivered to a doorman or dropped into a letter box, the thief uses the duplicate key and drives the automobile away.

Dealers in stolen automobiles are constantly seeking new tricks and ruses. A recent one is known as "Maceing" cars. Renting a large showroom on a prominent street, an advertisement is inserted in a newspaper announcing that fifty or more second-hand automobiles will be purchased at top prices. An owner, attracted by the advertisement, hastens to the showroom. The price he asks is $250. The dishonest dealer says he can get $300 for the car, and persuades the owner—in order not to lose an opportunity for a quick sale—to leave the car, keys and papers with the dealer. Ostensibly as protection and as a gesture of good faith, the dealer gives the owner a note for $300 payable at a designated bank in thirty days. Impressed with his good fortune, the owner leaves. Three weeks pass. The showroom is crowded with cars. Overnight all are removed out of town by confederates to divers localities. A visit to the bank by the seller discloses the fact that the notes are worthless.

A peculiar feature of automobile larcenies is that the thieves keep pace with the ever-fluctuating demand for the various makes of cars. The thief seems to feel the public pulse and plies his crime trade in accordance with the demand. Records of the police department should be scrutinized daily to check up on all transfers of ownership. In New York City there are approximately 600 transfers recorded daily, most of them being the late models of new cars.

B. Sneak Thieves

(a) *Office Sneaks*—Experience and records of police departments show arrests and complaints of young boys posing as messengers, middle-aged persons, elderly persons, well-dressed persons and shabbily-dressed persons, both male and female, stealing property from offices. There is the occasional thief on business in the buliding who sees an opportunity to steal successfully. Lone workers are the rule.

The professional sneak makes a survey and inspection of the building; familiarizes himself with the elevators, stairways, fire-escapes and emergency exits; also names of business firms, so that, if questioned, he can explain his presence. Firms having a large number of employees in one open office are avoided, as this type has so many persons in constant attendance that opportunity is limited. A small office where there are only one or two persons, or a general office subdivided into a number of smaller offices, is usually selected. Entry is made on the pretext of business or making an inquiry. Told to be seated in an outer office, or conducted into an inner office of a person sought, the thief is frequently left alone for a period of time. During the interim he looks around to locate anything of value, such as pocketbooks or handbags, petty cash, stamps, fountain pens, desk clocks, or other articles of value, which can be secreted on the person. Awaiting opportunity, he takes the property he has selected, and departs, either with or without the statement that he cannot wait any longer or that he will call again. If on some pretended business, he concludes it quickly and leaves.

(b) *Bank Thieves*—There are two types of bank sneaks: the one who steals from the cashier's cage and the one who loiters around for the purpose of picking up articles put down by persons making deposits, counting money, etc.

Those that steal from the cashier's cage generally work in a group of three. While this type is almost obsolete, it should be mentioned. One engages the paying teller or cashier in conversation under pretext of transacting some business, and while doing so places himself against the window with elbows on the ledge to cover the operations of a confederate who is next in line with a long hooked cane or wire, a straight cane, or a rolled newspaper with a gummy substance on one end. The wire or hooked cane is inserted into the cage and fishes out a bundle of bank notes. If the straight cane or rolled newspaper is used, the operation is practically the same, except that the cane or paper is placed on the top of banknotes and withdrawn. Another confederate has placed himself in position to observe the approach of anyone so as to give warning.

The other type observes people doing business in the bank, waits until their attention is diverted by filling in a deposit slip, counting money, or other tasks, and picks up pocketbook, handbag or money and departs.

(c) *Dishonest Employees*—This type includes all classes, from private secretary to night watchman, including the dishonest cashier, bookkeeper, clerk, checker, truckman, loader, stock clerk, and order clerk. Some are professional thieves. Others are occasional thieves.

The professional makes a business of obtaining employment under a false name with faked or forged references. He will work hard and faithfully to win quick approbation of employers. When opportunity to commit a theft presents itself, it is seized and flight made at a time when the loss is not likely to be discovered for several hours or until the next day.

The dishonest bookkeeper or cashier omits to record bills paid, and appropriates the money.

The checker in the mercantile establishment may be in collusion with a customer of the firm and permit a greater quantity of merchandise to be shipped than the order and bill call for.

The truckman may arrange with accomplices to leave his truck unattended in the street while he is in a restaurant having a meal, and permit them to drive off with it, loaded with valuable merchandise.

The loader may arrange to have accomplices drive up to his employer's business location with a truck, and permit or assist in the loading and removal of cases standing on the street waiting to be carted away or into the building.

The stock clerk and the order clerk, like the checker, may work in collusion with a customer by sending or wrapping up more merchandise than the order or invoice calls for. They may also steal by secreting merchandise on their persons. Silk houses have had experiences with employees who would wind a bolt of silk around their bodies under their shirts and walk out at closing time undetected.

(d) *Hotel Thieves*—Bogus or ostensible guests of either sex, dishonest chambermaids, bell-boys and other hotel employees having access to rooms may be found among this class of thieves. With the dishonest hotel employee the method is much the same as with any other type of dishonest employee. During employment he is constantly on the lookout for an opportunity to steal.

The professional hotel thief registers as a guest. He makes a survey of the hotel to become familiar with the arrangement of rooms, hallways, elevators and stairways; carefully studies habits of other guests, particularly those known to have money or valuable jewelry, noting when their rooms are occupied and vacant. Entrance is gained to the victim's room by means of an airshaft window, by a false key, and in some instances by forcing the door. Articles of value are usually packed in the victim's own suit-case or bag. The thief takes it to his own room, and checks out before the loss is discovered.

Others register in and out of large hotels on a number of occasions. Each time they register they keep the key to the room to which they were assigned. Some hotels pay small attention to such cases, concluding that the guest simply forgot to return the key, and another is made to take its place. With a number of keys accumulated, the thief may re-register at the hotel at any time, go to any of the rooms for which he has a key, enter and steal.

Another type of professional hotel thief is the ostensible guest who boldly walks into a hotel, ascends to an upper floor, walks along the corridor until he finds a door open, enters and steals anything of value, and decamps.

(e) *Dishonest Servants*—Among these are domestics, female and male; cooks, maids, laundresses, butlers, footmen, housekeepers, etc. There are two types. One obtains employment with but one idea in mind, and that is to steal. The other obtains employment and steals intermittently but continues in the employ until discovered. The former secures a position, usually giving a false name and address, with false or forged references. References are seldom investigated. Performing duties well, in a short period of time the domestic is liked and trusted. At the first opportunity, when the family is away, everything of value is packed, with the aid of an accomplice in some cases, and flight taken.

The second type steals one article at a time in such a manner as not to create suspicion. Thefts are timed so that when the loss is discovered it is recalled that a delivery boy, a plumber, an awning hanger, or somebody else was in the house at the time, thus diverting suspicion. Some of the articles stolen in the summer time are of the kind that would not be missed for months, such as a fur coat or an overcoat, or jewelry worn only on special occasions. As only one article is taken at a time, the owners do not, as a rule, remember putting it in any certain place and conclude it has been lost.

(f) *Furnished-Room Thieves*—Both sexes are found in this class of thieves. Some work alone, others have a male or female accomplice. A room is hired in a furnished rooming house. Habits of the owner and of the roomers are observed. At an opportune time a room, previously selected, is entered either by means of a pass-key or by forcing the door, and wearing apparel and other valuables are packed in the victim's suit-case or hand-bag. Flight is then taken.

(g) *Shoplifters*—Here we find the occasional thief, who may be a housewife, a shop or business girl or man respectably employed, or the so-called kleptomaniac. There is also the professional shoplifter.

The occasional thief is one who enters a store for a legitimate purpose, but when an opportunity to steal is presented, takes advantage of it.

The dress and gown shop thieves usually are two or three women operating in a group. One will try on one or more gowns, select a purchase, and ask that an alteration be made. While the salesperson takes the gown to the alteration department, usually located in the rear, another of the women takes a gown and hides it under her dress, coat, or cape, and leaves. Sometimes the gown selected is paid for. At other times word is left that it will be called for when alterations are completed.

No return call is made. Frequently the loss is not discovered until stock is checked, and the identity or description of the thief is not known. This makes it very difficult to trace the shoplifter.

Professional shoplifters usually operate in the larger department stores. They operate with the most success during the winter season when heavy outer clothing is worn. They may have a coat or cape with a very large inside pocket, sometimes extending across the entire width of the garment. Into this an article from a counter is slipped without attracting attention, or it may be dropped into an umbrella or other receptacle. If the theft is detected, protest is made that the article must have fallen into it by accident. Cases have been known where the shoplifter inserted an artificial arm into the sleeve of her coat, secured it to the front of the coat, and attached a handbag to the gloved artificial hand to give it a realistic appearance. She would then steal with the hidden member. Stolen articles are dropped into an inside pocket provided for that purpose.

Kleptomaniacs have a mania for stealing anything their hands can be placed on, usually without any apparent need for doing so. Very often persons in comfortable circumstances resort to petty thievery, taking articles which they neither need nor want.

(h) *Pennyweighters*—These are usually well-dressed adult persons, both male and female, who pose as customers. They sometimes work alone and sometimes with confederates, either male or female.

They operate in jewelry stores during business hours. They enter a store and ask to see a certain article of jewelry, usually a ring. They are shown an assortment of rings on a tray. The thief makes a mental selection of one, carefully noting its design, size, color, etc. He leaves, promising to return later when he will be ready to buy it. He has an imitation made, an exact duplicate of the ring selected. On the second visit to the store, while examining the original, he switches it for the imitation, advances some reason for not buying it, and leaves. The substitution is so cleverly made and the imitation is such a good one that the loss is often not discovered for days.

(i) *Bogus Advertisers*—These are professional thieves, usually males, of all ages. They sometimes work with female accomplices. An advertisement is inserted in a newspaper stating intent to purchase an article of furniture, such as a piano, or that a furnished room or an apartment is wanted. A post-office box number or newspaper-box number is given for reply address. Upon receiving replies, visits are made to the various places, and if opportunity offers, things of value are stolen.

(j) *Snatchers*—Snatchers are usually young and active men. They operate in quiet residential sections and in business and shopping districts. They loiter on the street until they observe the approach of a woman with a handbag, snatch it from her hand and run. In business districts, they get a line on employees conveying money through the streets, meet them in the hallway, grab the money and make their escape; or with the aid of an automobile they draw up at the curb, leave a man at the wheel with the motor running, snatch the money, and escape in the automobile. These thieves also snatch pocketbooks, bags and purses from automobiles stopped by traffic lights, just as the car starts with the lights.

(k) *Street Women*—Thieves of this sort are usually prostitutes. Sometimes they work alone and at other times with a male accomplice. They frequent hallways, furnished rooms, hotels and parks. They solicit a man for sexual intercourse and bring him to a cheap hotel or furnished room. While he is asleep, money and valuables are taken and departure is made. Others may have an accomplice come in and rifle the victim's pocket while they remain with the victim to divert suspicion. Where this is done, usually the same room is repeatedly used for the purpose. To avoid notoriety, the victim seldom makes a complaint. This type of thief may use a small dose of chloral or other potion to hasten the victim to sleep, and then rifle his pockets.

(l) *Overcoat Thieves*—Usually these are young men who enter a crowded restaurant where clothing is not checked, and where dancing is permitted. The thief observes an overcoat of good quality and size and somewhat similar to a coat to be hung up by an accomplice. The thief, without an overcoat, enters first. The accomplice follows and hangs his coat alongside of the one to be stolen. An order for food which can be supplied quickly is given to the waiter. The food is eaten and the thief puts on the coat to be stolen. If detected, an apology is offered. If not, the coat left behind is worn by the accomplice as he leaves.

Thieves of this type also operate in theaters. When a woman goes out during intermission and leaves her coat lying over the back of the seat, the thief walks down the aisle, picks up the coat and saunters out with it. The same method is used in restaurants where dancing is the vogue and no provision is made for checking women's coats.

(m) *Baggage Thieves*—These are usually well-dressed young men. They loiter around railroad stations and observe persons who set down baggage while waiting for a train or buying a ticket, walk alongside, and when the victim's attention is attracted elsewhere, pick up the bag and walk off.

Others get on a train and sit near a person who has left a bag near the aisle. Just before the train leaves, the thief picks up the bag and leaves, remarking to the trainman that he finds he is on the wrong train.

Others hang around the baggage rack in a hotel lobby and after the doorman has left and the guest is registering, they pick up a bag and leave. Or while a guest carrying his own bag is registering or paying a bill, they get behind him, pick up his bag and depart.

C. General Thefts

(a) *Package Thievery from Vehicles*—Criminals in this business have a get-up to simulate truckmen or delivery boys. They get a line on the vehicle, driver, and kind of merchandise carried, know the route to be taken and the stops to be made. Sometimes they follow the vehicle. They wait until the driver is in a building making a delivery, steal a package, and escape.

Sometimes they drive alongside of the victim's vehicle and boldly transfer goods from it to their own, and drive away. At other times they pretend they are hitching a ride and drop packages off to a confederate who is following.

(b) *Package Thieves*—This type steals parcel-post packages left on top of mail boxes. Some make a practise of stealing express matter from the sidewalk in front of buildings in the wholesale district. Customers deliver a number of packages to an express agent, whose office usually is a small table on the sidewalk or in the freight entrance of a building. As no wagon is available at the moment to cart them to the express office, the packages are left on the sidewalk. Opportunity thus presenting itself, the thief walks over, picks up one or two, and departs.

(c) *Letter-Box Thieves*—In addition to stealing checks and money orders sent by mail, this type of thief may extract a gas or electric-light bill from the box and then go up to the person to whom it is addressed, represent himself as a collector from the company concerned, and collect the bill.

(d) *Thefts from Automobiles*—This class of thievery is common in cities in recent years. If the car is locked, a section of pipe about six inches long, which can be fitted over the handle of a door, is used to break the lock and open the door. Anything of value is taken.

On cars having a fabric flap on the rear, which can be raised in warm weather or when passengers are in the rumble seat, they open the flap, enter and open the door, and steal any articles that may be in the car.

Other thieves get a small boy to go under the car, raise the floor boards, open the door and enter.

Automobile accessories that are easily detached, such as mirrors, emblems, tires, etc., are also stolen.

(e) *Package Thieves (Readers)*—These operate usually between the hours of 9 A.M. and 6 P.M. The "reader" locates an errand or delivery boy carrying a package on the outside of which there is a label, and walks a few feet behind the boy for a short distance, to permit his reading the name of the consignor and consignee on the label of the package. He then proceeds to the consignee's address, arriving there before the boy. He removes his coat. When the boy arrives he is standing at the entrance to the building or the receiving department, where he admonishes the boy for lateness of delivery. In some instances he directs the boy to return quickly to get and deliver to him another order. He then takes the package, signs a receipt, and when the boy has departed, recovers his coat and makes his getaway with the package.

Sometimes package thieves acquainted with the operations of a concern, and knowing from whom they purchase, will call the seller on the telephone and order merchandise to be delivered immediately. The thief then waits at the premises of the purchasing concern, which he pretends to represent as the boy arrives with the package. Receiving this, he departs.

(f) *Package Thieves* (*Senders*)—These usually operate between 9 A.M. and 5 P.M. The "sender" stops an errand boy or messenger who is carrying a package and requests him to deliver a message, giving or offering to give him a quarter or fifty cents for doing so. The thief then takes an envelop from his pocket and places a five- or ten-dollar bill in it, with instructions that it is to be delivered to the person to whom it is addressed. While the boy's attention is momentarily distracted, the money is switched back to the man's pocket. The empty envelop is then sealed and given to the boy for delivery, with promise of a gift if he will hurry. Meanwhile, he is told, his package will be guarded until he returns. When the boy returns after being unable to locate the person, he finds the "sender" has disappeared.

When two or more package thieves are arrested, they generally deny knowing one another and endeavor to place the burden of the larceny on the one who is carrying the bundle. The detective trailing package thieves should make a memorandum of the time and location in which he observed them together and endeavor to have some other person assist by observing the pair together.

(g) *Bogus Doctor*—This type of sneak thief has a limited knowledge of medicine. He obtains information as to expectant mothers who do not care to bear children. Securing information as to the employment of the husband, he visits the home of the woman while the husband is at work. He comes in the guise of a doctor, carrying a medical case, and tells the woman that her husband or a friend sent him. During an examination in the boudoir he tells her he has failed to bring a special required medicine, but while she remains in bed he will go and fetch it. Leaving the bedroom, the thief searches other rooms, steals valuables, and decamps.

(h) *Bogus Purchases*—This class operates by selecting jewelry, furs or other articles of value, and directing delivery to a hotel or business premises C.O.D. Upon receipt the article is taken to another room on a pretext. While the delivery clerk waits, escape is made.

D. Pickpockets

Among the types of pickpockets may be included patch-pocket workers, fob workers, pants-pocket workers, lush workers, toilet workers, and bag openers.

(a) *Patch-Pocket Workers*—This type of thief operates mostly in the spring, fall and winter, but not in the summer time, because then women do not wear coats in which their pocketbooks are carried in an outside pocket. This primary-class pickpocket usually starts his day's work around 7:30 o'clock in the morning and continues until about 9 A.M. He starts again about 4:30 P.M. and quits around 7:30 P.M., when the evening rush of homeward-bound working people is over.

The patch-pocket worker's methods vary in three respects, depending upon the amount of experience he has had. He usually carries a newspaper in one hand or has his overcoat over one arm. When he sees a bulging pocket—and usually he picks out a woman's coat pocket—he feels to see whether the bulge is a pocketbook. If it is, he extracts it from the owner's pocket, using the overcoat or newspaper as a shield for his hand.

Some members of this class of thieves operate with a newspaper held in the left hand. After one of them puts his hand in somebody's pocket, he removes the contents of the pocket and places it between the newspaper pages and backs away from the crowd. The patch-pocket worker usually operates in five-and ten-cent stores, at parades, or wherever there is a gathering of women.

The patch-pocket worker is particularly easy to catch because of his inexperience. Nevertheless, detectives have to exercise great care in dealing with this elementary class of "dips." The victims are nearly always working people who often prefer to lose the small amount of money the pickpocket has stolen from them rather than go to the trouble and expense of losing a day's work by appearing in court against the thief.

(b) *Fob Workers*—In the main the fob workers are men between fifty and seventy years of age. They have been working in every branch of pocket-picking and are now hopelessly rounding out a misspent life. They look and act like mendicants, and follow wherever a crowd collects, usually working from 1 P.M. until 2:30 P.M., depending on the season of the year.

There are only two pockets in a person's clothing from which the fob worker can steal; that is, the outside overcoat pocket or the right-hand inner coat pocket. This class of pickpocket carries a handkerchief in his left hand, and standing beside his victim, covers his own right hand with the handkerchief in his left hand, inserts a couple of fingers in the victim's pocket, takes out whatever money is there, backs out of the crowd, looks around and edges away. If no one has noticed him, the fob worker looks at his loot, gives the crowd the once-over again and repeats his illegal activity. Generally the fob worker has a long criminal record.

(c) *Pants-Pocket Worker*—The pants-pocket worker's method calls for the highest degree of skill, and he is recognized by pickpockets as being at the top in this particular class of thievery. The pants-pocket worker often operates alone, altho sometimes he has a partner and occasionally he operates in mobs of three or five. His favorite time is during the rush hours of the morning and evening, and he likes motion-picture theaters, subways, piers on a sailing day—any place where there is a crowd.

Operating by himself, he carries as a rule either a coat over his arm or a newspaper in his hand. Skilful tho he very often is, an experienced detective can spot him rather easily because he does not act naturally. He has more purpose in his expression than an honest man, there is more of a sharp look about him—it's something hard to explain, but easy to detect. The lone pickpocket of this class nearly always operates in the subway because most people are in a tremendous hurry getting on and off subway trains.

When pants-pocket workers go in pairs, one who does the actual pocket-picking is known as a "tool"; his partner is called a "stall." The "stall" has three objects—to cover the hand of the "tool" when it is in the victim's pocket, to bump into the victim and divert his attention from the "tool," and to receive the pocketbook which the "tool" has removed from the victim's pocket. When such thieves work in groups of four or five, there are two "tools" in the outfit. One "tool" takes his position on either side of the intended victim. This is done so that the "tools" will not have to shift from one side to the other to locate the victim's pocketbook.

(d) *Lush Workers*—Thieves of this type usually operate from midnight until 7 o'clock in the morning. However, they may be busy as early as 9 o'clock at night. Their field of operation mainly is along subway transportation systems, particularly at terminals. Generally they travel in pairs, but at times there may be three or five thieves operating in concert.

The victim is generally asleep in the car or on a station seat. One of the thieves will sit on one side of him and another thief on the other side. If there are others they station themselves in front of the victim, blocking the view of any other person who might be at the station or in the car. One of the thieves, who is sitting alongside of the victim, will open a newspaper and hold it in such a position as to cover the front portion of the victim's body. The confederate sitting on the opposite side will extract whatever property he can from the pockets of the victim. In operating in moving trains, the thieves generally enter the train by way of different cars and then meet at the point where the victim is asleep. To detect and apprehend this class of thief, observation must be had of trains as they enter stations. From there the victim may be seen. In station cases, observation should be had from a distance on the platform or from a ticket booth thereon.

(e) *Toilet Workers*—This type of thief may operate alone or in pairs, and often there are four or five in a group. Generally, however, two or three comprise a group. They enter a wash-room, comfort station or toilet, and one of the thieves stations himself at the urinal as a lookout. Another thief goes to a particular door alongside of an occupied toilet, and throws some coins on the floor. The third thief then approaches the toilet. The second thief is starting to pick up what he has dropped. The selected victim does not want to be annoyed and naturally helps to look for the coins or whatever has been dropped. The victim has his coat hanging on a hook in the compartment. The second thief inserts his hand into the pocket of the coat hanging on the wall, takes its contents and passes them to the third thief, who leaves the premises, to be followed by the second thief and then by the lookout. To detect and apprehend this type of criminal, surveillance of comfort stations is necessary. Observation must be had in a natural way without creating suspicion. If the same men are seen making repeated trips into the comfort station there is ground to suspect a criminal intent.

(f) *Bag-Openers*—Bag-openers are nearly always woman pick-pockets who operate in the daytime in department stores. There are three types—all very smart and all very difficult to catch. Bag-openers may be classified as main-floor workers, elevator workers and upper-floor workers.

The woman pickpocket selects a department store which is having a bargain sale, and enters by the last door—that is, the door farthest away from the main entrance. Having entered as inconspicuously as possible, she glances around with assumed carelessness to see if she has been recognized and is being fol-lowed. If she is satisfied that no detective has recognized her, she proceeds directly to the crowded sales counter, around which a large number of women are thronged with their bags dangling from their arms.

Most women shopping in department stores are careful buyers. They will, for instance, run their hands through stockings to assure themselves that the stockings are of good quality, before purchasing them. They examine other merchandise with equal care. While the honest buyers are thus occupied, the well-dressed bag-opener stations herself beside her chosen victim. The pickpocket's left hand is concealed by a fur piece she is carrying, and with it she opens the victim's bag, her act being concealed by the fur. Under pretense of examining the stockings the female dip looks into the opened bag, and while replacing the stockings on the counter she takes the contents of the bag.

Since the majority of department-store detectives are stationed on the main floor, and all persons must enter and depart through that floor, the most astute women pickpockets work the elevators and upper floors. It is hard for a man to get on the same elevator with a woman pickpocket if she wishes to avoid him. When the bag-opener is on the elevator she gets behind a woman, opens her bag without much trouble, since all are wedged tightly together, and takes the contents without looking at them. Then when the victim steps out of the elevator the loss is discovered or called to her attention.

Of course a clever woman pickpocket knows that after she has stolen the contents of two or three bags, the store detectives will be on her trail. She therefore leaves immediately after the bell is put on for the shop's sleuths. The pickpocket on an upper floor always departs from the extreme opposite end of the building, as far away as she can get from the elevator in which she made her "touch."

There are men as well as women bag-openers, altho not so many, and the men do not frequent the department stores because they know they can't get by there, as women do. If a man pickpocket went into a department store and approached the stocking counter the sales girl would at once give him her undivided attention, because she would expect to sell him more quickly two or three times as much as she could sell to a woman. If the man pickpocket operates in a crowd of women and one of them discovers she has been robbed, the first thing she will do is to suspect the lone man.

Therefore the masculine bag-opener usually confines his efforts to five-and-ten-cent stores and chain stores where a good percentage of the purchasers are men. His presence there attracts no special attention.

E. Swindlers and Confidence Men

(a) *Money-Making Machine*—A money-making machine generally simulates a highly polished wood cabinet. Its size is generally about 3 x 3½ inches. It contains an electric motor operated by a switch on the right side of the box. The motor has no real purpose other than to make a humming noise when the switch is on. The cabinet also contains about four small electric bulbs, lighted by dry-cell batteries from within. It has a drop-slot drawer which falls to the bottom of the cabinet. A hidden button on the left side, when touched, operates the drop. One hundred pieces of fine white paper cut the size of a twenty-dollar Federal Reserve or National Bank note form part of the paraphernalia.

New bills only are used in the operation of the money-making machine. The confidence man or swindler in demonstrating the machine to a victim places a new bill with a piece of the white paper together in the drop-drawer. The switch is opened and the motor rotates. Pressing the hidden button, he drops the box to the bottom. This brings into view another similar drop-drawer in which two new banknotes are found when the cabinet is opened. The victim believes the machine printed one of them.

The persons who operate this class of swindle are usually foreigners, averaging in age from thirty to fifty years. They work slowly and cautiously. The following illustrates one manner of approach:

The swindler becomes acquainted with a man who in his judgment can be used for his purpose. He imparts little information regarding himself but gains the confidence of the other and gradually finds out whom he knows, his business and, if possible, his financial standing. Victims are usually foreigners who are not overly sharp or suspicious.

With a victim selected, the confidence man frequently visits the latter's place of business, spends money freely, and pays for purchases with new twenty-dollar bills. The victim comments on this custom of always paying with new money. The swindler replies cautiously that a relative or friend who formerly worked in a mint in Germany or Austria told him how to duplicate new money, using a chemical and a money-making machine, and that it is very easily done if one is able to get the kind of special paper that the government uses. He then offers to sell the victim a couple of twenties at ten each, or he gives him a couple to pass, warning him to tell no one. After a couple of days the swindler returns and learns that the victim has passed two genuine twenty-dollar bills and collects a share thereof. Of course, the victim is interested. An invitation to see the machine follows. The victim is told that if he invests one or two thousand dollars in a machine he will sell him the one he possesses and get the former employee of the mint to make another. If the victim agrees to enter the deal, the swindler has a confederate watch his movements to see if he informs the police. Everything clear, the swindler gets the machine ready, usually planting it in a furnished room. The room is darkened if he demonstrates it in the daytime, or a very dim light is used if in the evening. The machine is not brought into the room until after the arrival of the victim. This is a precaution. Satisfied that the way is clear, the swindler goes to another room in the premises and returns with the machine.

He explains and demonstrates its mechanism and operation. The sale of the machine is accomplished. The swindler takes leave with the promise that if anything goes wrong he or the former mint employee will fix it.

The more modern criminal paraphernalia used in this type of swindle consists of a number of glass tubes containing colored liquids, a quantity of blank white paper cut to the size of bills, and a simple pressing device. This paraphernalia is generally carried in a brief case or portfolio.

(b) *The Sick Engineer*—The dupe is taken by a swindler to a large office building in the financial district and is introduced to a confederate swindler posing as a broker. The "broker" expresses willingness, and even eagerness, to buy a particular mining stock that has suddenly become valuable, naming the price he will pay for as much of the stock as he can secure. The guide swindler then leads the victim uptown to a furnished-room house or hotel, where he is introduced to a "sick engineer." The subject of the mining stock is brought up and the "engineer," not knowing of the rise in value, offers to sell the lot he holds for a nominal sum. Seeing an opportunity to resell profitably to the broker, the dupe buys the stock. This transaction is generally timed to take place on a Friday or Saturday afternoon, after the broker has left for the day. On Monday, when the victim presents himself at the broker's office, he learns that the man he is looking for had simply hired desk room for one day and that he departed without leaving an address. Returning to the home of the "sick engineer," he is informed that that person too has left for parts unknown. He soon finds out that the eagerly sought stock is valueless.

(c) *Gambling Swindles*—Meeting an "easy mark" with a few thousand dollars, confidence men will, on short notice, stage a fake prize-fight, a fake wrestling match, or a fake gambling house. Of these, the gambling swindle is the most popular. The victim is introduced to the dealer of a gambling house, who agrees to play into his hand and "double-cross" the house. He is taught a code of signals and is instructed to play his hand according to the dealer's signals. However, during the progress of the game, the signals become mixed and the dupe loses. If it is apparent that he can raise more money, the dealer shows him just how he misinterpreted the signals, and his newly made friends induce him to try again, giving him two or three thousand dollars of their money to play with his own, to inspire confidence. He fares no better at the second attempt and usually loses about the same amount of his own money as the others gave him to play for them.

(d) *Handkerchief Switch*—An elderly man of seventy years walking on a prominent street of a metropolitan seaboard city shortly after 10 o'clock in the morning was approached by a young fellow in shirt sleeves, who struck up an acquaintance and engaged in a conversation about the weather and business slackness.

The elder showed a patent lock he was endeavoring to sell. After walking a few blocks they came upon a very bewildered old man who appeared lost.

"I wonder what's the matter with the old fellow," said the young man. So his companion went over to the old man and asked, "What is the matter?"

The stranger, sighing, replied, "I have just arrived from the West and my brother has just died and left me $10,000 in insurance money. If I return to the old country with this money, my mother will wonder where I got it, and will soon realize that my brother, whom she loved so much, got killed, and I would not want to grieve her. I don't know what to do with this money. I am a stranger here and I am afraid to trust it to anybody."

Tears dropped from his eyes as he held the inside pocket of his overcoat open and showed a small canvas bag in which there was something that had the appearance of money.

Both elderly men were natives of the same foreign country. The locksmith agreed with the young fellow to be one of the old man's guardians. They were business men and knew the dangers of a big city for strangers who had money.

The old man, still with tears, asked, "How will I know you are honest people?" The young man turned to the locksmith and asked him if he had any money in a bank or on his person. "Yes, I have a bank account," was the reply.

Thereupon the young fellow said to the old man, "We will show you how to keep your money safely by letting you see how banks operate." The old man, glad to meet honest people, wiped the tears from his eyes and promised them a good day's pay of twenty-five dollars for guarding him and his money.

They went to the bank. En route the old man was amazed at the large buildings and asked many questions about landmarks and city life. Holding the locksmith's hand and caressing it, with tears of gratefulness in his eyes, the old man kept repeating his obligation to such honest people.

The locksmith withdrew a thousand dollars. The young fellow suggested that the old man put his money in a package along with the locksmith's so that the latter could carry it safely to the bank for deposit. They repaired to a hallway. The locksmith took the money he had withdrawn from the bank and placed it in a handkerchief. The old man placed his money in the same handkerchief. The handkerchief was tied in a four-cornered knot. While doing this the young fellow kept cautioning the locksmith to be careful with such a large sum of money. With much ceremony the young fellow unbuttons the locksmith's vest, stressing the matter of carefulness. The old man switches the handkerchief and substitutes another while this is going on. Then the old man excitedly declares, "You got safety pin, I got safety pin, here, here, place it so," pinning the handkerchief to the inside of the locksmith's vest, then buttoning the vest and the coat.

The locksmith returns to the bank and discovers that the handkerchief contains clippings from newspapers cut about the same size as paper money.

The thieves were subsequently located by visiting cider stubes and coffee houses. Arrests and convictions followed.

(e) *Coin Matchers*—Not long ago Mr. A. from York, Pennsylvania, stopping at a prominent New York hotel, reported to a detective that while walking west on Forty-second Street he was approached by a man who asked him where the Museum of Natural History was located. Mr. A. replied he was a stranger in the city and unable to furnish him information.

The man then asked Mr. A. where he was from, and Mr. A. told him. The stranger expressed surprize and told A. that he lived in Wilkes-Barre and was more than glad to meet a fellow Pennsylvanian.

The stranger invited Mr. A. to attend a show as his guest. After the play they walked north on Broadway. On reaching Forty-seventh Street they were approached by a man who asked them where he could find the Hippodrome. They were strangers and did not know.

The newcomer said he was from the South, had been in New York only two days, but found that it was a very funny city. Everybody he spoke to seemed to be a stranger and nobody could direct him to any place he wanted to visit. The Southerner stated that he had been left a large sum of money by his mother, who had died recently, and that he had come to New York to spend part of it having a good time.

He said it was hard to get acquainted in New York, and proposed that the three of them go to luncheon.

They all entered a cigar store and bought cigars. The Southerner insisted on paying for them, and an argument arose on the subject. They finally decided to match coins to determine who should pay. The man from the South lost, and paid for the cigars; but he remarked that he had bad luck every time he gambled, and pretended that he was sore. He then suggested that they match for five dollars. The swindlers continued to match. The Southerner continued to lose. The more he lost the angrier he got. They kept walking north on Broadway and entered Central Park.

The Southerner excused himself to go to a lavatory. His confederate said to Mr. A., "Let us work together and get this fellow's money." Mr. A. refused at first, but finally consented when the swindler suggested returning the money after winning it.

After the Southerner's return, they resumed matching. The Southerner lost approximately $300 and Mr. A. about the same amount. An argument then arose between the so-called Southerner and his confederate, the Southerner claiming that the two were playing in conjunction with each other to swindle him. He threatened to call the police and have them arrested.

Mr. A. became excited and pleaded with them to be quiet, and asked the swindler to return the money to the Southerner and settle the argument. He refused and told Mr. A. to leave the matter in his hands, instructing A. to go to his hotel, where he would meet him later.

Mr. A. then returned to his hotel and waited. After waiting two or more hours, it finally dawned on him that he might have been swindled. He referred the matter to the police. Mr. A. failed to identify any criminal from photographs shown. However, with the information which he furnished, detectives continued on the case and some days later, in a hotel, a detective observed a man—apparently from out of town—conversing with a criminal who had been previously arrested for swindling.

The criminal answered the description of one of the men in Mr. A.'s case. The criminal and victim were trailed to the same cigar store visited in the case of Mr. A. The same mode of procedure was employed by the swindlers in this case. A man who fitted the Southerner's description met them at the cigar store and started to talk to them.

They were followed to luncheon and to Central Park. There the sharpers were placed under arrest. The victim gave the same story as Mr. A. Mr. A. was summoned from York, Pennsylvania, to New York and identified the men. They were convicted and sent to jail.

It might be well to note, in cases of this kind, that after swindlers are arrested, identified and held for trial, they usually try to buy the complainant off and send what is generally termed a "fixer" who not only offers reimbursement for the original amount he was swindled out of, but offers him an additional sum or "bonus" to drop the charge.

Types:

1. Very well dressed; generally an American twenty-two to thirty-five years of age; affable and friendly; affects English or Southern accent.
2. Very well dressed; twenty-five to thirty-five years of age; affable, friendly, polite, affects foreign accent; displays large roll of bills.

(f) *Diamond Switch*—Not many months ago a woman was walking along a busy street in a metropolitan city when she was stopped by a well-dressed man who was talking to a very poor-looking male foreigner. The well-dressed man asked the woman if she could talk Yiddish or Polish. She could speak Yiddish. The well-dressed man, pointing to the foreigner, said to the woman, "Ask him what he wants." They conversed.

The foreigner asked the woman how much he could get for a solid gold Russian coin he displayed to her. She explained the situation to the well-dressed man. After negotiating through the woman, he purchased the gold piece, which was alleged to be worth fifty dollars, for five dollars.

Thereupon the well-dressed man said to the woman, "Ask this greenhorn if he has anything else to sell." She did. The immigrant brought out a number of diamonds and showed them to the woman, telling her in Yiddish that he had just come over from Russia and these were Russian crown jewels.

The well-dressed man, speaking English, said, "These diamonds are the most beautiful I have ever looked at. However, I wouldn't purchase them unless I had them examined. If they are genuine, there is a fortune in it for us, as this greenhorn doesn't know their value in American money." The woman suggested going to an appraiser whom she knew. The appraiser informed them that they were genuine jewels and were worth plenty of money.

The immigrant then put the jewels back into a bag and slipped the bag carelessly into his coat pocket. Said the well-dressed man to the woman, "This is the greatest break I ever had in my life, but I haven't any money with me. I live in Jersey, and by the time I go to my bank it will be closed. Will you please go to your bank and buy these jewels from this greenhorn before he becomes educated, and I'll come over tomorrow and buy half of them from you. It is only fair that you let me buy half, because he was talking to me when you came along."

While this conversation was going on, the immigrant switched the genuine jewels into his hip pocket and substituted another bag with glass diamonds in his coat pocket.

The woman went to her bank and withdrew $1,500 and gave it to the immigrant for the "jewels," agreeing to let the well-dressed man purchase half of the jewels for $750 the following day.

Of course, the well-dressed man never returned. Some days later, while showing her friends the wonderful jewels, the woman was informed that they were not genuine. She immediately ran to the appraiser. He told her that these were not the stones he had examined a few days previously. The woman described the immigrant to detectives. The description fitted a notorious con man.

A few days later detectives arrested both of the swindlers as they were about to enter a classy roadster. Both were tried and found guilty and sentenced to State's Prison.

Types: The greenhorn is always poorly dressed and speaks a foreign language very well, often being a genuine foreigner. The well-dressed man is an American and a very convincing talker.

Sometimes three swindlers work this racket, the third being the jeweler, whom they meet rushing out of a jewelry store on the way to the hospital where his wife is sick. He appraises the diamonds in the street, offering the greenhorn a large sum in cash right on the spot.

However, the modern swindler uses genuine diamonds and allows the victim to get them appraised, and the switch comes in after they leave the jeweler or appraiser.

This racket is not confined to Russians; it is used by Italian and Polish confidence men, who pick victims of their own nationality.

(g) *Lemon Men*—Last year an alumnus of an eastern university came to a metropolitan city to witness a football game between his Alma Mater and another university.

He registered at a first-class hotel and mingled with the football crowd staying there. Conversing with a group of collegians, one of them suggested that they take a walk to get away from the group. They found themselves in the billiard room, still talking about college life. The stranger suggested that they play a few games of pool.

The stranger lost the first few games purposely, letting the alumnus beat him with the agreement that the loser should pay the check. The stranger then suggested playing for a small bet, saying that if he was lucky enough to win a game it would help him toward paying the check.

The stranger lost the first game on which a bet was placed. When he suggested doubling the bet, the visiting alumnus did not hesitate to agree. The stranger won the next game by one point, remarking that he was getting lucky, as he never was very good at pool. He then proceeded to win more than the amount of the check, and soon was leading.

The alumnus soon found himself losing money and suggested that they double the amount of the bet to allow him to recuperate his losses. The stranger agreed, and kept beating the alumnus by one or two points and losing an occasional game to make it look good.

The alumnus was down to his last few dollars and was on the verge of borrowing some money from his fraternity brothers when a detective making the rounds of the hotels stopped to watch the game and to ask the players some questions. The detective informed the alumnus he was playing with a criminal who belonged to the fraternity of "lemon men" or "pool sharks" making a living on winnings from such games. A conviction and jail sentence ensued.

Lemon men usually hang out around hotels, steamships or other places where people are enjoying themselves. Some of them dress very nicely and can carry on an intelligent conversation. There is also a lower grade of lemon men who frequent disreputable pool rooms and dress in common with the men of such a neighborhood.

(h) *Dropping the Leather*—Pocketbook dropping is one of the oldest of confidence games. It has not changed in its methods, apparently, since Smollett was fleeced by this swindle in London two hundred years ago.

In cities the game is usually worked on immigrants and seldom constitutes more than petit larceny. It is worked with two operators. Number 1, striding past, drops a pocketbook in front of the victim, who is not given an opportunity to pick it up, for it is instantly seized by Number 2. Number 2 agrees to divide and leads the selected victim to a near-by doorway. When the pocketbook is opened, it is found to contain one or two one-dollar bills and a Confederate or counterfeit one-hundred-dollar bill. Number 2 points out that it would be unwise to change such a large bill in the neighborhood, and as neither has change and he must catch a train, suggests that the victim retain the bill until the following day, when they will meet and divide equally. As security the victim gives Number 2 whatever money he may have with him, perhaps adding his watch or other valuables.

F. Problems in Connection with Letters

Unsealed Letters—The criminal or spy who tampers with a letter may do this for the purpose of reading the contents or of stealing the whole or part of the contents. His procedure will differ according to the purpose in mind.

If his desire is only to read the letter, he may try transillumination by means of a strong light coming from the back, with the hope of reading through the translucent paper. This, however, will not be possible if the paper and envelop are thick. He may then resort to the method of making a print of the contents, by putting the letter, instead of a plate, in a frame with sensitive bromid paper behind and using powerful light for some time. The contents will then appear on the print—white on black background. To decipher the contents will, however, be a difficult matter if the letter is folded and closely written. This difficulty is also encountered when using X-rays for the same purpose. By this latter method a plate, instead of the paper, is placed in the frame and the letter is then illuminated with very soft X-rays for a short time.

No one of the above-described methods will leave markings, and whoever wishes to protect his mail against such attempts is advised to use thick envelops and thick paper. In order to make it impossible to read by means of X-rays, envelops whose lining contains lead have been put on the market. The lead will not allow penetration by the X-rays.

A frequently-used method of opening a letter is to draw the sharp point of a knife across and through a thick printed line on the envelop. When the contents have been removed, the slit is covered with very thin, silky, transparent paper which is pasted over it.

The classic method, of course, is to let the vapor from boiling water act on the sealed back of the envelop and dissolve the paste, allowing the envelop to be opened. This method, however, inevitably leaves traces on the paper in the form of waves. All stamps or marks of indelible ink or pencil writing will also be dissolved to a certain degree, leaving blurs. The clever thief, instead of using water vapor, employs thin strips of blotting paper soaked in water, passing these over the sealed edge of the flap. This method injures only a small part of the flap.

Another method employed by thieves is to roll the flap open. A blunt instrument, such as a lead pencil, is inserted in the opening which almost always occurs at either extremity of the flap, where the paste layer ends. This opening represents the weak spot in the envelop, and it is the starting point of the mail thief's maneuvers. The lead pencil is now carefully and slowly rolled along the edge of the flap, which will easily open in most cases. Many mail thieves start on the under flap because this generally has inferior glue and loosens more readily. In the latter case he opens only one part of the bottom flap and the opposite part of the upper flap.

When this method of opening letters has been used, however, the shrewd investigator can detect it. Fibers from the paper will be detached from the upper as well as the under surface of the layer of glue. Often thin laminæ will be detached from the paper. There is no possibility whatsoever for a thief to hide these marks. To reseal the envelop a different glue than the one originally present on the envelop is generally used, and if the thief be a clerk he may use the glue of the office. Many post-office departments abroad mix their paste or glue with some easily detectable reagent. Generally such reagents have a strong luminescence and an examination of a letter under an

Fig. 79

Investigation of a mail theft. Note the curled tissue on the flap ultra-violet light will immediately reveal whether it has been tampered with. Such reagents may also be used to set special traps. If, for example, a clerk is suspected of tampering, the paste may be mixed with some characteristic reagent. If several clerks are suspected, the glue of each may be mixed with a different reagent.

Another difficulty encountered by the thief in sealing the flap for the second time is the production of a double glue line and the difficulty, not to say impossibility, of making the divided cancellation stamp, which runs across the edge of the flap, look as it did originally. These differences are encountered irrespective of the method used in opening the flap. The double glue line is made when the flap is pressed against the envelop for a second time. It is almost impossible to match the former edge of the glue line with the new. This can be seen with the magnifying glass or microscope.

Through the above-mentioned opening at the extremity of the flap the contents of the envelop may be taken out without opening it. For this purpose two knitting-needles fastened together by means of a cork are used, or even a special instrument consisting of a small steel rod having sharp steel points projecting from it. By rotating the knitting needles or the steel rod, the letter, if it is sufficiently thin, is grasped and rolled on the needles or the rod and drawn out through the opening. The letter may then be read, rolled back on the object used, inserted again in the opening and replaced. Such a procedure will surely leave marks on the letter.

The examination of letters suspected of having been opened and closed again is begun by studying the envelop while illuminated from the back by strong light. Places where the fiber or thin particles of paper have been detached will show up brighter than the rest of the glued border. Such places are then encircled with a fine lead pencil and examined closely. Two incisions running through the edge of the flap are now made with a sharp knife so that only this part of the flap between the two cuts can be lifted. A piece of filter paper soaked with water is put on the suspected spot so that it is thoroughly soaked. When the glue has been dissolved the small flap is carefully lifted with the aid of forceps. Great precautions must be taken in lifting this flap so as not to cause new fibers to become detached. The under surface of the flap and of the envelop is now examined with a magnifying glass. Detached paper fibers, detached thin particles, may be easily seen, and may be looked upon as a sure sign of previous opening.

Before this procedure is carried out the edge of the flap is carefully examined and any stamp glue on the edge is scrutinized to see if the parts of it match. Eventually the clues present are photographed. It should be pointed out that altho the examination is a simple one a very experienced eye is required. Some mail thieves proceed with the utmost care and leave very few traces of their work, but a careful examination should nevertheless solve the problem in most cases.

The possibility of getting the fingerprints of the suspect on the contents of the letter should not be overlooked.

Wax-Sealed Letters—A letter sealed with wax may be opened in exactly the same manner as described above except for the seal. The seals may be removed in many different ways.

The simplest method is to lift the whole seal either by pulling it away directly or by inserting under it a thin, electrically-heated platinum wire. This method is most likely to succeed if the seal is thick. The seal is then replaced either by pasting it back or by heating its under surface and roughening the paper to bring about better adherence.

The method most commonly used is the one in which a cast of the seal is made, and this is later replaced by a new seal made from the cast. This cast is made of plaster of Paris. The thief builds a wall of plastelina around the seal and pours a plaster-of-Paris mixture on it. When this has dried the plaster cast reproduces quite faithfully the original seal. Sealing wax of the same color is used by the thief to make the new seals. It has been reported that clever thieves have been able to make a plaster cast of the seal, open a letter, remove the money, close it and put on a new seal in about twenty minutes. The fact that the letter has been in the possession of the suspect for only a short time is not, therefore, proof of his innocence.

The seals made with the false plaster cast have some drawbacks. While reproducing all the faults in the original seal, the outlines of the letters are never as sharp and clear-cut as when made with the metal signet. Besides, minute traces of plaster lodged in the false seal may be detected by slight enlargement. It should, therefore, almost always be possible to detect this type of tampering, altho an experienced eye is always needed. In order to overcome the drawbacks of the plaster cast certain thieves have used some dental composition, such as copper amalgam.

In the more crude methods of years ago, the thief made an impression of the seal in soft lead plates. He put a piece of lead plate over the seal and struck a strong and absolutely vertical blow with a wooden club. The seal naturally broke in pieces but a faithful reproduction of it on the lead plate resulted. This was then used to make new seals.

As the thief seldom bothers to open all the seals, the first part of the examination should be directed to the sealing wax. It should be determined if a similarity exists in all the seals. Examination with ultra-violet rays may be very useful, as sealing waxes which look quite alike may have a different fluorescence. Slight differences in the luminescence do not always mean, however, that the seals have been made with different sealing waxes, as the method of melting or burning the sealing wax alters the fluorescence of the same stick of sealing wax. Experiments must be carried out with the same sealing wax to determine the slight differences. A chemical or microchemical analysis of the sealing wax may also be helpful in this case. When the seals have been lifted away the thief will in many cases be compelled to repair them by piecing them in place. The different sealing waxes used can then easily be detected by means of the ultra-violet rays.

G. Setting Traps for Thieves

In places where epidemics of thefts occur, as in schools, offices, clinics, etc., the thief may be detected by setting a suitable trap. This may consist either of some mechanical device or of a dye. It is naturally impossible to describe how the traps should be applied. This depends entirely upon the circumstances of the case and the sagacity and cleverness of the investigator.

The use of the mechanical trap can best be exemplified by an actual case. Students attending a private school were accustomed to hang their overcoats, and often even their coats, in a corridor adjoining a laboratory. Some of them carelessly left their pocketbooks in their coats. Within a few weeks several thefts were reported. To catch the perpetrator a coat was rigged up with a pocketbook visibly protruding from one of the pockets. The inside of the pocket contained two wires leading to the janitor's room, where they were connected with a battery and a bell. The pocket was also supplied with a contact. Removal of the pocketbook would then cause the bell to ring. The thief was soon apprehended.

The dyes can be mixed with a slowly drying glue and applied under doorknobs, the edge of a drawer, on coins, in pockets, etc. Three kinds of dyes may be used for this purpose. The first embraces dyes which will immediately stain the hand; for instance, methylene blue, magenta fuchsin, malachite green, and carbol fuchsin. Of these the methylene blue and the carbol fuchsin, which has a brilliant red color, are difficult to wash away. The second category embraces less noticeable dyes, which, however, by the action of the perspiration, will stain the hand very markedly. Blue of bromophenol, a light yellow powder which turns dark blue after a short time, is used. It has, however, the disadvantage that it can be very easily washed away. The third category embraces dyes or, better, chemicals with strong luminescence. The thief in this case gets some white powder on his fingers and does not as a rule pay any attention to it. Even if he washes his hands once, traces of the powder will remain adherent to the skin. If the hands of the suspected person are examined in the ultra-violet rays the particles of powder will be detected by the brilliant luminescence given off. A powder commonly used for this purpose is naphthionate of sodium.

QUESTIONS

1. Describe some different methods of automobile thievery.
2. What is meant by a sneak thief? Describe two types from your own experience.
3. How would you operate if you were sent out to look for pickpockets?
4. Describe briefly the psychological conditions which make a "switch game" possible.
5. How would you examine a letter which you suspected had been previously opened?
6. What would you look for on a seal which you had reason to suspect was forged?
7. Describe some of the traps which may be set for thieves.

XX

ROBBERY

ROBBERY is one of the leading forms of major crime with which the police must deal. There are innumerable types of robbery. Some do not require much planning on the part of the criminal, while others, due to the protective measures taken, not only require a survey of the premises and neighborhood, a study of habits of the individuals to be attacked, the hour most opportune, traffic flow and impediments in the area, but also the organization and assignment of confederates to act definite parts and to transport swiftly the band of robbers from the scene in high-powered motor-cars, stolen weeks in advance and carrying fictitious or stolen license plates. These cars are quickly abandoned at a location unlikely of instant observation, and transportation again taken by other motor-cars, buses or speed-boats.

In the main, robbers operate in mobs of from two to five. They generally range in age from seventeen to twenty-five years, and may specialize in holding up certain classes of persons, stores or premises. In the following pages many types of robbery are mentioned. It must not be assumed, however, that the list is anywhere near complete. Many volumes could be written without covering the topic completely. Only a limited attempt is made.

In the investigation of robbery all methods of police science may be useful. Fingerprints may be found on abandoned cars and on other paraphernalia. On discarded arms filed-off numbers may be revealed, thereby disclosing at least the original buyer of the weapon. Footprints are left at the scene, etc. Even in seemingly hopeless cases a careful investigation will almost always reveal some traces of a technical nature which may be utilized to track the criminal.

Robbery of Bank Messengers—This type of crime is seldom attempted by amateurs, but usually is the work of experienced criminals, generally in groups of from three to six. Sometimes they work in collusion with a dishonest employee who tips them off with information as to movements of messengers, the procedure followed in making deposits and withdrawing funds, and the methods of transportation. The crime is planned in advance. Each criminal is drilled in the part he is to act. High-powered cars are stolen days in advance, the number depending upon the need for escape and transfer. License plates are removed from the stolen cars. Others under a fictitious name and address replace them. The cars are stored until the day of the crime. About thirty minutes before the messenger leaves, the robbers drive to a spot adjacent to the bank. One remains at the wheel. Others act as lookouts to prevent interference with the hold-up. The motor of the car is left running or, if stopped, is started up a few minutes before the messengers are expected. The hold-up men trail the messenger from the bank. If he is riding in an automobile, his car is forced to stop by an argument over some alleged traffic offense or discourtesy in driving. With the messenger off-guard, he is disarmed at pistol point and the money taken.

Another method is for the criminals to await the approach of the messenger in the hallway of the place of delivery, and there hold him up at pistol point. This may be done without the knowledge of elevator operators, as flight from the building is by stairway. At other times the elevator operator is brought to the floor in which the hold-up is to occur, compelled to remain there until the crime has been committed, and forced to take the criminals to the main floor. Upon letting them out, he is forced to ascend immediately with the elevator.

Bank Robbery—Bank robbers are professional criminals who organize carefully, plan with ingenuity, attack boldly, and are equipped with machine guns or sawed-off shotguns or rifles and sometimes tear-gas grenades. One of their early-morning methods has been for a member of the mob—dressed as a letter carrier, telegraph messenger, or policeman—to knock on the bank door and, under a subterfuge, to get the watchman to open it. Upon doing so, he is confronted and subdued with a revolver. The bandit enters the bank, admits his confederates, makes the watchman lock the door, and then handcuffs or ties him.

As other employees and officials arrive, the watchman is compelled to open the door and admit them without giving warning. The robbers take the employees and officials to a certain room or corner until the one who has the combination to the vault arrives. At pistol-point he is forced to open the vault at the regular time. In many instances, if he could use the wrong combination and prolong the attempt to open the vault, the robbers would be apprehended.

With the vault opened, the money is put into bags, and escape made. Officials and employees are covered in the getaway. The individual covering the getaway may have a tear-gas grenade in his hand. As he steps out of the door, he releases the cotter pin and throws the grenade to the floor, distracting his victims' attention from alarm devices until the criminals are on their way.

Another method used by criminals is to drive up to the bank in an automobile, leaving a confederate at the wheel with the motor running, and another as lookout, while the actual robbers enter. Each takes up a definitely planned position. At a signal, guns are displayed and employees compelled to move away from alarm devices. Some of the robbers force their way into the cages of the paying and receiving clerks, or climb over the partitions. The employees are forced at pistol-point to a certain location in the bank. Money is swiftly gathered into bags, and one or two armed robbers cover the getaway.

Small banks not amply protected are sometimes entered at night through an upper floor by forcing a door or window, or from an adjoining building by rope or ladder. When the watchman arrives on an upper floor, he is overpowered and disarmed. If he is required to punch a time clock, they compel him to do so under their supervision. He is compelled to admit employees in the morning. The criminals follow the same procedure as those who operate with a confederate in uniform as described before.

Armored-Car Robbery—This crime is committed by thoroughly experienced criminals who go to the greatest pains in preparing plans for its commission. They have been known to use two or more high-powered automobiles, speed-boats, and airplanes. Even a hearse, a pushcart, and other business vehicles have formed part of their strategy. They dress as pedlers, mechanics, street cleaners, policemen, or otherwise. Equipped with machine guns, shotguns, revolvers and even tear gas, they work rapidly. At times the automobile in which they are fleeing may discharge a gas cloud from the exhaust pipe. Sometimes they operate on tips furnished by dishonest employees.

In a recent case where the *modus operandi* was especially developed, one of the perpetrators in the guise of a pushcart pedler arrived with a cart and stopped near the curb a few minutes prior to the arrival of the armored car at the premises from which money was to be collected. Others had trailed the armored car to this place. As the guard stepped off towards the premises, the ostensible pedler pushed his cart to the side of the armored car, the door of which was open. A sub-machine gun was drawn from among the vegetables. The chauffeur on the armored car was covered. Accomplices covered the guard inside the car, while another covered the guard who was about to enter the premises to make a collection. Other accomplices entered the armored car, removed money therefrom, and escaped. They sped away, changing direction, to a near-by waterfront. Transfer was made to speed-boats. The boats were scuttled and submerged. They had been repainted; registration number and identification marks were changed or removed.

In the robbery of armored cars, the technique used is nearly always similar to the method described. However, the criminal paraphernalia is not always so elaborate.

Payroll Robberies—The large payroll entrusted for transport to an officer or paymaster is taken by criminals numbering from four to six men. The small payroll entrusted to the girl cashier who draws it from the bank is taken by a lone worker or criminals who operate in pairs. The large payroll is usually taken from a plant or factory in the manufacturing or industrial section. The smaller one is taken at any time anywhere. The large payroll bandits work in a manner similar to that of the bank messenger robbers. They make a survey of the environs and plan in detail. Sometimes they are supplied with information by a dishonest employee working in collusion with them. If the payroll is delivered by an armored car, their time of operation is a few minutes after the car has left the premises.

Where the cashier is armed and accompanied by a guard, the robbers wait until he returns to the plant. They arrive in a car—usually stolen—carrying fictitious license plates. One criminal remains at the wheel; another at the door as a lookout. In some instances the man in the car has a sub-machine gun or sawed-off shotgun. They enter the office, hold up all present, and disconnect the telephone or cut the wires. Seizing the money, they run to the waiting car, covering their escape with guns, and giving warning to their victims not to move for three or four minutes. They either abandon the car in which they take flight for another, or separate and take different directions, taking other cars, a taxicab, bus or train. Where they take a payroll from a cashier riding from a bank in a taxicab or auto, they operate in a manner precisely the same as with the bank messenger.

When they have definite information of a large payroll protected by a guard or policeman who is not on the alert, they approach quickly, shoot the guard, cover other persons with revolvers, take up the payroll and flee. This type of robbery is always carefully planned and executed, for the reason that the robbers have to perform the act and make their getaway in a very short interval to avoid apprehension.

The small payroll criminal is usually a young and active man —not always a professional criminal. He observes a young girl going into a bank and drawing out two or three hundred dollars for the weekly payroll. Generally she carries this money in an envelop in the same hand with her pocketbook. The robber perhaps precedes her into the building where her office is located. As she approaches, he usually strikes her with his fist or with some blunt instrument, takes the money and escapes. This thief seldom has a gun, but has been known to use a piece of pipe wrapped in paper. As a rule he is not inclined to resort to grave assault. He mostly works alone and attempts to lose himself among pedestrians on the street or will run through alleyways, buildings or courts to escape. Or he may enter the office when the girl is making up the payroll at lunch hour when other employees are out. He applies for a position or attempts to sell some article. Then, locating the payroll, he seizes the money. If the girl resists he strikes her with his fist and flees.

Jewelry Robbers—Experienced criminals working in a group of from two to five rob jewelry stores. The better-class store is generally selected. The time chosen is just after opening or just before closing time, when trays of jewelry are being put in or taken out of the window. Criminals of this type generally use a stolen automobile which is provided with fictitious license plates.

The automobile conveys the robbers to the scene. A confederate remains at the wheel of the parked automobile with motor running. Another acts as a lookout while the others enter. One or two carry small leather bags into which jewelry may be placed. At revolver-point they hold up the clerks and owner, remove jewelry from the safe and show-case trays and decamp, warning that an outcry or pursuit will cause them to shoot. In stores equipped with an alarm system, they force the owner or clerks into the rear, tie and bind them, and escape. If two automobiles are used, they ride a few blocks in the first to the point where the second car is waiting for them with a driver accomplice. This type of mob may have one of its members known as a "killer" who acts as the lookout. He generally loiters in a doorway close by. He will not enter the car in which the actual robbers have escaped after the hold-up, but may casually walk away and enter another car parked in the vicinity and follow along to impede pursuit. Robbers of this type are desperate and dangerous.

Another method is for two criminals to visit a store ostensibly to buy jewelry. A certain piece is selected. Pay by a check is offered. The clerk refuses to take the check. One of the thieves leaves to cash the check. The other remains in conversation with the clerk. The thief who left to cash the check phones the store. As the clerk or owner answers the phone, the criminal remaining covers him with a revolver. Another accomplice enters and steals jewelry available. Or they may force the clerk to open the safe, tie and gag him, cut telephone wires, and flee from the premises with their plunder.

Robbery of Outside Salesmen—Professional criminals working in a group of two or three operate against the jeweler or sales-man calling to show his line to a prospective customer. Or they may hold him up while he is riding in a taxicab or automobile. Then again they may hold him up in his hotel room.

The criminal operation may occur any time during business hours. At times the thieves are tipped off by a member of the trade working in collusion. They may also follow him into a building, hold him up at the point of a gun, assault him if he resists, take the jewels, and direct him to walk up the stairs to the floor above or to the roof. They warn him against making any outcry and flee.

If the jeweler or salesman is riding in a cab or automobile, he is trailed in another. When traffic pauses, the criminals quickly enter his car, cover him with a gun, direct the driver to continue, take the jewels, drive to a distant point, put the victim and driver out, take his automobile and drive away in it, later abandoning it. In buildings equipped with elevators, they may follow the victim into the elevator, and if he is the only other passenger when the car starts up, commit the robbery and order the elevator operator to stop the car at the first floor. There they get out, ordering the operator to proceed up with the car while they escape.

If the salesman is stopping at a hotel, the criminals engage a room on the same floor. They gain the confidence of the salesman, enter his room under some pretext, and commit the rob-

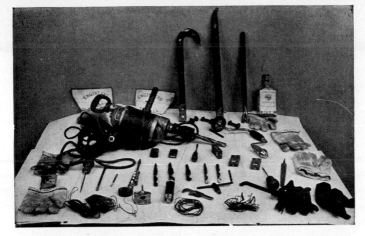

TOOLS USED IN A SAFE BURGLARY

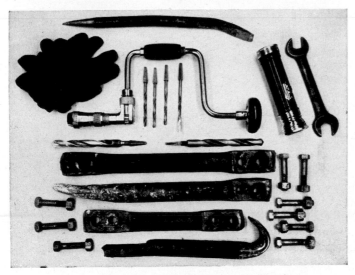

ANOTHER SAFE BREAKER'S OUTFIT

[PLATE 22]

MODUS OPERANDI OF A "DRAG JOB"   TOOLS USED IN A "PUNCH JOB"
(Page 301)   (Page 301)

[PLATE 23]

bery. At other times they do not hire a room, but gain entrance under pretext of being a bell-boy or other employee.

Chain Stores and Shops—All classes of criminals operate in this field. They select stores where there is a large turnover of money in a day, where there are only one or two clerks on duty, or where there is a large week-end business. Time of operation is usually prior to closing. It may be a Saturday night when banks are closed, or when the money is held for pick-up by company collector on Monday. Several such robberies may be committed in succession. The perpetrators drive up to a point near the premises in a car, oftener than not a stolen one. An accomplice remains at the wheel, sometimes accompanied by a woman to avoid suspicion. The motor is kept running. The criminals enter, ask for an article which the clerk turns to get. When he faces about he is looking into the muzzle of a gun. In some cases it is an imitation one. Ordered to the rear of the store, sometimes he is tied up, locked in a washroom or ice-box, or made to remove his trousers, the legs of which are immediately knotted. In a few cases the female accomplice enters alone or with a confederate and removes the money from the cash register while her accomplice handles the revolver.

When two male robbers enter, one usually forces the clerk to the rear of the store with a gun while the other with hat removed rifles the cash register, even waiting on a customer should one come in. At a favorable moment they run out, get into a waiting car and escape. While these robbers in the main operate prior to closing time, police officers may also find them in the field shortly after the opening morning hours.

Restaurants—Criminals robbing small restaurants, lunch wagons and coffee houses work alone or with a partner. The more experienced criminal mob selects the busier and better restaurant, usually after 11 o'clock at night. In the former, two will drive up in a motor-car, enter, order food, eat and await opportunity. They hold up the counter man or cashier at the point of a gun and take the money from the cash register. They will shoot to effect escape. The lone worker seldom has an automobile, but hails a taxicab, and sometimes at the point of a gun compels the driver to speed away. In the larger restaurants the crime is planned in advance. The criminals select a place frequented by the moneyed clientele, and alight from a motor-car adjoining the premises. One is left at the wheel and a lookout is on the street. The doorman, if any, is forced to go inside the restaurant. The leader enters and orders patrons to line up against the wall. Thereupon his confederates go through the pockets and handbags of the diners, taking jewelry and money. The job completed, they escape by motor-car.

Theater and Motion-Picture Houses—The cashier or treasurer of a motion-picture theater or continuous vaudeville and burlesque house is apt to be attacked between 10 and 10:30 P.M. In the legitimate playhouse, shortly after curtain time is the hour usually selected. In the case of motion-picture houses, two or three criminals operate. Previously observing the time for the cashier to transfer the money from booth to office, one of the criminals waits at the wheel of a parked car with the motor running while his confederates enter and at the point of a revolver thrust through the wicket of the booth demand and take the receipts. Or they may wait inside the door of the theater and hold the employee up as he enters with the money. Again, they may wait until the money is delivered to the office, knock on the door, and when it is opened display their guns, subdue the manager and cashier, tie them up, take the money and flee.

Gasoline Stations—Criminals operate against these stations in groups of from two to four. At times a female accomplice or male so disguised may assist. Gas stations situated on roads in outlying sections or less frequented highways are attacked, generally after 11 o'clock at night. The criminals drive up in a stolen car, which may also have fictitious license plates. They order a quantity of oil or gas for the car. When it is time to pay the attendant, guns are displayed. The attendant is forced to enter the station, is tied or bound or handcuffed to an object, or locked in the washroom. The cash register is rifled and escape effected.

This crime may be irregular in its incidence, criminals operating for a week in certain sections and then stopping for a week or more.

Garages—Usually professional criminals operate against this class of premises in groups of from two to four. They select a garage with an office that cannot be seen from the street—one that does a large cash business. To steal a high-powered motor-car to be used in some future crime, a higher-class garage is selected. Driving into the garage, gas, oil, or storage is sought. Covering the garage workers with revolvers, selection of a car is made, and it is driven away by one or two of the group, the others covering the escape as they drive away. Usually late at night or early morning is the time of operation.

When in quest of money, one man removes it from the cash register or drawer while confederates hold and tie up employees. At times they place automobiles near the entrance to prevent quick pursuit.

Drug Stores—Here may be found the professional and amateur criminal operating alone or with a confederate with real or imitation pistols. The female as an ostensible buyer may be an accomplice who enters and orders something; while the clerk is filling the order, the criminal draws a revolver and compels him to go to the rear of the store. Thereupon one empties the cash register. Perpetrators may also take narcotic drugs. Selecting a store where their actions cannot be observed from the street at night, they drive up in a car, usually stolen or hired. One criminal remains at the wheel. The other enters, purchases and pays for an article, and as the clerk deposits the money in the cash register, the criminal draws a gun, orders the clerk to the rear behind the partition, makes him remove his trousers or locks him in a washroom. Returning, the register is emptied. At other times the confederate enters at the moment the clerk is confronted with the gun and while his partner covers the clerk and forces him to rear of store, the confederate rifles the register. They may repeat at another store in the area, when the druggist is closing and the patrol force is changing tours.

Clubs—The hardened criminal mob commits this type of robbery. Clubs where gambling is the vogue are a fertile field after

10 P.M. One member of the gang may have frequented the place to make observations of members and players. The number of robbers is in proportion to the number of the players to be held up. If known to the players, the criminals mask. If the club has a doorman, he is forced into the clubrooms. One remains at the wheel of a waiting automobile, another at the entrance as a lookout. The players are lined up against a wall at point of revolver, and their pockets are rifled. The criminals flee the premises, covering the players until all are in the waiting car.

These criminals are usually bold and desperate and do not hesitate to shoot to escape. They may overcome resistance by striking a resister over the head with the butt of a revolver.

Gambling Games—Professional criminals operate on crap and other gambling games conducted in lofts, garages, cellars, pool and wire rooms, and at construction sites on payday if crap games are conducted by the workers. After 10 o'clock at night, when the game is in full swing, is the usual time chosen to "stick up" such players; Sunday mornings to attack garages; Friday evenings or the noon hour on week days to rob workers on construction sites. Like the club bandits, the criminals have had a survey made of the place and plans laid in advance. Their operation is the same.

Robbery of Residences—The criminal operating in this field, sometimes with one or two accomplices, selects only homes of the wealthy. They usually operate about 8 P.M. or about midnight. In the larger homes and apartments they usually gain entrance without the knowledge of the occupants via a rear door or through a window, or by climbing a porch at a time when servants are not about. They surprize their victims, who are dressing or undressing. Money or valuable jewelry is stolen. Sometimes the victims are tied up. If resistance is offered there is no hesitation to assault. Flight is usually by car. At other times the criminals may enter the house and secrete themselves therein until their victims return.

In smaller apartments and residences the perpetrator may be admitted by the woman of the house on supposedly legitimate business; he may deliver a radio or other article of household use, saying it was ordered. Then, distracting her attention, he may strike the woman with a blunt instrument or even with his bare hand. Criminal assault may be attempted to insure quick turning over of money and jewelry.

Robbery of Individuals—Criminals use various techniques in robbing an individual. A female accomplice may lure the victim to a hallway, to the second floor or to a vacant apartment, or even to the roof. Here the male accomplice is waiting and proceeds to hold up the victim at the point of a gun, or with a knife or razor. Together they relieve him of money and valuables, and trousers. The woman flees first and her companion follows. If the victim resists he is assaulted. Criminals of this type know the neighborhood in which they operate.

Rent collectors, milkmen and bill collectors may be held up at the point of a revolver by two men waiting in the hallway of the house entered. Sometimes the money is taken in the hallway; at other times the victim is forced to the roof, tied up there, and robbed.

In sparsely settled areas, two may wait for a man on his way to a bank, take the money from him at the point of a gun, and flee in an automobile.

Other criminals make a practise of following women and girls from subway and elevated stations, market places or homes late at night. On the street, at entrance door of home, or in vestibule they threaten with a revolver, steal money, jewelry and valuables, or take a fur piece and flee. Most cases of this class show only one man operating. Such criminals may assault to overcome resistance. Others loiter in the vicinity of hotels, restaurants and saloons, and wait for an intoxicated victim, whom they pull into a hallway and rob. This last-named class may operate with an automobile, pretend to assist an intoxicated man, get him into the car, strike him over the head with a blunt instrument, remove his money and valuables, and dump him out in an unlighted street or highway.

Others work in groups of two to four. Frequenting the better-class hotels, restaurants, and cabarets as guests, they take special note of a couple spending freely, especially if the woman is wearing valuable jewelry. When the couple leaves, usually in a car or a taxicab, they follow in another car, and commit the robbery with the aid of a gun in the vestibule or foyer which the victims enter.

It is also customary for two females driving an automobile and flirting to pick up a male. Getting him into the car, they drive to a secluded spot, take his valuables, order him out of the car, and flee.

Some colored male criminals dressed in female attire—in colored neighborhoods—will solicit white men on the street. The victim is then taken into a hallway or to the roof of an apartment or tenement house, and there robbed. Here indeed is a dangerous robber. Resisted, he may shoot, stab, or throw the victim off the roof. Some have impersonated a female with such skill that only after they were in the detention prison undergoing examination was their true sex apparent.

Taxicab Robbery—The amateur criminal sometimes operates in this field. The taxicab robber operates mostly at night. He directs the driver to proceed to a lonely spot or street, alights, confronts him with a gun, takes his money, forces him to enter a hallway, then drives away in the cab, which is abandoned a short time later. This type sometimes commits four or five such hold-ups the same night and may have an accomplice.

The Department-Store Delivery Truck—Robbery of department-store trucks and delivery vehicles is usually the work of professionals. Three or four criminals in a stolen or hired car follow the truck to a quiet thoroughfare and force it to the curb; money collected is taken at revolver point. Sometimes the driver and helper are put into the thieves' car, forced to lie on the floor, and driven to a distant point where they are discharged. In cases of this type the hold-up men may drive the vehicle containing merchandise to a drop, remove the contents, and abandon the vehicle.

Subway and Elevated Stations—This type of robbery is usually committed by criminals of experience who work alone or with an accomplice. They select stations during non-rush hours.

The lone robber generally waits for a minute or so until after a train has left the station. Then he introduces a pistol through the window of the ticket booth, orders the agent to, open the booth door, seizes the money, and flees to the street. Or he may tie up or render the agent unconscious to prevent pursuit. When working with an accomplice, one is the lookout. With the agent covered and the door open, the lookout enters the booth and takes the money. Escape is covered with a revolver. An automobile may be used to expedite escape.

Warehouse—This type of robbery is generally committed by a group of four to seven criminals, who may work in collusion with one or more employees. At times the robbery is planned on information and connections provided by an agent or lieutenant of the fence or receiver. Warehouses or sheds where valuable merchandise, liquor, or tobacco is stored have become a field of criminal activity. Such gangs operate in the early morning hours. The place has been previously surveyed, habits of watchmen studied, location of merchandise learned. Heavily armed and equipped with criminal paraphernalia, two of the robbers proceed to the warehouse or shed, enter by pretext or force, cover the watchman with a gun, assault and subdue him if he resists. Telephone wires are cut. Some minutes later two or three confederates arrive and select the goods to be stolen, using hand trucks to transport them to the door. The criminals' motor truck arrives at the premises. Lookouts are at each corner and warning signals have been arranged. To illustrate: As a sign of danger, the outer lookout will wipe his face with his handkerchief. The inside lookout will warn his confederates that the road is not clear or that a policeman is approaching. If the road is clear, the truck is loaded and driven away. As this happens about five or six o'clock in the morning, and interstate and market trucks are moving, one truck more attracts little notice. Generally one or two members of the band drive the truck away, while the others scatter in various directions. The merchandise, of course, is taken to a prearranged drop; marks of identification are removed from the goods, and they are disposed of to the fence or receiver.

Hotels—A hotel with one clerk on night duty is usually selected by the robber, who engages a room and then calls the clerk to his room. There he assaults and ties him up, proceeds to his desk, and removes the contents from the money drawer, having also taken whatever valuables the clerk possessed. This type of criminal is generally a lone worker who seldom uses an automobile, preferring a taxicab. Two or three operations in one night may be the rule. At other times he may commit the hold-up after entering and finding no one but the clerk present.

Robbery of Dentists—Criminals who specialize in robbing dentists usually operate alone but at times with the aid of an accomplice. They are experienced criminals. One selects a time when no clients are likely to be in the office. Invited to sit in the chair, he draws a revolver and forces the dentist to turn over money, valuables, and sometimes gold and certain drugs used by the profession to lessen pain.

Robbing Private Cars—During recent years, particularly in seasonable weather, couples parked in secluded spots in outlying areas have been taken by surprize by a lone hold-up man who at pistol point relieves them of their valuables, and in some instances the car as well. This type of criminal may have an accomplice when operating in public parks. Not content with plunder secured, one of the pair may attempt a criminal assault on the female victim.

The lone criminal also operates by soliciting a lift or ride and shows quick appreciation by holding up his benefactor, relieving him of his valuables and forcing him out of the motor-car, thus enabling himself to continue to a point he desires to reach, where he abandons the car.

QUESTIONS

1. Enumerate some elements of procedure and strategy employed by bandits in one or more robberies which have occurred in your locality.
2. Can you expect to use any method of police science in the investigation of robbery?

XXI

INVESTIGATION OF ARSON

A. Aspects of the Evidence in Arson Cases

As in no other type of crime the successful prosecution of an incendiary depends upon a close collaboration between the prosecutor and the investigator. It may be said that arson cases are the most difficult of crimes from the viewpoint of the investigator. In most cases the fire will have destroyed all traces of the arson, so that the prosecution is compelled to build up the case almost entirely on circumstantial evidence.

Definitions of the crime of arson, and of what constitutes arson, differ in the different States, and this lack of uniformity makes it difficult to give any definite hint to the investigator as to the methods of prosecution, altho it cannot be too greatly stressed that the successful arson investigator must have a thorough knowledge of the legal aspects of the problem. The difference in the arson laws of the various States extends not only to the methods of trial but also to the nature of the evidence which may be introduced. There are, however, three things that must always be established in order to conduct a successful prosecution: the existence of the fire, its incendiary origin, and the proof of the guilt of the accused. The establishment of the motive is also most important, especially from the viewpoint of the investigation.[1] Here must be emphasized the necessity of a careful physical examination of the premises in which the fire occurs.

The Fire—Proof must be introduced that the fire actually occurred at a specific time and within the jurisdiction of the court. The mere scorching, smoking or discoloration of a building with-

[1] See also *Suggestions for Arson Investigators*, published by the National Board of Fire Underwriters, 85 John Street, New York City.

out fire actually set thereto is not sufficient. There must be some
actual burning or ignition of some part of the building to constitute the offense. The time of the fire may be ascertained from
the Fire Department or from the neighbors.

The Incendiary Origin of the Fire—To constitute arson there
must be an intent to burn the building. It has also been held
that if a person, while engaged in the commission of some felony,
sets fire to a building, it is arson, even tho there be no intent in
the mind of the accused.

To accuse a person of arson it is, of course, not necessary that
the fire be started by the accused with his own hand, nor need
he be present. It is sufficient that he procured, aided or abetted
the commission of the crime.

All fires are presumed to be of accidental origin, so long as
there is no proof to the contrary; hence it is necessary to introduce positive evidence to overcome this presumption and prove
the *corpus delicti*. In most cases, even if a confession is obtained,
it will be impossible to prove the *corpus delicti* by direct evidence,
so that circumstantial evidence must be employed.

"All the evidence of *corpus delicti* may be proved by presumptive or
circumstantial evidence where direct evidence is not to be had." (St.
Clair *vs.* U. S., 154 U. S. 136; Commonwealth *vs.* Williams, 171 Mass.
461; State vs. Dickson, 78 Mo. 438, etc.)

One may, however, succeed in getting direct evidence showing
the incendiary origin of the fire, such as time burners, saturation
of the premises with inflammable fluids, or the existence of several distinct and separate fires. This will be dealt with later in
the chapter.

A good description of evidence admissible in arson cases is
given in *Corpus Juris:* [2]

Any circumstances tending to rebut the presumption that the burning
was accidental may be given in evidence as proof of the *corpus delicti*
(the body of the crime), and when the fact of the burning is clearly and
satisfactorily proved, and the circumstances are such to exclude accident
or natural causes as to the origin of the fire, a foundation is thus laid for
the introduction of any legal and sufficient evidence, direct or circumstan-

[2] *Corpus Juris*, vol. 5, p. 572.

tial, that the act was committed by the accused and that it was done with criminal intent. Accordingly, it is proper to receive evidence tending to fix the description, character and surroundings of the building at the time of the fire, and its possession, occupancy or control. For this purpose, evidence of the contents of the building is admissible, except when the character of the building is not controverted.

Not only the burning of the building in question, but also the extent of the conflagration and the burning of other buildings by the same fire, may be shown in evidence: and while evidence that other fires occurred in the vicinity at or about the same time as the burning of the building alleged in the indictment, or that the same or other property of the accused or prosecutor was on fire on previous or subsequent occasions, is not generally admissible in the absence of anything directly to show defendant's connection with the charge for which he is on trial, yet if it directly tends to connect defendant with the burning alleged in the indictment, or to establish intent, or to show the incendiary origin of the fire in question, it may be received. So evidence of the burning of other property belonging to the same owner at almost the same time is admissible to show that the two fires were parts of a scheme concocted and carried out by the assured. The fact that defendant, a few months before the burning charged, requested another to burn the house is admissible in evidence.

Evidence of incriminating circumstances, tending to show accused's motives, malice or intent is admissible. Thus on the question of motive, evidence is admissible which tends to prove that assured set the fire for reward, or gain, to secure employment as watchman, to destroy evidence of title, to destroy the record of a pending indictment against him, or to conceal a murder of another. The acts and declarations of the accused showing the intention to burn the property in order to collect the insurance money are admissible against him.

Threats made by accused against the person or property of the prosecutor, regardless of whether it is the identical property burned or adjacent property, may be shown, not only for the purpose of proving malice, but also to connect the accused with the commission of the offense; and the competency of testimony of threats is not affected by a considerable lapse of time intervening between their making and the burning of the building, or the fact that the ownership changed in the interim, or that the threats were general, vague, or indirect. However, evidence of a threat made after the fire is not admissible.

Ill-feeling or unfriendly relations between accused and owner may be shown.

It is proper to admit evidence of incriminating circumstances tending to show that the fire was of incendiary origin, and that the accused was connected therewith, such as evidence of defendant's act, conduct and whereabouts, at or near the time of the fire, and his acts or preparation or his possession of goods proved to have been in the building immediately before the burning, or that he removed insured goods from the building immediately before it was burned.

The proof of the *corpus delicti* is always strengthened if it can be shown that valuable furniture or stock or articles held dear by the suspect were removed before the fire, or if there were arrangements to retard the work of the firemen, to facilitate the spreading of the fire, or to cover the origin of the fire.

The Proof of Guilt—As has already been stated, the accused person is equally guilty if he procured another person to set the fire, or if he aided or abetted the incendiary. When the *corpus delicti* has been established, every fact and circumstance which may throw light on the case is usually admissible as evidence.

If a confession is obtained, it should be remembered that an extra-judicial confession in itself is not sufficient to sustain a conviction of the crime. Some corroborative evidence must be offered before such confession is competent. The following case on record is significant in this respect:

Where evidence shows that certain buildings have been burned and there are marks of a carriage having been driven through such premises and footprints leading from the place where the carriage stopped to the house, there was sufficient proof of the *corpus delicti* to justify the admission of confession of the defendant. (People *vs*. Jones, 123 Calif. 35.)

The Motive—In order to conduct the investigation successfully it is most important to ascertain the motive on the part of the suspect or accused. The establishment of the motive, on the contrary, is not absolutely necessary for the prosecution. Motives naturally vary, but the most common may be said to be desire to defraud the insurer, and revenge. There are, however, many other motives for committing arson, such as concealing crimes, pyromania, and vanity.

The desire to defraud the insurer may not always be manifested by the raising of the insurance just before the commission of the crime. Cases are known where the insurance has been reduced to some extent before the setting of the fire, in order to avoid suspicion. In many cases the arson will be the outlet for a desire for "quick sale," and there, too, the insurance fraud is not so manifest. The insurance angle of arson cases is, however, most important and should be carefully investigated. It goes without saying that the financial status öf the suspect, as well as dates of embarrassing payments due about the time of the fire, should also be ascertained.

Revenge is not an uncommon motive for arson. The movements of persons having a grievance against the owner of the burned property should be investigated.

Arson sometimes will be committed in order to conceal a previously committed crime. A murderer will set fire to a building to destroy all traces of the homicide and make it appear to be due to accidental death. The fraudulent business man will plan the setting of a fire to destroy his account books, etc. It should be pointed out that when persons have been burned to death accidentally, the charred bodies—owing to the contraction of the tissues caused by the heat—often will assume the most peculiar positions, sometimes indicating that they had died defending themselves. Only an autopsy can give any basic foundation for such a suspicion.

It has frequently been observed that when fraudulent business men are about to burn their account books, these are opened at the pages which they wish destroyed, as it is well known that it is almost impossible to burn a thick account book if it is closed. Hence, if the account books are found opened at the incriminated place, this is a reason for suspecting arson.

It should be noted that there are arson fires that are indirectly due to trade conditions. These are commonly referred to as trade or business fires. A change in the fashion of wearing apparel finds the merchant overstocked. A financial loss confronts him. If unscrupulous he may resort to arson and sell his unwanted goods to the fire insurance company after arranging for the incendiary fire. Or he may surreptitiously remove the most valuable goods from the premises on a bogus sale or shipment thereof, leaving the unwanted goods to be damaged or destroyed by the fire.

The unsuccessful or fraudulent merchant may employ a professional arsonist to apply the torch. On the other hand, he may arrange, in order to avoid having what is known as a fire record, to have the fire started on the floor above his occupancy, where another business is conducted, so that he will sustain a water loss and collect insurance fraudulently.

Intimidation is another motive. The fire may be set to intimidate a witness in a civil or criminal case.

There are also fires set in cases of trade rivalry, where one competitor burns out another in order to get the latter's business.

Racketeers resort to the torch in their extortion rackets when they want to intimidate contractors, firms or individuals in various building or other trades and thus force the victims to meet their illegal demands.

Strange as it may seem, vanity sometimes has played a part as a motive for arson. There are cases on record where, for instance, a proud member of a voluntary fire brigade or company set fire to different kinds of buildings in order to be able to wear his uniform and operate as a fireman.

Pyromaniacs—Certain monomaniacal persons, commonly called pyromaniacs, delight in setting fire to dwellings and other property. There has been a good deal of discussion as to whether pyromania is a special psychopathological condition or can be attributed to other sources, generally of a sexual nature. Pyromaniacs often are found to be mentally defective boys and girls of ages ranging from seven or eight years to their teens, as well as half-witted tramps, farm hands, maidservants, alcoholics, etc. Sometimes they set fire only for their own pleasure, and at times the setting of the fire is due to their natural reaction against petty wrongs. They can often be found among the first onlookers at the fire or at least in the neighborhood. It is not uncommon that such persons are members of the local fire association or patrons thereof.

However, as a rule, the pyromaniac commits this crime for no reason other than the impulse which urges him on. In explanation of his act in nearly every instance he will state that he did it to get a thrill, to create excitement. Whenever a series of fires of mysterious origin occur under similar circumstances in any particular district—in unoccupied or isolated buildings, or in a particular part of a building, such as cellars, storage rooms, hall-ways, etc.—it is safe to conclude that a pyromaniac is operating.

The alcoholic pyromaniac usually operates at night and fre-quently wanders a considerable distance from his home or place of employment to apply the torch.

Pyromaniacs, by turning in alarms and aiding firemen or help-ing persons from the building they have set afire, often avert suspicion from themselves.

The pyromaniac is the most difficult to detect because of the lack of motive. Peculiarly characteristic is the fact that he always works alone.

B. Points to Be Observed by the Investigator

The following will give a survey of some important questions which the arson investigator should ask himself:[3]

1. Who observed the fire first, and what did the person observe?
2. Where was the fire first observed, or where did it originate? In which building and in which room?
3. How was this room furnished? Was there a fireplace or stove of any kind?
4. Who was in the room when the fire was observed, or who was the last to visit the room? For what purpose did this person visit the room?
5. Did the visitor use fire or light in some form? Did he smoke?
6. Did the children use matches, and where were the matches kept?
7. Was there a fire in the fireplace or stove? When was it lit and what fuel was used?
8. Were inflammable objects lying on or hanging near the stove or fireplace?
9. Were the stove, or the fireplace and flue, well insulated, and were all clean-out doors and other openings in the flue carefully closed?
10. Was there soot in the flue, and when was it cleaned the last time?
11. When were the ashes last removed? In what container were they kept, and where was this placed?
12. In what manner were lamps, candles or lanterns placed in the room? Distance from ceiling, window or inflammable material?
13. Were there electric wires for light and power? When were they in-

[3] From *A Guide to the Investigation of Fires*, published by "Norges Brandkasse," Oslo, Norway.

stalled or repaired? Who did this work and when was the last time it was tested? How many watts?

14. Was heat in the electrical contacts observed at any time?
15. If there was an electric motor in the room, how was this safeguarded against dust?
16. Was the electric current on or off at the time of the fire?
17. Were there machines in the room? What machines? What power was used? When were they used last? When were they last tested and lubricated?
18. Had there been any fire, or attempt to set fire, before at the place?
19. Were there substances which might be subject to spontaneous combustion? What were they? How were they stored?
20. How, when and for what amount were the building and other property insured?
21. What is the relation between the amount of the insurance and the actual value of the property?
22. Was there other insurance than fire insurance, as, for instance, Use and Occupancy Insurance? For what amount?
23. Were there fire-extinguishing devices installed in the premises? What were they? How did they function?
24. Had anyone a personal interest in the fire? Who? In what manner?
25. Was some business conducted in the building? Were account books kept? Were they saved, or what was done to save them?

It is impossible within the scope of this book to deal with all problems connected with the investigation of arson. Some of them are of a highly technical nature and some could not be described in a book intended for the general public. We will therefore confine ourselves to a few remarks on the more important points in connection with the foregoing schedule of questions.

The origin of a fire may belong to any one of the following classes:

(1) Natural causes without human aid.
(2) Accidents where a human action is involved directly or indirectly.
(3) Arson.

It is naturally difficult to draw an absolute distinction between these three classes of causes. All investigations of arson must, however, begin with this classification. The investigator should be careful to eliminate Causes 1 and 2 before arriving at the conclusion of arson.

C. Natural Causes of Fire

Lightning—Lightning as a rule strikes high points and places connected with subsoil water. It may strike several places at the same time and may pass from one object to another. Very often an odor of sulfur (ozone) may be detected and the lightning is often accompanied by a sound of rustling. The traces are very characteristic, especially on metallic objects which melt or show beads of melted metal or deformations. Iron objects may become magnetic, as evinced by the compass. The traces of lightning in brick walls may be very characteristic: pieces of plaster are broken and shattered, whole bricks may be scattered about, some of them may be glazed on the surface, etc.

When there is a suspicion of arson, the lightning rod should be examined especially as to traces of lightning and of the rod's efficiency. Ascertain that there really was a thunderstorm at the time of the fire. Lightning is very often mentioned as a pretext by the arsonist.

Action of the Sun—We know that the rays of the sun concentrated in a lens or in a concave mirror may set fire to inflammable material. A bubble in a windowpane may also act as a lens. Such cases are, however, very rare; and yet it is not uncommon to hear an arsonist use this as an explanation for the origin of a fire. Where such a question arises, one must ascertain the direction of the sun's rays at the time of the fire (if possible, the day after the fire), the focus of the supposed lens and the position of the inflammable material in relation to the focus.

Explosions—These may be caused by unstable explosives, fireworks, kerosene or gasoline lamps, cooking gas, gasoline, alcohol, ether, acetylene, etc., and dust of flour or coal. Explosions generally occur from leaking gas pipes or gas containers, from the use of gasoline, or from fires originating from other causes where explosive material is reached by the fire. Arsonists seldom use explosives for their purpose.

When an explosion is suspected, the investigator should ascertain the position of the origin of the explosion in relation to the place where the fire originated, the nature of the explosive material (which can sometimes be determined by a chemical analysis of surrounding material), and the characteristic traces of the explosion. The aid of a specialist on explosives is essential, and the investigator should confine himself to gathering the traces.

Animals—All animals fear fire to such an extent that only by pure accident will they come near it. Animals therefore rarely cause fires. Sometimes a dog or a cat will accidentally upset a carelessly placed lamp or cooking device. A kerosene lamp generally goes out when upset and only in rare cases explodes. If it does happen to explode, the traces of the explosion and the remains of the lamp will always be found if the room has not been destroyed by the fire.

A few cases are reported where insects, birds and mice, by contacting bare electric wires, have caused short circuits and thereby endangered a house. In all such cases, however, the fuses have functioned and broken the circuit.

Spontaneous Combustion—Several materials have the property of retaining and concentrating the oxygen of the air on their surfaces. This phenomenon is followed by the generation of heat which, on account of the insufficient circulation of air, finally leads to spontaneous combustion. Such spontaneous combustion occurs especially when the material is stored in a pile or bales. Coal dust, charcoal, flour, hay, and vegetable oils, such as linseed and resinous oil, soaked in porous material, as cotton waste, paper, etc., are especially susceptible to spontaneous combustion.

In the spontaneous combustion of hay the origin of the heat is not the same as in the other materials, because the development of the heat here depends on fermentative processes in the hay, which will occur only when the hay has been stored before drying. The combustion of hay does not start with an open flame. The heat begins in the interior of the pile. A heavy odor arises, the hay begins to smolder in the interior, and the fire slowly finds its way to the outside.

When spontaneous combustion of hay or other vegetable matter is suspected, one must ascertain when the hay was cut, how it was dried, how the weather was on the day it was stacked, and, if it was still moist, if any odor of fermentation was apparent or if any sinking of parts of the stack was observed; also how long a time elapsed between the day of the cutting and the day of the stacking, between the day of the cutting and the day of the fire, and between the day of the stacking and the day of the fire. It is important to ascertain whether some neighboring farmer cut his hay on the same day and stacked it under the same circumstances. If so, his hay can be used for comparison.

It is generally held that spontaneous combustion in a haystack cannot occur before 8 to 10 days after the stacking. The danger of spontaneous combustion will cease after 70 to 80 days.

Spontaneous combustion of oil-soaked waste is a fairly common occurrence; hence plants, garages, etc., where it is used, have strict regulations regarding the disposal of waste. Spontaneous combustion of oil-soaked waste may occur after a few hours if the waste is in a small pile and the circumstances are favorable. If such combustion is suspected, one has to ascertain the presence of vegetable oils on the premises and make reconstructions and experiments under the same circumstances as prevailed at the time of the fire.

Other materials reported to be subject to spontaneous combustion are lime, bone meal, moist wool or cotton, guano, dung, sawdust, nitric acid which has touched organic material such as straw, sacks, etc., and saltpeter which has been packed in sacks.

New observations about substances susceptible to spontaneous combustion are made constantly. In one case, for instance, a bottle containing laundry ink began to burn and set fire to some paper in its vicinity. Laundry ink is made by dissolving nitrate of silver in ammonia. When such an ammonia-silver compound evaporates, the remainder is the highly explosive nitrid of silver (AgN_3). In this case the cork must have been loose; the ink dried up, and the explosive silver compound caught fire because of the presence of gum arabic or dextrose in the ink. In another case a box of rat poison was the origin of a fire. Rat poison is generally made by dissolving phosphorus in lukewarm water. The oily layer which is formed on the surface of the water is then stirred with flour until a thick porridge results. In the case just mentioned, some of the poison had been used in 1921 and the remainder had been stored near a window and forgotten. Some barrels containing kerosene and oil had been placed below this window. In July, 1933, the porridge had become absolutely dry, and under the action of the sun the phosphorus caught fire, and the fire was communicated to the kerosene barrels. This "time burner" then acted after twelve years.

The chlorate of sodium or chlorate of calcium used to clear grass from railroad banks may, even in such weak solutions as 1 to 2 %, render the grass, pieces of wood and paper along the banks highly inflammable.

Miscellaneous Causes. Corrosion of electric cables underground, damage to electric cables through earthquakes, and the breaking of gas pipes because of low temperature, have sometimes caused fires.

D. Accidents in Which a Human Action is Involved Directly or Indirectly

It is naturally impossible to give a list of all the accidents that may cause a fire. The most common ones are faulty flues, drying clothes too near a hot stove, careless handling of inflammable material, children carelessly handling fire, smokers' carelessness, leaking gas pipes, forgetfulness in the use of electric irons or electric heating pads, short circuits, carelessness with firearms, carelessness in the use of torch blowers, friction caused by insufficient lubrication of machines, etc. We will deal only with faulty stoves and firing devices, faulty flues, and the problem of short circuits.

Faulty Stoves—In cases where the origin of the fire is supposed to have been in a faulty stove, the position of the stove in relation to the wall, the kind of substructure upon which the stove stands, leakages in the pipes, faults in the stove itself, and the position of inflammable material in relation to the stove should be ascertained.

In the case of gas stoves one should ascertain the working order of the pipes, the position of the jet, how the burner functioned, whether the rubber hose was on, and whether there had been some perceptible odor of gas before the fire.

If necessary, reconstructions and experiments should be made to ascertain the origin of the fire; the facilities which the fire had to spread from the place also should be carefully examined.

Faulty Flues—In most cases the flue will be preserved after the fire, and faults in it can be ascertained by the presence of holes and smoky places. The position of the faults in the flue in relation to the place where the fire originated should be determined.

In examining flues it is recommended that experiments be made to ascertain their faults. Dry wood should be ignited at the base of the flue, directly in the flue, or in the stove if this is preserved. When the air in the flue is sufficiently warm, some moist material is placed on the fire and the smoke permitted to escape. If the top of the flue is now covered for a moment the smoke will find its way out of all faulty places. The distances between the faults in the flue and the inflammable material should also be ascertained.

Short Circuits—It has become almost a habit today to accuse the electric system of a house as being the cause of fire when no other plausible explanation can be found. The electric system, however, is seldom to blame, especially when the installation is up to date and the fuses are working.

Examination of the electric system in an arson case demands much knowledge, theoretical as well as practical, and should preferably be done by a specialist. A German specialist in the field says, and not without reason, that one often has to work with slide-rule in hand to determine if there is a possibility of an electric system being the cause of fire. The following factors are of importance: [4]

The kind, the system and the voltage of the current.
The fuse system from the source of power to the scene of the fire.
The diameter of the cables and wires and the distance to the first fuse which did not react.
The number of consumers and the amount of power they use.
Date of the installation and name of contractor.

[4] See Hoppe in *Kriminal. Monatsh.*, vii, 9.

Condition of fuses and the whole installation before, during, and after the fire.

Plan of installation.

Fires caused through an electric system may be due to *overloading* (short circuit, grounding, exaggerated consumption), *faulty contacts* (high resistance), *sparks* (by short circuits, grounding or breaking of the current), *carelessness* in the handling of electrical apparatus, or *intentional acts*.

The most important thing to ascertain when the electric system is suspected is the condition of the fuses. See if they have functioned, if they have been replaced by heavier fuses, if they have been bridged over, and if the fuses were in the right proportion to the diameter of the wires and the consumption.

A fire may sometimes occur without reaction from the fuses. Such an occurrence is possible where, for instance, the insulation of the wires is faulty and a bridge where a part of the current passes is formed. This may be regarded as a hidden short circuit. The part of the current which passes through this point is so feeble that the fuse will not react. The resistance at the point is, however, so high that under certain circumstances fire may result. Certain resistances used in commercial apparatus may also be put into the circuit and heated to a dangerous heat without reaction from the fuses. In order to bring about such a fire one must, however, have a thorough knowledge of electricity. The average arsonist would certainly not be able to carry out his plans on this line without abundant experience.

The investigator should sketch the circuit throughout the house, looking for traces of short circuits and other suspicious places, and these should be noted on the sketch.

E. Arson

Arson is a major felony calling for a most thorough and careful physical examination of the scene and environs at the earliest possible moment. Doors and windows must be examined to determine whether or not they were locked when the fire was discovered. If found forced the identity of the firemen or persons who forced them must be learned. Witnesses must be interviewed without delay. Occupants, if absent, must be immediately located and questioned to ascertain their time of departure, who locked doors and windows, who had keys to the premises, where insurance policies are or were at time of fire, financial status, outstanding liabilities, business and personal; time, date and manner of last receipts and shipments of goods, and so forth.

An inspection and inventory of stock should be made by an expert appraiser, for the purpose of determining possibility of overinsurance or overstock of unseasonable goods on hand.

Ever fearful of detection, the modern firebug has in recent years resorted to the practise of leaving an electric iron in circuit on a table, close to which is a quantity of combustible material. The electric iron generates sufficient heat to set fire to the material. Gas irons have also been used in the same way. Of course, the accident excuse is offered, but it has not been as successful as arsonists expected.

The presence of oil-soaked rags or waste in premises with doors and windows locked, the departure of the occupant shortly before the fire was discovered, coupled with the fact that recent insurance was taken out on the property or chattels, presents opportunity for prosecution on the basis of exclusive opportunity and circumstantial evidence.

Sketching and Photography—The scene of an arson case should always be sketched and photographed. In the sketch the building material in different places should be marked—also the electric circuits.

Sifting—It cannot be sufficiently pointed out that the scene of a fire should be most carefully searched and the remaining ashes and coals carefully sifted. Even if the work is dirty and time-consuming it will often pay. The ashes may reveal remains of time fuses, paper soaked with inflammable oils, candle wicks and other devices which are used to set a fire and sometimes in a miraculous way have escaped destruction. The sifting of the ashes will also permit a check-up on the claims of the owner against the insurance company and establish the fact that insured property really was in the burnt area.

Reconstruction Work—Trying to reconstruct the conditions under which the fire started is of importance for the investigation. Especially in cases where the building or the room has escaped destruction such reconstructions may have the most valuable results.

If, for example, the fire started in a room and this room is intact altho burned, one should immediately—after having carefully cleaned the floor and sifted the ashes—begin to reconstruct the appearance of the room, place the furniture where it was at the time of the fire, and try to account for every unusual displacement. Tables and chairs will leave unburnt marks of their legs on the floor. Objects which have been placed on tables or on chairs will leave the same marks and allow an exact replacement. By such reconstructions it is often possible to get a clear view of the whole occurrence. Numerous cases can be cited where painstaking reconstructions have thrown light upon seemingly hopeless cases of investigation.

Time Fuses—Time fuses used by arsonists consist either of mechanical or chemical devices. The mechanical devices often prove to be dangerous for their inventors as they may escape the fire and be found afterwards more or less intact. For this reason, perhaps, their use is becoming less and less frequent. Chemical time fuses (candles included) often betray their presence by the chemical analysis carried out after the fire. Candles especially will often leave traces of paraffin, which soaks deep into the wood. Even in cases where the wood has been quite deeply burned it is possible by a microchemical analysis to determine if candles have been used.

Oils and Other Inflammable Materials—Inflammable oils, such as gasoline or kerosene, and materials with similar effects, as motion-picture film, etc., are often used by arsonists to facilitate the spreading of the fire. The arsonist then generally calculates that the fire will destroy all traces of the inflammable material. In many cases, however, enough of it remains in the coals and ashes and soaks into unburnt wood to allow a determination by chemical analysis. In many cases, too, a chemical analysis of the soot will lead to a determination of the material used. The ap-

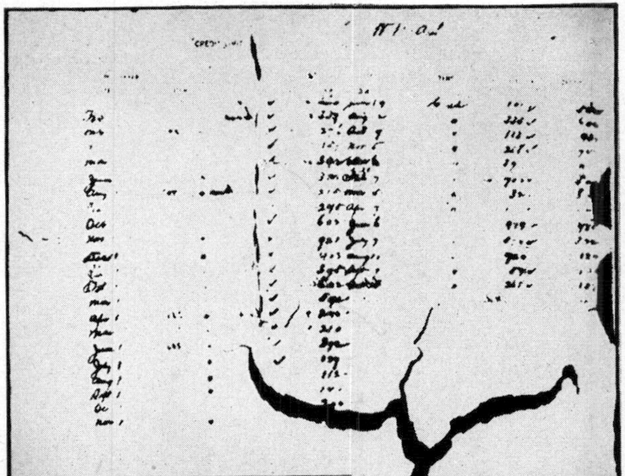

Fig. 2. Print made from negative showing writing and printing on the charred paper

Fig. 1. Showing Appearance of Charred Paper

Federal Bureau of Investigation, U. S. Department of Justice

DECIPHERING CHARRED RECORDS BY CHEMICAL ACTION AND PHOTOGRAPHY

(It will be seen from the tear that Fig. 2 is a print from the reverse side of the sheet shown in Fig. 1)

[PLATE 24]

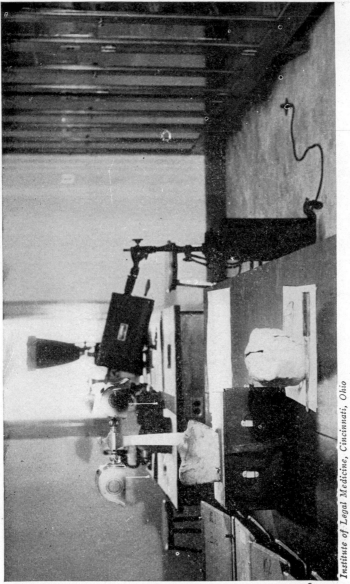

Institute of Legal Medicine, Cincinnati, Ohio

A SECTION OF THE CRIME LABORATORY AT THE SERVICE OF THE CINCINNATI POLICE

[PLATE 25]

pearance of the soot is highly characteristic for different inflammable oils, and it is recommended that the arson investigator produce smoke experimentally from different inflammable oils in order to familiarize himself with its appearance.

Sometimes the smell of the inflammable oil will allow an immediate determination. If kerosene, for instance, has been used, the coals will have an odor of kerosene for quite a while. There is a simple method of examination based upon the odor. Pieces of charred wood from the suspected places are put into a wide-mouthed glass container which is carefully closed and heated in water to 60 or 70 degrees Centigrade. If the container is then opened it is often possible to determine by the odor if an inflammable oil has been used. Naturally such an examination should be made as soon as possible.

Another method now employed with increasing frequency for the determination of inflammable oils is the use of a red dye called rhodokrit. The suspected area is powdered with rhodokrit, which is allowed to remain for twelve hours. If the wood contains traces of kerosene oil, gasoline, or any other material which dissolves fat, the wood will turn red. This test can also be carried out under a microscope with small pieces of wood or charcoal which have been in contact with the dye for several hours.

F. Reconstruction of Burnt Paper

It is often possible to read writing on burnt paper if the remains are carefully collected. If in searching a house, or in an arrest, burnt paper is found in a stove, the damper should be immediately closed, also the window, and if necessary an armful of wet rags, towels, or something similar, should be put in the stovepipe. Water should under no circumstances be used to extinguish the fire. When the fire is choked the paper is removed in the following manner. A glass pan is taken in the left hand, and, keeping it as near the paper as possible, the ash is gently fanned over to the glass pan. The ash is now moistened with Fixative (a mixture of shellac and alcohol, such as artists use on a charcoal drawing) using an atomizer. Thereafter, with the utmost precaution the ash is flattened and another glass pan is placed on the top so that the ash is pressed between the two glass pans, and the whole is placed in a printing frame. It is then photographed on an orthochromatic plate and printed on compression paper.

Another method consists of preparing a hot solution of 1% gelatin in water. This solution is put in a flat developing pan. The ash is placed on a glass plate in the above described manner and the plate is sunk in the pan so that the surface is just covered with the solution. When the ash has been so moistened it is flattened, another glass plate is put on the top, and the whole is pressed firmly in order to prevent the appearance of air bubbles.

This sort of work must be done with the utmost care if any success is to be expected. The handling of the ashes must be done with a very gentle hand and sometimes the process may take several hours.

QUESTIONS

1. What are the essential facts necessary to build up an arson case?
2. Describe how spontaneous combustion may occur.
3. State briefly how a flue is examined.
4. Tell what should be looked for in the electric system in an arson investigation.
5. Describe out of your own or others' experience some chemical time fuses.
6. Describe some methods of detecting inflammable oils.
7. Why is it necessary to reconstruct all circumstances prevailing at the time of the fire?

XXII

SABOTAGE

A. The Use of Stench Bombs by Racketeers

THE present era has brought into the hands of the criminal new weapons with which to force the merchant, manufacturer or business man to accede to unlawful demands for money or to force him to join a union of mushroom growth, or other "protective" organization, to which he must pay monthly, bi-monthly or semi-annual dues. When he refuses to submit to this kind of extortion, he is threatened with violence, or at least with serious annoyance. In the larger cities, chemical bombs have frequently been used to cripple the business of restaurants, dress shops and other mercantile establishments. Some of these are so-called "stench bombs." The chemicals are carried in bottles or in glass vials tightly corked, which when thrown will break upon striking the ground or floor. The disagreeable odors thus produced compel the discontinuance of business, sometimes for several days. Some of the agents commonly used for this purpose are:

    (a) Valerian
    (b) Valerianic acid
    (c) Butyric acid
    (d) Hydrogen sulfid
    (e) Asafœtida
    (f) Ethyl mercaptan

The first three are the ones most commonly used, because of their heavy, lingering, disagreeable odor and the difficulty of getting rid of it.

Materials Used—By far the most commonly used materials in stench bombs are the "valerian" preparations. Valerian itself consists of the rhizome and roots of Valeriana officinalis, a large perennial plant of which there are two varieties—the *European* or *Asiatic,* which is also cultivated to some extent in New Jersey and New York, and the *Mexican.* Valerian has a strong, characteristic, disagreeable odor. The most common valerian preparations used for stench bombs, and easily obtainable in the market, are *zinc valerate,* a pure white powder, and *valerianic acid,* small water-white crystals, the tincture of valerian (the alcoholic extract), the fluid extract and ammoniated valerian.[1] In these preparations the characteristic smell of valerian is still more penetrating and repulsive.

Butyric acid is a colorless thick liquid with a disagreeable odor and a taste resembling rancid butter. It is obtained from a double fermentation, whereby milk and sugar are transformed through lactic and butyric ferments into butyric acid. The final product is obtained through distillation.

Hydrogen sulfid in aqueous solution is a slightly yellowish light fluid with an unpleasant odor similar to rotten eggs or putrid fish. The gas emanating from the liquid is poisonous and the presence of large quantities in the air may be dangerous. Mixed with $1\frac{1}{2}$ volumes of oxygen and ignited, it explodes. The gas is easily obtained by treating iron sulfid with an acid. Silver, copper and lead objects are tarnished by the action of the gas.

Asafœtida is a product from Asia, sold in the form of powdered gum or in lumps. It has an overpowering, nauseating odor resembling that of garlic.

Mercaptans are organic compounds with an exceedingly offensive odor. Even the slightest trace of mercaptan in the air may be detected by smell.

Preparation of the Bombs—The following methods have been used by racketeers in preparing powdered valerian, zinc valerianate and valerianic acid for use in stench bombs:

(a) The powder is dissolved in a small quantity of alcohol or ether, to which warm water may or may not be added.

(b) The powder may be mixed with warm water.

[1] The New York Department of Health has included these products in a Sanitary Code to be sold on prescription.

(c) Sometimes strong ammonia is confined in a separate vial, which will also break at the time of contact. With this mixture the occupants of the premises damaged may suffer from a severe smarting of the eyes as the result of the ammonia fumes.

(d) Another method is to mix the valerian preparations with water and put the mixture into a glass container. Some ether is then carefully poured on top of it so that it remains unmixed, thus preventing the valerian fumes from escaping around the cork or stopper.

(e) Another method used is to put the powdered or crystallized substance on the floor about the revolving door of the entrance to the premises, and as persons keep entering through this revolving door the powder or its odor is taken up by the air current and carried throughout the interior of the premises.

The mixing is generally done in a thin-glass bottle, a vial, or the glass container of a thermos bottle. The container is corked, sealed with wax, carried to the premises, and thrown with enough force to cause it to break. In the case of a thermos bottle, the outer metal protection is discarded before throwing the glass container. Occasionally the mixture is put in an atomizer and sprayed throughout the premises.

Butyric acid, hydrogen sulfid and *ethyl mercaptan* are also put into containers. Certain staining chemicals are sometimes added to cause damage in addition to the disagreeable odor.

B. Treatment of Damaged Property

A neutralizer or counteracting agent used to overcome the odor should, from a practical viewpoint, have the following safety factors:

(a) It should act not only on the basic body but on the disagreeable vapors in the air as well.

(b) It should not be injurious to health, property, merchandise or food to any greater extent than the stench bombs themselves.

(c) It should be non-inflammable and non-explosive.

The agent used in counteracting stench bombs must be placed on every particle of the offensive chemicals. It should also be sprayed in the air to neutralize the disagreeable fumes. If possible, electric fans should be placed on the floor to drive the odor to the windows, as the fumes, being heavier than air, remain at low levels. The following principles have been found practical in dealing with stench bombs:

(a) Remove all affected material to the outside air. If the offensive agent is on the carpet, cut out all affected pieces and remove them to the outside air, fire-escape, etc.

(b) Confine the fumes to the one space or room, if possible.

(c) Ventilate quickly by opening all windows and doors leading to the outside.

(d) Place electric fans on the floor to blow the fumes out through open doors or windows. Strong ammonia could be used to advantage during this operation, by sprinkling it on the floor to neutralize the odor.

(e) Spray the counteracting agent—such as oil of wintergreen, etc.—on the air affected.

(f) Objects which cannot be removed, such as floors or walls, may be covered with a paste made from caustic soda and water.

(g) If the odor is too disagreeable, a cotton-fabric pad impregnated with dilute caustic soda in glycerin should be put over the mouth and nostrils. The pad should be wrung out before applying it in order not to cause injury to the skin. Care should be taken not to bring the pad in contact with the eyes.

(h) To prevent the offensive odor from getting into another room, a heavy cotton cloth should be placed over closed doors, window crevices and other openings, and the paste of caustic soda placed against the lower cracks will help to keep the odor out.

(i) A rubber raincoat and old clothing should be worn in the premises affected, as it requires several hours in the open air to get rid of the odor on the clothing.

The following agents will counteract to a certain extent the offensive chemicals and their fumes: (1) a solution of alcohol and sodium hydroxid, (2) a solution of sodium carbonate or milk of lime. Other agents which give results if placed over the offensive agent and sprayed into the air are activated charcoal, which absorbs all gases, and copper sulfid, which absorbs ammonia.

To counteract the action of valerianic acid, asafœtida, butyric acid, hydrogen sulfid, and similar substances, one of the following precautions may also be taken:

(1) Wash the premises with denatured alcohol and absorb as much of it as possible with absorbent cotton.

(2) Wash the object affected with 20% ammonia and allow to stand for

five minutes. A diluted alkali solution, for instance, 5% sodium hydroxid solution, can be used instead of the ammonia. If the material used in the stench bomb is entirely volatile this treatment is certainly of no use.

(3) Soak up the offending solution with some absorbent material, and when as dry as possible cover the area which has been in contact with the obnoxious agent with carbon tetrachlorid. There must be ample provision for ventilation, as the fumes of this substance are poisonous.

(4) Rub dry with newspapers and remove all the materials used in the cleaning process from the premises to the outside air.

(5) Spray the area of the entire room with oil of rosemary. This pleasant odor will disappear within two days.

When mercaptans have been used in the stench bombs it is extremely difficult to remove the odor. The treatment with carbon tetrachlorid should prove to be of value. The damaged area can also be covered with chlorid of lime, which tends to neutralize the odor. This substance must be handled with caution, since, after releasing chlorin, lime is left as a residue. Every particle or object must be covered.

One of the most common neutralizers to be bought on the market consists of denatured alcohol and chromic acid. The following procedure is employed. Rubber gloves should always be worn:

The parts affected are saturated with denatured alcohol, whereupon crystals of 99½% chromic acid are placed thereon. This preparation is rubbed into the floor with a damp cloth and allowed to remain for three to five minutes, whereupon the objects are washed with water and caustic soda. The operation is repeated until the odor has disappeared. When such a neutralizer is used the fumes in the air must be counteracted by some other agent, as the above procedure only applies to the basic body of the stench bomb deposited on the part affected.

Another commercial preparation consists of a liquid which can be sprayed upon the basic body as well as in the air. This agent seems to have some effect on the disagreeable odor, tho its own odor may be objectionable to some. It can be used in a sprayer and does not ignite.

Strong vinegar has also been used as a counteracting substance with some effect. Its only disadvantage lies in its pungent odor.

C. Other Acts of Sabotage

Staining—Any markedly adhering and coloring dye, as, for instance, henna or anilin, is mixed with water or turpentine and put into an easily broken glass container. Christmas-tree balls are often used for this purpose. Such a container is thrown against the merchandise, walls of the shop, etc.

Damage through Acids—Strong acids, such as oil of vitriol (concentrated sulfuric acid), hydrochloric acid or nitric acid, are sometimes thrown by criminals against objects of merchandise which they wish to destroy. Sometimes hydrofluoric acid is thrown against plate-glass windows to destroy the surface of the glass.

D. Explosives

For obvious reasons a description of the most common bombs likely to be encountered by police forces and other law enforcement agencies is not given here. It must be constantly borne in mind that there will always be a hazard in handling bombs, infernal machines and other forms of explosives. To reduce the hazard to a minimum, the New York City Police Department has issued orders that whenever the attention of a member of the force is called to a suspected container of this kind, the premises on which it is found shall be evacuated immediately of all persons therein, and the investigating officer shall notify Police Headquarters by telephone of his findings. The Telegraph Bureau (which is the central office for communication service by telephone, radio, teletype and telegraph) at Police Headquarters immediately dispatches an Emergency Service Squad motor truck with a police crew to the scene, and also notifies the Bomb Squad, the Police Laboratory, and the Desk Officer of the precinct concerned, in addition to other routine departmental and extra-departmental notifications. Upon arrival of the Emergency

Service Squad at the scene, the officer in charge of the Emergency Service Squad causes a sufficient quantity of lubricating oil—which is carried on the truck at all times for such purposes—to be brought to the place where the suspected container was found, and designates one member of the squad to immerse it in the lubricating oil. All others present, except the member so designated, are kept at a safe distance. Any bomb, upon explosion, will cause damage to property and fatal or serious injury to persons within three hundred feet from the point of explosion. If there is a vacant lot or a roadway near by, which can be closed to traffic, and which will furnish a free radius of three hundred feet from a central selected point, the officer in charge of the Emergency Service Squad will cause the container of lubricating oil in which the bomb, suspected bomb, infernal machine or other explosive has been immersed to be removed thereto. Under no circumstances will the suspected container be removed from the oil by anyone other than a member of the Bomb Squad or of the Police Laboratory. When lifting the suspected bomb to transport it or immerse it in the lubricating oil, extreme care must be exercised to keep it in the identical position in which it was found, so that it will not be jarred, tilted or turned. Police safety lines must be established and maintained at proper distances by the officer in charge until the removal of the suspected explosive by proper authority. Suspected bombs should not be immersed in containers of water.

Metropolitan and State Police Departments maintain a personnel service especially assigned to the investigation of suspected bombs or infernal machines, and have technical equipment, including the fluoroscope and an x-ray unit for radiographing purposes, available for use by the specialists assigned to this class of work. Lubricating oil will stop the works of a clock while in the oil, and will desensitize a number of chemicals, provided the oil can penetrate the package. Police officers should always remember that the investigation or handling of bombs or suspected infernal machines of any kind requires the services of an expert. Disposition of the suspected container should be made under the direction of the expert.

QUESTIONS

1. What are the most common chemicals used in stench bombs?
2. State briefly how you would deal with the situation when stench bombs have been used in a store.
3. Describe briefly some other sabotage methods.

XXIII

QUESTIONED DOCUMENTS

O F the many problems connected with questioned handwriting we will discuss only a few which have special importance in detective work.

Three types of ink are chiefly used today in the United States, namely, gallotannic, chromic (logwood), and anilin (nigrosin), inks. In addition there are the colored inks, China ink, and a small number of rare dark inks, as vanadium and wolfram. The different types of ink may have a very similar appearance on paper, but they are easily distinguished on account of their different compositions.

A. Determining the Kind of Ink Used

The gallotannic ink was originally an Arabic invention—a solution of iron salt and nut-gall. When these substances were mixed, a thick black precipitate consisting of tannic acid, gallic acid and iron was obtained. The inconvenience of this precipitate was conquered in the middle of the nineteenth century when small amounts of hydrochloric and sulfuric acids were added. These dissolved the precipitate, giving a clear, almost colorless liquid which turned black as the result of the oxidizing action of the atmosphere. However, it took some time before the ink turned black, and in order to render it visible and usable for writing, a so-called primary dye—an anilin dye resistant to acids—was added. When the ink is oxidized, the color of the primary dye is obscured by the deep black color which results. Modern gallotannic inks may be regarded as sulfuric or hydrochloric solutions of tannic and gallic iron salts with some anilin dye and a quantity

TABLE OF INK REACTIONS—BLACK INKS *

REAGENTS

INK	Oxalic Acid 3%	Tartaric Acid 10%	Hydrochloric Acid 10%	Nitric Acid 10%	Chlorid of Tin in Hydrochloric solution 1/10 N	Na$_2$S$_2$O$_3$...1 Ammonia..1 Water....10	Hydroxid of Sodium 4%	Hypochlorite of Calcium 20%
Gallotannic Ink	Disappears	Bleaches	Disappears giving a yellow color	Disappears	Disappears	Dark red	Dark red	Disappears
Logwood with K^{2}CrO^4	Violet	Violet	Purple	Red	Red	Unaltered	Brown	Disappears
Logwood with CuSO^4	Orange	Orange	Red	Purple	Red	Dark blue	Dark red	Disappears leaving a yellow color
Nigrosin	Unaltered	Dark blue	Almost unaltered	Unaltered	Unaltered	Dark violet	Dark violet	Brown
Vanadium	Bleaches	Bleaches	Bleaches	Bleaches	Bleaches	Dissolves	Dirty brown	Unaltered
Resorcinol	Brilliant red	Disappears	Brilliant red	Brilliant red	Disappears	Brown	Unaltered	Brown

* After Robertson and Hofmann in *Chemisches Central-Blatt*, 1892, Leipzig. For analysis of the various colored inks in the market we recommend the tables of Robert Poix, which may be found in Locard's *Manuel de Technique Policière*, Paris, 1934.

of sugar and gum arabic or similar substances to prevent rapid drying. Copying ink contains greater quantities of dye and glue. Gallotannic ink is regarded as the most stable of all inks and is certainly the one mostly used.

Chromic ink consists of a watery solution of logwood, bichromate of potassium or chromate of potassium, and alum. Logwood contains a blue-red dye, hematoxylin, which is turned black by bichromate of potassium.

Anilin inks are water solutions of anilin dyes. Generally they also contain a small quantity of sugar and an acid to render the color more brilliant.

The different classes of inks may be determined by many different methods. We may mention the use of reagents on the ink lines, the spectrographic method, and the photographic method of Miehte.

The reagents are applied on the ink with a glass rod, and the resultant color allows one to determine the nature of the ink used. The reagent should be put on unimportant parts of the document, and if the text to be examined is very brief the document should be photographed first. The drops should be as small as possible and the reaction observed under the microscope. The most common reagents are oxalic acid (3%), tartaric acid (10%), mineral acids (1% to 20%, generally 10% solutions of hydrochloric and nitric acids), ammonia (10% to 17%), hydroxid of sodium (4%), hypochlorite of calcium (20%), chlorid of tin in hydrochloric solution (1/10 N). To determine the presence of iron in the ink a hydrochloric solution of ferrocyanid of potassium (1/5 N) and rhodanid of sodium (20%) in a weak nitric acid solution is mostly used.

The weak oxalic acid solution is used first. If it is a gallotannic ink the primary dye is first dissolved. The speed with which the ink is dissolved may, to the experienced eye, represent an approximate index of its age. The colored drop is then absorbed with a small piece of white filter paper. The primary dye is generally blue or bluish red, and the filter paper is examined to determine the nature of the dye. If there are several anilin dyes in the ink there will be different colored zones on the paper as a result of the different capillarity phenomena.

When strong acids or alkalies are used, they should, immediately after the reaction has taken place, be treated with a counter agent, *i.e.,* for the acids, ammonia, and for the alkalies a weak hydrochloric-acid solution.

The value of the iron reactions showing the presence of gallo-tannic inks should not be overrated, because a corroded pen may dissolve in acid inks and give a weak iron reaction. The iron reaction must then be a very decided one.

The presence of chromic inks is best determined under the microscope with the diphenylkarbazid reaction of Stover as advocated by Metzger and Heess. The ink line is oxidized with a drop of a solution of hypochlorite of barium obtained by the action of a 2% chlorid of barium solution on a ½ N hypochlorid of sodium solution. The reagent should be allowed to act about double the time necessary for the destruction of the ink. The drop of hypochlorite solution is then absorbed with filter paper on which a drop of diphenylkarbazid reagent is applied. If chrome is present the area will turn violet. The reagent must be freshly prepared by mixing 1 cc. of 2% alcoholic solution of diphenylkarbazid with 9 cc. of 5% hydrochloric acid. Control reactions on chrome free and on chromic ink writing should be made.

Spectrography may be used to some advantage for the differentiation of anilin dyes. A microspectrograph is used. The different anilin dyes will show absorption bands at different places in the spectrum.

The old method of Miehte consists of photographing a text which is suspected of having been written with two different inks. It is photographed in transparency if the paper was written only on one side and with reflected light if it shows writing on both sides. To render the paper transparent vaseline or tetrachlorid ethane are used. The text is at first photographed on an ordinary plate with blue filter. Then it is photographed with a specially prepared plate sensitive to red and with a red filter. If the ink shows differently on the different plates it may be assumed that we are dealing with two different inks.

With the aid of the above-mentioned methods one may determine that two inks are chemically different, but one cannot prove that a document is written with only one ink, because within the types there are innumerable compositions. Inks of different manufacture within the same types may differ as to the strength and depth of the color, as to the contrast of color between the different parts, as to their secondary color by oblique reflected light, and as to the appearance of the borders of the ink lines, which may be even or irregular. They may also differ as to the amount of pigments shown in thin or blotted strokes, and as to their glossiness. A careful examination of these properties will sometimes show differences or similarities between two inks of the same type.[1]

The chlorid and sulfate picture mentioned on page 410 may also give some information as to special makes of inks within the different types. The dye in the ink must then be completely oxidized. When dealing with gallotannic and chromic inks, nitrous acid will do; with anilin ink a solution of 1% nitrate of silver, 1% nitric acid or 2% permanganate of potassium is used. The separated precipitate is removed with sulfate of hydrazin in a weak solution of nitric acid, and the excess of nitrate of silver is removed by washing with a 1% nitric-acid solution.

The intensity of the negative or positive chlorid picture can be compared with the intensity of the chlorid picture of the incriminated addition to the text. An experienced eye is needed to judge accurately. This method will, however, have a very limited use because of the obliteration of the writing.

Determination of the color of the ink with the naked eye is difficult because of the personal element involved. There are at least three objective methods for determining the colors of inks, i.e., filter photography, examination in an Osborn-Lovibond tintometer, and by photometric examination.

In filter photography the writing is photographed through a

---

[1] See also Osborn, *Questioned Documents*, New York, 1929.

light filter, which allows only certain colors to pass on to the plate. If one color is to be made stronger than the others, a filter having its complementary color [2] is used. As the filter with the complementary color does not allow the color of the object to pass through, the sensitive plate will be lighter on the place in question and the print darker. On the contrary, if one removes a color one uses a filter of the color to be suppressed which allows the light to pass through. A thick, black precipitate will be found on the sensitive plate and the print will be light-colored. The ink specimens to be examined are photographed on the same plate. The difference in the colors will be shown on the plate. With proper filters and panchromatic plates some results may be achieved.

The Osborn-Lovibond tintometer is built on the same principle as the comparison microscope used in examining bullets. Each lens has an opening in which a Lovibond filter glass may be inserted. These consist of red, yellow and blue stained-glass slides representing all gradations of these colors.

The specimen of writing to be examined is placed under one of the lenses. The various stained slides are inserted in a groove placed immediately above the opposite lens until the same color as that of the ink is obtained. This procedure is repeated with comparison specimens and if there is a difference this may be ascertained by means of the numbered slides. This method, however, is delicate and can only be applied to a limited number of cases.

Another method of determining the color of the ink is by the photometer. As microphotometric methods are now being developed to a great extent, we may expect that within the next few years dependable ways of determining the colors of minute objects such as ink lines may be found.

---

[2] Two colors which by being mixed produce a white light are called complementary colors. They may be simple or complex. Simple complementary colors are, for instance, orange/blue, gold-yellow/blue, yellow/indigo blue, greenish-yellow/violet, etc. Green, on the contrary, has a complex complementary, purple.

B. Determining the Age of the Ink

Efforts to ascertain the age of ink are seldom successful. It is possible only when the ink has been recently applied and when it is of the gallotannic type. There is no possibility of determining the age if chromic (logwood) ink, anilin (nigrosin) and China ink, violet, red, light blue, green and other inks have been used.

In order to understand the possibility of determining the age of gallotannic ink we must describe the alterations taking place in the writing during the lapse of time. As already stated, the color of the gallotannic ink before use is due to the presence of an anilin dye. When applied to the paper the ink still shows this primary color. The process of oxidation will, in time, turn the ink to deep black. In summer the ink will seem black to the eye after a few weeks, and in winter after one to several months. During these periods, however, the black color is only superficial; the pure, densely black color is only obtained later. Gallotannic inks require from one to two years to attain their intensest blackness, and this will then last for several years more. After that period the ink begins to turn yellow along the traces made by the pen point. This discoloring will continue for several years more, until the writing becomes a dark yellowish brown. This latter color will last indefinitely. The above-mentioned periods of time can be stated only approximately, because the oxidation processes are retarded or accelerated according to the degree of atmospheric humidity, the light, the ink itself, and the paper.

If the ink under examination still shows the fresh primary color it cannot be more than a few weeks old. This may be ascertained in the following manner. The document to be examined is covered with a thin metal plate having an aperture through which only one letter is exposed. The plate is then flooded with the ultra-violet rays, without filter, for about a quarter of an hour at a distance of about five inches. The unfiltered light is not only very rich in all of the actinic rays of the sunlight but during the exposure ozone is also developed.

During this time the exposed letter undergoes an artificial oxidation which causes it to appear blacker than the surrounding letters if the ink is of recent application. If a few weeks have elapsed since the writing, and the ink is already fairly black, its property of dissolving in water may be put to use to determine its approximate age. A recently applied ink is immediately dissolved in a drop of water placed on the writing, the drop assuming a blue color. This may be due either to the fact that the ink is fresh or that it contains a dye soluble in water. In the first case the occurrence is temporary, as the ink will not be dissolved when oxidized. In the second case the occurrence is constant, as the ink colors the drop regardless of its age. To determine whether the ink is fresh or whether it contains a soluble anilin dye, the process of oxidation must be completed. The quartz-lamp method (see page 432) may be used for this purpose. A drop of distilled water is put on the already-treated portion of the writing. If the ink does not become dissolved after 20 minutes, while the other untreated parts of the writing do, it must be concluded that the document has been written recently. On the other hand, if the ink on both the treated and untreated parts is dissolved, the test is negative.[3]

The later-mentioned chlorid method of Metzger and Heess may also be used to determine the approximate age of the ink. The shape of the chlorid picture will give some indication as to the age of the ink. The chlorid picture of ink not more than a few days old corresponds entirely to the form of the original writing. With the lapse of time the chlorid picture is blurred because of the spreading of the chlorid ions. After a period of one-half to one year the chlorid picture is entirely blurred. Naturally with this method it is only possible to determine the difference in age between two writings which are supposed to have been subject to the same influences from the moment of the writing.

Errors may arise both when determining the age of an ink and when comparing inks. These errors may be due either to

---

[3] This method was invented by Van Ledden-Hulsebosch in Amsterdam.

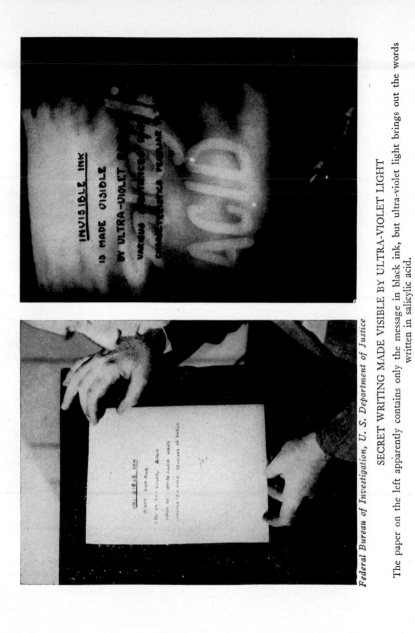

Federal Bureau of Investigation, U. S. Department of Justice

SECRET WRITING MADE VISIBLE BY ULTRA-VIOLET LIGHT

The paper on the left apparently contains only the message in black ink, but ultra-violet light brings out the words written in salicylic acid.

[PLATE 26]

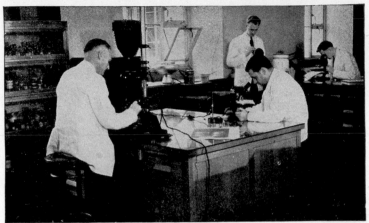

Federal Bureau of Investigation, U. S. Department of Justice

STUDYING EVIDENCE WITH TWO DIFFERENT MICROSCOPES

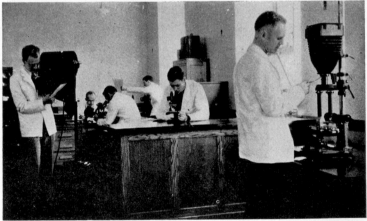

Federal Bureau of Investigation, U. S. Department of Justice

LEFT: EXAMINING A DOCUMENT UNDER ULTRA-VIOLET LIGHT.
RIGHT: TAKING A PHOTOGRAPH THROUGH A COMPARISON
MICROSCOPE

[PLATE 27]

the writing having been dried with blotting paper or to the fact that the ink was diluted. Writing dried with a blotter never becomes deep black, but looks light and dull. The blotting can be recognized by the blurring of certain lines. The blotted writing contains a reduced quantity of the ink substance, but it will nevertheless show the characteristic reaction.

Writing made with diluted ink appears like blotted writing. It is, however, uniformly light, and there are no traces of blotting. Microscopic examination shows small black grains due to the settling of the ink.

Handwriting experts are often able to arrive at conclusions as regards the age of a document, or the age of additions in relation to the text, by other means besides the studying of the ink. Examination of the sequence of strokes and the writing on the folds as well as the examination of slants, position while writing, watermarks and other signs of the manufacture of the paper, etc., may lead to definite conclusions.

C. Erasures

Ink may be erased with a knife, rubber, or ink eradicator.

When the erasure has been made with a knife or rubber it is generally easy to detect the area involved, as it is translucent. This is seen by holding the paper against the light. A simple method consists in putting a few drops of benzin in the vicinity of the suspected area. The benzin spreads to the border of the erased portion of paper, continues to spread along the border, and later penetrates the erased spot. The iodin-fumes treatment [4] may also give good results and even allow the reading of the erased writing.

If the erasure has been made with ink eradicators it may be difficult to detect it, especially if a great deal of time has elapsed. Newly applied ink eradicators can be easily detected with the ultra-violet rays, which bring out the contrast quite sharply. As clever forgers have been known to wash away with distilled

[4] See pages 105-106.

water all residue of the eradication, the examination with the ultra-violet rays should not be too much relied upon.

If the eradicated ink is a gallotannic one it is almost always possible to get at least some traces of the original writing, because small particles of ink will always adhere to the paper. The suspected area is then treated with sulfite of ammonia. A quantity of the sulfite of ammonia is put in a glass container, which is then covered with the document to be examined, the suspected spot pointing downwards. The sulfite of ammonia gas is allowed to act on the paper from five to fifteen minutes, until the invisible residue of iron oxid is transformed to black sulfite of iron and thereby made plainly visible.

Each ink, even if it does not contain iron, contains other inorganic compounds, such as chlorids and sulfates, which spread in the surrounding paper independently of the ink itself. They can never be removed through erasures and are out of the reach of the forger. These invisible chlorid and sulfate ions will not only spread on the surface but will also penetrate into the paper itself. Spreading and penetration of the ions will go on for years. A method of making this latent chlorid or sulfate picture visible was invented by Metzger, Heess and Rall.[5] So far as the examination of erasures is concerned, the method is quite revolutionary.

Two solutions are used. The first is composed of 10% sodium nitrite ($NaNO_2$), which is added to a 1% silver nitrate solution until a heavy precipitate of nitrite of silver is obtained. This latter is then dissolved by the addition of a 10% solution of nitric acid. The second solution is made by adding one part of a 35% solution of formalin to 10 parts of a 2% solution of sodium hydroxid. The suspected document is immersed in the first solution. If this process is prolonged, the visible writing still existing over the erased area will be completely destroyed. If that is not desired, the reaction may be controlled and stopped from going on by soaking the area with a 10% solution of nitric acid followed by distilled water to which a few drops of

[5] *Beiträge zur kriminalistische Symptomatologie und Technik*, Graz, 1931.

nitric acid have been added. The now insoluble chlorid of silver is turned to black silver by soaking the area with the second solution. The latent chlorid picture is transformed into a visible picture by washing it several times in distilled water and drying. The reaction must be carried out in the dark room by red-light illumination and requires a certain amount of training on the part of the operator to insure success. The suspected areas should not be touched with the fingers. Only glass rods and forceps should be used.

If the ink is highly acid the result of the procedure may not be a positive but rather a negative chlorid picture, the original showing up white against a black background. A picture absolutely similar to the original writing can be expected only when the document is fresh. If this is not the case, the picture will appear blurred because of the spreading of the ions in the paper. If the chlorid picture cannot be seen on the front of the paper, it can, at times, appear clearly on the back of the paper.

Sometimes it may be necessary to develop the sulfate instead of the chlorid picture, but it must be kept in mind that the sulfate ions do not spread as much as the chlorid ions, and the paper itself may often contain sulfates of aluminum or barium which will interfere with the reaction. Test reactions to determine whether the chlorid or sulfate reaction should be made are to be carried out on unimportant parts of the document.

If the sulfate reaction is attempted, the suspected area is treated with a 4% nitrate-of-lead solution. If some of the writing has remained behind after the erasure, it may, if necessary, be removed by treating it with a 4% solution of perchloric acid and some drops of permanganate of potassium solution. A few minutes later all the sulfate in the ink has been transformed into lead sulfate and all the iron of the ink has been dissolved. The erased area is now washed with a saturated solution of sulfate of lead in distilled water to get rid of the excess of nitrate of lead. If necessary some drops of dichlorid of hydrazin should be added to the washing solution in order to reduce and dissolve the dioxid of manganese. The erased portion is now washed with distilled water and treated first with a solution of 2.5% of sulfid of sodium (Na_2S) and then with a 2% hydroxid of sodium solution. The paper is finally washed with distilled water.

D. Problems of Lead-Pencil Writing

It may be said at the outset that it is very difficult to determine whether two lead-pencil writings have been made with the same sort of pencil or not. There are different proportions of graphite and clay in "lead pencils," but on account of the very small quantities of material at the disposal of the expert the proportions cannot be determined. A microanalysis requires at least 2 milligrams of substance, and to obtain this quantity several pages of lead-pencil writing must be scraped. Besides, it is almost impossible to get pure material free from foreign substances in the paper itself. However, it may sometimes be possible to reveal foreign substances in the lead pencil by the application of different reagents on the pencil lines in the same manner as that used when dealing with inks. The presence of such a foreign substance in lead-pencil writing should at least be able to furnish negative proof, *i.e.*, the presence of such a substance in one lead-pencil writing and its absence in another indicates non-identity. The most common foreign substances in lead-pencil writing are titanium, chlorids and sulfids, as well as iron. Owing to the fact that the paper itself may sometimes contain titanium, iron and chlorids, control experiments must be carried out on the paper.

The German scientist, Kögel, has invented a method which differentiates one indelible pencil writing from another to a certain degree and distinguishes indelible-pencil writing from lead-pencil writing with certainty. A filtered ultra-violet light is played obliquely on the writing to be examined. The lead-pencil writing will reflect the ultra-violet light in such a manner that it appears chalk-white, while the indelible pencil, which contains only anilin dyes, shows up jet-black. Indelible pencils of inferior quality, which contain graphite in addition to the anilin dyes, disappear more or less completely by blending in the violet tone of the paper.

Lead-pencil writing often shows traces of having been written on an uneven substructure, and it is possible in some cases to show that a certain sheet has been written on a certain substructure, or that several writings have been written on the same underlying surface. For this purpose a piece of paper is put over the suspected surface and the pencil writing made on it is compared. It is not possible to compare the substructure directly with the paper.

Erased lead-pencil writing may be made visible by different methods, *i.e.*, iodin fumes, the addition method, examination in polarized light, and photography in oblique light.

The use of iodin fumes has been described on pages 105-106.

By the addition method the erased writing is photographed on a wet collodion plate of the same type as that used in half-tone work. Several plates are made and marked in such a manner that they may be absolutely matched together later on. Several negatives, each of which is too weak to show the traces of the original writing, are now at hand; the collodion skins are taken away from the glass plates, and are superimposed on each other according to the markings. This adds the feeble impressions to each other, producing a stronger negative, which may be printed with good results. The so-called diapositive method is very similar. A hard plate is made of the area to be examined. A still harder diapositive is printed on the hard plate. From this diapositive a harder plate is made, and so on, until the original writing can be read.

Examination in polarized light with crossed Nicols will sometimes give good results. All mirroring is prevented through the polarization when the Nicols are crossed so that the particles of graphite remaining in the paper appear jet-black.

If the paper on which the writing appears is very dirty, it may be bleached by treating it for a short time with a strong solution of peroxid of hydrogen. This, however, must be done very carefully to prevent the particles of graphite from being loosened by the liberated oxygen.

If there are any traces of writing on the back of the paper, reconstruction of the original writing is possible by photographing this in an oblique light, thus giving relief to the impressions.

E. Sequence of Strokes in Writing

When two ink lines cross one another it is often of great importance to determine which is superimposed on the other. The solution of such a problem often answers the question as to whether a number has been altered, whether words or sentences have been added to a document, or whether the whole text has been written after the signature was affixed. There is no absolutely infallible method for arriving at such conclusions, but in the majority of cases a solution will be found. In all examinations of the sequence of strokes comparison tests should be made with the same paper and with the same ink, if possible.

If the second line is superimposed on the first before the latter has become completely dry, the ink from the second stroke will spread out on the first line at the crossing in such an obvious manner that there can be no doubt about the second line lying over the first one. One reason is that the paper which is covered by the first line, being moist, is more absorbent and therefore causes the ink from the second stroke to spread more pronouncedly than on bare paper. Another is that the paper has been roughened by the pen point during the act of making the first stroke, and is thus rendered more porous. This is also shown by the fact that the additional ink spreads out only along the traces of the first stroke. This part of the phenomenon may be observed even when the first stroke is entirely dry.

The appearance of the crossing is quite different if the second stroke is immediately blotted. If the second stroke was made before the ink in the first line was dry, a part of the ink from the first stroke will dissolve in the ink from the second stroke. In blotting, however, pigments will be absorbed from the second as well as the first stroke. The first one will then appear lighter at the crossing than the rest of the same stroke, but the second will be uniform. If the two strokes were each blotted immediately after writing it is almost impossible to determine the sequence. If the traces of the pen point from the second stroke show up more clearly at the crossing than the traces from the first one, however, there is a possibility of determining the sequence.

If the first stroke has not been blotted and is fully dry, but the second is blotted immediately, there are great possibilities of making mistakes. In most cases the dark stroke underneath will seem as if it were over the blotted one. Such mistakes often occur when the strokes are of different width and intensity of color, even if there has been no blotting. At first sight a broad line looks as if it were superimposed over a thin one. A thin light line also often does not spread out on the broad one.

Ink lines *over* lead-pencil lines will show the same spreading underneath as has been described above. The pen point will also smooth the graphite at the crossing so that the grains of graphite acquire a glossy surface. If the ink line is *under* the lead-pencil line the latter will show a continuous metallic glossiness even at the crossing.

Ink lines over rubber stamps will spread out if the stamp is not dry. The reverse is true if the stamp is dry. Ink lines *over* typewriting will not spread even if the typewriting is still wet. On the contrary, the typewriting repels the ink in the same manner as does oily paper, so that the sequence may often be determined. In most cases it is impossible to determine the sequence of strokes in lead-pencil writing which crosses rubber stamps or typewriting.

Examination of the sequence of strokes should be done by slight enlargement and with the light from behind the paper, in front, or obliquely, according to circumstances. In examinations with the light placed back of the paper it is often necessary to make the paper transparent. This is done by depositing a drop of resin oil or some similar substance on the back of the paper at the crossing. The minutest possible quantity of oil should be used.

F. Crossings in Folds

When a paper has been folded, the fibers in the fold are broken, and as paper does not possess elastic qualities it is not able to return to its normal position. The properties of absorption are altered in the fold, which can be regarded as a strip of blotting-paper over the surface of the folded document. In most cases it is easy to show that an ink line running over the folded part has been written before or after the fold was made. If the line is first drawn and the paper is subsequently folded, the line will appear evenly and uniformly over the fold, and if the paper in the fold is very much worn the protruding paper fibers will not appear stained. If the ink line, on the contrary, is written *over* an already existing fold, the ink will not only spread out over the fold but the protruding paper fibers will become stained. Thin inks show this phenomenon more clearly than thick inks, and different papers also give different results. It is therefore often necessary to make practical tests with similar ink and similar paper.

It is almost impossible to determine whether a lead-pencil line was drawn before or after the folding of the paper.

Crossings in folds are very important in questioned documents. Most documents will be written on unfolded paper, and if the incriminated part of the text appears to have been written after the paper had been folded, this fact certainly makes the document more open to suspicion.

There are many cases on record in which forgeries of this kind have been solved entirely by the examination of ink lines running over folds.

G. Tracing

By tracing we mean a forgery in which the original writing was traced on a forged document. In most cases the tracings apply only to signatures, but in a few cases larger pieces of text have been copied. The latter procedure is, however, not a tracing in the real sense of the word, but could be called forgery by

Detroit Police Department

IDENTIFICATION OF HANDWRITING

Institute of Legal Medicine, Cincinnati, Ohio

CRIME LABORATORY OF THE CINCINNATI POLICE

[PLATE 28]

AT WORK IN THE BALLISTICS SECTION OF THE BUREAU OF IDENTIFICATION, DETROIT

[PLATE 29]

piecing words or letters together. The forger picks out words or letters from a written communication or other document, arranges them in the order in which he wishes to have them, and traces them on another paper.[6] Such forgeries are to be examined with very strong enlargement. In the original and uniform writing the height of the letters, the distances between words, etc., will be arranged in a constant manner. When the forger picks out letters from different parts of the document and arranges them again, the slight disarrangement in height and other differences may not be observed on the forgery unless the document is greatly magnified.

Different methods are used in common tracing. The simplest is that of copying the signature with the aid of carbon paper and filling in the tracing with ink. Such a procedure may be detected immediately by microscopic examination, as parts of the carbon tracing will be seen under the ink. Another method is to put the paper containing the genuine signature against a windowpane, place the document to be forged upon it, and draw the transparent signature. We use the word "draw" to describe the writing made by the forger while in this unnatural position. A tracing of this sort is conspicuous because of the strained writing obtained. Clever forgers use the apparatus which photographers employ in retouching—an oblique ground glass with an electric bulb underneath. The hand will then have the natural position when writing, and if the tracing is repeatedly made, so that the forger acquires familiarity, it may be very similar to the original. Upon close examination, however, it should be possible to detect the forgery.

The forger will often lift the pen away from the paper, pausing for a moment to gaze at his handiwork or to determine the manner in which he has to continue. These interruptions in the writing are hidden through a retracing, so that the new stroke is begun over the previously unfinished stroke. Such a retrace differs from the normal lifting of the pen, not only on

[6] See Locard, "Les faux sur découpage," in *Revue de Droit Penal*, 1927.

account of its unnatural position—often in the middle of a letter —but also because the natural retracing is not hidden.

The forger will often retouch his work, especially when the tracing has not closely followed the outlines of the original. These retouches should not be mistaken for the retouches which many persons, called "retouchers," do on their own writing. Such normal retouching may be the result of exaggerated carefulness or of a nervous affliction. Quite often, however, the retoucher's handwriting is not very legible, so that he improves parts of it which seem indistinct to him. Here we also see the difference between the forger and the normal retoucher: the forger retouches even parts of letters which are clear and understandable in order to obtain similarity with the original, but the normal retouchers retouch only illegible letters.

Traced strokes do not show the speed and steadiness of normal handwriting, consequently the letters often show that they have been written by a hand affected with more or less pronounced trembling. The trembling may, however, be natural so that it becomes necessary to differentiate the trembling of the forger from that due to age, cold or certain illnesses. The trembling of the forger will especially be noticeable on the upward strokes and on the places where the pen, during its tracing, covers the original writing. Furthermore, this trembling is irregular, while that due to the ataxic movement of the hand is regular. The trembling due to old age is mostly noticeable in the initial strokes. Cold, rigid fingers often cause angular writing. The pathological trembling of the different illnesses, such as paralysis and Parkinsonism, may be very characteristic.

The wrong starting-point in the tracing of a letter is often quite evident. If the forger, for instance, is writing a closed "o" it seems unimportant to him if he begins to trace from the top or elsewhere.

Sometimes one is able to obtain the original of the tracing. This is especially possible in cases of forged due bills and checks. It is then very simple to detect the forgery because two signatures can never be alike in all their proportions. It is impossible to write a second signature absolutely similar to the first. If two such signatures are found, one of the two must be a forgery. The shape of the initial strokes and the punctuation may be found to vary if the original and the tracing are compared, because the forger will often trace them after having completed his work. The end strokes may also vary. However, the distance between the letters and that between important parts of the signature are absolutely alike. This may be shown to the court after photographing the original and the tracing on exactly the same scale and printing them on a network, which will show the similarity. This similarity may also be put in evidence if the print is made by superimposing the two plates. The tracings above mentioned are shown by photomicrographs moderately enlarged. The trembling is shown in common photographic enlargements.

H. The Comparison of Handwriting

The examination of forged and disguised handwriting is one of the most difficult problems in police science. The expert must have not only an extensive theoretical knowledge of the manifold problems connected with questioned documents and a long practical experience, but also the ability to detect small differences in shape. The last is not the least important, because many persons are blind to forms and cannot perceive the slight differences upon which the handwriting expert bases his conclusions.[7]

Examinations of handwriting in former days were almost exclusively based on the calligraphic method, *i.e.,* the comparison of the outer shapes of the letters. It is, however, precisely these which the forger seeks to imitate, and it was only natural that the experts should sometimes make mistakes. The most widely known miscarriage of justice based on an examination of questioned handwriting was the famous Dreyfus case. In recent

---

[7] It should perhaps be pointed out that graphology and the examination of handwriting from the viewpoint of criminal investigation are two quite different things. Graphology is in its worst form a quack science similar to astrology; such graphologists think they can read the past and future of a man by studying his handwriting.

decades, however, the examination of questioned handwriting has attained a more scientific character owing to the work of Locard, Schneickert,[8] Osborn,[9] and others. We cannot within the scope of this book give a comprehensive account of the methods employed by the comparison of handwritings, and we therefore refer the student to the special textbooks on the subject.[10]

I. Problems Connected with Typewriting

In connection with typewritten documents questions may arise as to whether the whole document was written with the same typewriter in the same continuous writing, whether the typewriting was done on a certain machine, or whether the make of the typewriter corresponds with the date of the writing. Most of these problems can be solved.

It can be said that each typewriter gives an individual writing which, if properly enlarged and measured, can be identified with the machine in question. Pioneer work regarding the identification of typewriting has been carried out by Albert Osborn in New York. The glass measures invented by him have facilitated the work of the expert to a high degree.

It can always be shown that a part of a document has been added later to the original writing. It is almost impossible to insert the paper in the typewriter exactly as it was before. Appropriate enlargements and measurements will clearly show such a forgery. The identification of typewriting done with a certain machine is also almost always possible if the incriminated writing is sufficient to show the constant peculiarities of the typewriter. In order to determine whether the age of the machine

---

[8] Schneickert, Hans, born 1876, Doctor of Law (Tübingen), director of the identification bureau of the Police Department of Berlin until 1928, instructor in criminology at the University of Berlin since 1920. Schneickert is a well-known handwriting expert on the Continent.

[9] Osborn, Albert S., born at Sharon, Mich., 1858. Examiner of questioned documents in New York City since 1887. Author of *Questioned Documents*, New York, 1910, 1929, and *The Problem of Proof*, New York, 1922.

[10] See Osborn, *Questioned Documents*, second edition, New York, 1929; Locard, *Manuel de technique policière*, Paris, 1934; Schneickert, *Leitfaden der gerichtlichen Schriftvergleichung*, Berlin, 1918; and Mayer, *Gerichtliche Schriftuntersuchung*, Berlin, 1934.

used corresponds to the date of the writing, it is necessary to have a comprehensive collection of typewritten specimens showing the dates when the different manufacturers changed letters and other signs of identification in their typewriters. It should be the aim of each police laboratory to build up such a collection. For further study of this question we refer to the previously cited work of Osborn.[11]

J. Standards of Comparison [12]

Standards Obtained through Dictation—In the taking of standards of comparison by dictation the circumstances prevalent in the original writing should be reproduced as much as possible.

The same sort of paper should be used, as, for instance, letterheads, post-cards, telegraph blanks, money-order blanks, bills, receipts, etc. If the suspected handwriting is written on lined paper the standards should also be written on lined paper having the same spacing. In emergencies the lines may be drawn with lead pencil.

The same writing material should be used, *i.e.,* the same ink, lead pencil, crayon, fine, broad, hard or soft steel pen, inkograph pen, and smooth or rough paper.

If the handwriting in question has been written very slowly and carefully, very quickly and carelessly, very slantingly or upright, or very large or small, the standards from the suspect should also embrace specimens written correspondingly (slowly, quickly, slantingly, etc.). The investigator should note the manner of writing on each sheet of paper.

If the suspect tries to disguise his handwriting he should not only be made to write as fast as possible, but a considerable quantity of text should be written.

When the writing under investigation appears on doors or walls, the standards should be made in such a manner that a sufficiently large paper is put on the wall at the same height as

---

[11] Osborn, *Questioned Documents*, New York, 1929.
[12] Partly from the excellent *Regulations of the Berlin Police Department*, September 1, 1911, by Dr. Hans Schneickert and Dr. Georg Meyer.

the suspected writing and the suspect made to write thereon. (It should be noted that persons writing on walls will hold the pencil at a height corresponding to the height of their eyes, thereby furnishing a clue as to their stature.)

The standard should reproduce the entire text, or at least a considerable part of its beginning and end. Special attention should be paid to parts of the text in which errors in spelling are common.

Short texts should be written several times, especially when dealing with forged signatures or brief additions to the text. It is advisable to have the suspect write the signature twenty to thirty times. It is also advisable to have him write a short continuous text in which the words or letters from the forgery appear in other connections, as, for instance, a short autobiography.

Standards of comparison should only be dictated. The suspect should not be allowed to see the document, either before or after the dictation, and words should not be spelled for him. Foreign words should be dictated with their usual pronunciation.

If the suspect declares that he cannot print, for instance, block letters, have him make the standards with a newspaper as a copy. In important cases it is advisable to obtain standards from the schools attended by the suspect, especially when he denies his ability to write.

Exceptional circumstances prevalent at the time of the writing of the standards of comparison, as, for example, strong agitation of the writer, imperfect light facilities, cold, heat, inferior writing material, etc., should be noted and recorded by the investigator.

Other Standards of Comparison—In addition to the standards obtained by dictation, other samples of handwriting from letters, note-books, income-tax returns, checks, account-books, automobile registrations, leases, receipts, marriage licenses, voting registration, applications for gas and electric service, public-library registrations, purchases made on the instalment plan, etc., should be sought.

If there are any doubts as to the origin or age of the standards of comparison, these should be noted. The standards should, if possible, have been made at the same time as the suspected document. It is preferable that the standards embrace the time of the origin of the document, so that one part comes from the time before the origin and one part from the time after the origin.

In major cases when a raid on the house of the perpetrator or suspected person is necessary in order to gather standards of comparison, special attention should be paid to the seizing of writing materials, such as paper, lead pencils, crayons, ink, blotting paper, stamps, carbon paper, hectograph pads, envelops, writing experiments on discarded paper, torn or burnt paper in the waste-paper basket, stove, etc.

As specimens for ink testing, some words written with the suspect's ink and with a clean pen are sufficient. If the bottles of ink are not seized, each specimen of ink should be used on special paper.

If the document has originally been a sheet in a book or a part of another sheet, search for the book or sheet in question should naturally be made.

When and How Should Standards of Comparison Be Taken? —The taking of standards of comparison at the first interrogation if determining the identity of a writer—whether he be a suspect, anonymous complainant, or merely a witness—is of importance for the investigation. They should also be taken in all cases where the suspect may seek to avoid further interrogation by changing his residence or by disappearing.

In order to facilitate the work of the handwriting expert the standards of comparison should be written on one side of loose sheets which are put in a special envelop. Suspected documents and anonymous complaints together with their corresponding envelops should also be put in a special envelop and not attached to the record. Under no circumstances should suspected or incriminated documents be pasted to the record, as is sometimes seen, or have their words underlined or annotations added to by others, thus making the work of the expert very difficult. The standards of comparison should have no other notes than those already described.

In important cases a handwriting expert should always be consulted before obtaining the standards of comparison.

If several anonymous letters originate from the same person and there is reason to believe that more will be received, the recipient should be advised to turn them over to the police laboratory unopened in order to determine the presence of fingerprints.

K. Contact Detection

Handwriting which has had contact with any paper for at least a few hours may leave invisible traces. For instance, the envelop containing a letter often carries a latent picture of the writing which has touched it.[13] Such traces are left only by gallotannic inks. The latent picture may be made visible by the method of Paul Ermel. The surface of the paper or envelop is treated in the dark room by red light with a solution composed of 5 grams of silver nitrate, 1 gram of citric acid, 0.5 gram of tartaric acid and three drops of nitric acid in 100 grams of distilled water. The writing is developed in ordinary daylight and fixed with ordinary fixation. Since the process of fixation weakens the intensity of the letters it is advisable to photograph the writing first.

L. Restoration of Torn and Chewed Paper

Paper can only be torn in a few ways, so that it is possible to detect the manner by examining layers of paper fragments which, as experience shows, always adhere to one another. The number of fragments and the succession of smooth and torn edges gives the clue to the system of tearing. There is a special table made by Friedendorff for the purpose of reconstructing torn paper. The use of this table will save time in more complicated cases.[14]

It is also possible to reconstruct the fragments when the paper

[13] See Schneickert, "Sichtbarmachung latenter Abdrücke eisenhaltiger Tintenschriftzüge" in *Archiv für Kriminologie*, 1912, and the excellent work of Mayer, *Gerichtliche Schriftuntersuchung*, Berlin, 1933.

[14] Friedendorff, "Zusammensetzen zerissenen Papiers" in *Archiv für Kriminologie*, 1906.

has been destroyed by chewing or otherwise. Water should not be used, as the paper will easily become putrefied. The dry pieces of paper should be soaked in some thin clear lacquer, as, for instance, sapon lacquer, which will be absorbed very readily, rendering the pieces resistant and elastic. They can then be handled with microscopic preparation needles, unfolded, put on a glass slide and covered with another glass slide in the same manner as a mounted lantern slide.

QUESTIONS

1. Describe briefly different types of inks used in this country.
2. Are there any possibilities of distinguishing between different classes of ink?
3. Is it possible to distinguish between inks of the same class?
4. What are the possibilities of determining the age of ink?
5. Is there any way to determine the difference between different lead pencil writings?
6. Describe a case where the question of the sequence of strokes would be of importance.
7. What is meant by graphology?
8. Describe some methods of making erased ink writing reappear.
9. What is meant by contact detection?

XXIV

THE POLICE LABORATORY

A. General

To establish a modern police laboratory, something more is required than the mere engaging of a chemist or physician to do technical work. The work of the police laboratory, properly managed, runs deep into the different parts of the detective division and has an immediate and practical as well as an educational influence on general detective work; hence it must not be underrated. There is no doubt that practical detective work, in some cases, nowadays leaves something to be desired in so far as the methods are concerned. Too much reliance should not be placed upon the spontaneous ability of investigators to comprehend and judge; nor should luck be relied upon. But the place of the detective will never be taken by a police laboratory. It is an agency of aid in crimes amenable to phases of technical investigation, supplementing other phases of detective work.

The police laboratory, serving as an educational institution for the police force, teaches not only the rules for evaluating details and working in a methodical and scientific manner, but also how technical evidence, growing more important year after year, must be handled.

A mere chemist or otherwise scientifically trained civilian is seldom the right man to be chosen as the head of the police laboratory. Experience shows that a detective with his practical training is the ideal person to act in this capacity. He knows the detective side of the problems and how they must be approached to suit the viewpoint of the investigation. However, special training is a requisite. Experience gained by working for a time in a police laboratory other than that of his own force is quite helpful. As in almost all other sciences, an exchange of students is desirable in police science.

Police science is eclectic in that the principles of physics, chemistry and other allied sciences must be utilized and co-ordinated in order to yield the unique solution required for any case which is being studied. For this reason the detective heading the police laboratory should work hand in hand with a scientific adviser—a chemist, physicist or physician having the basic scientific training necessary to conduct with ability and authority the work of the laboratory and to testify before the courts. This man must be carefully chosen; much depends upon him. In larger laboratories several such men may be employed, each a specialist in his field.

The personnel of the laboratory should be composed of detectives and specialists, such as a physicist, chemist, etc. Young men with some years of practical detective work and, when available, those whose academic background is such that they are well schooled in the fundamentals of science should be chosen. In addition, these men must be animated by an intense and lasting interest in the work, for frequently at the scene of a crime great patience is required, and sometimes the work is tedious and arduous; for example, making casts of tire marks or other impressions when the temperature outdoors is very low.

Younger members of the detective division or bureau should be required to attend the laboratory for periods of time to obtain knowledge of police science from practical and technical angles. It must, however, be understood that it is not proposed to convert all detectives into scientists.

The police laboratory should be maintained to assist detectives who gather traces, clues and other materials for examination when these have value, evidential or otherwise, in an investigation of a criminal act. In many instances laboratory examinations will effect a saving in man-hours of investigation applied in field work.

B. Outline

An outline, using a somewhat arbitrary classification of topics —which serves, however, to indicate the work generally performed in a police laboratory—is given below:

1. Chemical examinations
   Narcotics
   Liquors
   Blood
   Semen and other stains
   Explosives
   Spectrographic analyses
   Unknown specimens—general chemical analysis
2. Physical examinations
   Automobile and headlight lens
   Broken windows
   Electrical appliances
   Locks, keys, etc.
   Hair
   Microscopical examinations
   Ortho-stereoscopic examinations
   Physical tests—specific gravity, index of refraction, hardness, etc.
   Rope, wire, textile, fabric and fiber examinations
   Tool impressions and automobile tires
   Ultra-violet light
   X-ray examinations (fluoroscopy and radiography)
   Etching deleted numbers
3. Personal markings for identification purposes
   Fingerprints
   Foot and shoe impressions—casting methods
   Teeth
   Laundry and dry-cleaning marks
4. Documentary examinations
   Questioned handwriting
   Obliterated writings
   Paper, ink and pencil problems
5. Ballistic problems
   Comparison microscope
   Powder residue tests
6. Photography
   Indented writings
   Infra-red plates—photography in the ultra-violet
   Photomicrography
   Copying

In the preceding chapters of this book many of the topics have been discussed in detail. Some, however, have not been touched upon, and this chapter will be devoted to indicating a few of the techniques employed.

C. Chemical and Spectrographic Examinations

In conducting chemical examinations a thorough training is presupposed, so that any discussion would be wholly inadequate. The reader is referred to the chemical texts and literature for a complete treatment of the approved methods. In passing, however, mention must be made of the spectrograph and its very great usefulness, especially where only small samples of materials are available. Thus paint scraped from a bicycle frame onto an automobile bumper as a result of a glancing collision, or metal filings found on a file after its being used to cut a lock, or rouge and lipstick found on a defendant's hands or clothing after an attempted assault or rape may be successfully analyzed and identified as being originally part of the "known" sample. Aniline inks, blood, gunpowder traces, glass or any substance containing inorganic materials can be analyzed by this rather new but very powerful tool of the modern criminologist.

Indeed, it is only in the last few years that the spectrograph has come into its own as an important instrument in aiding in criminological investigations. In order to have a better understanding of the application of the spectrograph to criminology, it is necessary to be somewhat acquainted with some of the principles of the allied sciences, physics and chemistry, upon which spectrography is based. The following discussion of light energy, photography and the chemistry of the elements is necessarily very simplified, so that the average policeman without any particular background of scientific study will be able to perceive the ideas behind spectrographic analysis.

Light is a form of radiant energy in which a minute particle (corpuscle, quantum or photon) travels in the form of a wave. The graphic illustration on the following page indicates the essential characteristics of light.

Wave Length—The wave length is the distance from the top of one wave to the top of the adjacent wave. The frequency of the light is determined by the number of waves which pass point F in one second. The wave length multiplied by the frequency gives the velocity of light. Thus $W \times F = V$. Generally, the symbol λ is used for wave length, v for frequency and C for velocity. Therefore $\lambda v = C$, where C is a constant regardless of the type of light. That is, all light has the same velocity, so that the different types of light have different wave

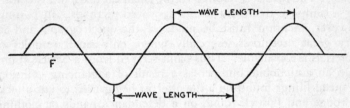

WAVE FORM PROPAGATED WITH VELOCITY V.

lengths and different frequencies. Radio waves, for example, have very long wave lengths and small frequencies; infra-red waves (rays) have somewhat shorter wave lengths and slightly greater frequencies—similarly, for visible waves, ultra-violet rays, X-rays and gamma rays in ascending order the wave lengths grow smaller and smaller and the frequencies higher (larger) and higher (larger). The human eye can only see a small portion of this scale of distribution of energy according to wave length, but photographic plates can be sensitized so that the light ray, altho invisible to the human eye, will affect the photographic plates, and in this manner we are able to detect its presence. The instrument used to separate or disperse the various types of light into their component parts is called a spectroscope when used in the visible region, and when used in the other regions with a photographic plate as the recording agent it is called a spectrograph. Thus a spectrum is the ordered arrangement of the various types of light (light radiations) according to their wave length or frequency. The developed photographic plate containing this spectral arrangement is called a spectrogram, The unit used for measurements of wave length varies with the region of the spectrum being worked in, but for our purposes we shall use the Angstrom unit (see footnote on page 436 for definition). The limit of the visible region of the spectrum is from about 4,000 to 7,500 Angstrom units.

Fortunately it is not necessary to comprehend completely modern theories of the atom to be able to use the spectrograph in many chemical problems. The following diagram indicates the principal parts of a spectrograph leading to the dispersion of the light waves and their impingement upon the photographic plate.

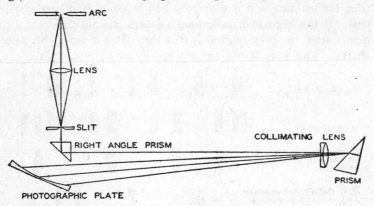

LITTROW   TYPE   SPECTROGRAPH

When the light source is two iron bars and the proper amperage and voltage drop applied across them and the apparatus adjusted for focus and the proper exposure given for the slit opening used, the spectrogram shown below is the result.

This is a spectrogram of iron and the lines are in relation to each other in such a way that no other element has the same combination of all the lines. There are ninety-two elements in nature which in combination form all the substances (earth, air, animal and vegetable matter, etc.) of which the world is composed. A great many of these elements have had their spectra very thoroughly studied and a vast amount of literature is available for reference. An element has a unique spectrum—that is, the combination of lines on a spectrogram is always the same for the particular element being analyzed and is different from any other element. If the same elements, particularly trace elements, or elements usually foreign to the substance being examined and hence usually present in only very small amounts, are present in both the known sample and the unknown sample, then the presumption is that both had a common origin in the past. If the known or unknown samples contain different elements, then the presumption is that they are not from the same source. This may be shown graphically as follows:

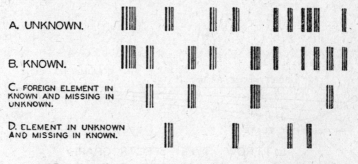

A. UNKNOWN.

B. KNOWN.

C. FOREIGN ELEMENT IN KNOWN AND MISSING IN UNKNOWN.

D. ELEMENT IN UNKNOWN AND MISSING IN KNOWN.

WHEN A AND B ARE THE SAME, THE MATERIALS BEING COMPARED ARE THE SAME.

WHEN A AND B DIFFER, AS IN THE ILLUSTRATION ABOVE, THE MATERIALS BEING COMPARED ARE NOT THE SAME.

With regard to the method that is used to determine which lines in a spectrogram composed of several elements belong to which element, mention must be made of the use of the iron spectrogram as a sort of standard; that is, iron is employed because it has many lines covering the spectral region the crimi-

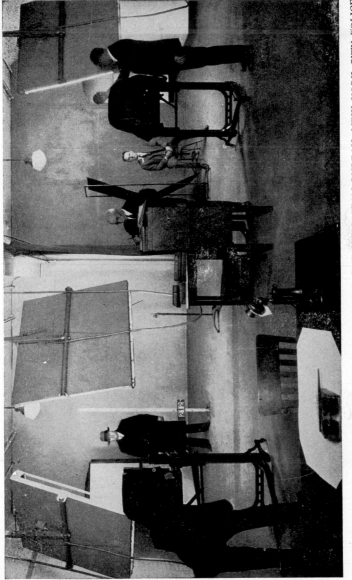

PHOTOGRAPH GALLERY, STATISTICAL AND CRIMINAL IDENTIFICATION BUREAU, NEW YORK CITY POLICE

[PLATE 30]

Philadelphia Police Department

SECTION OF BALLISTICS LABORATORY

Detroit Police Department

PHOTOGRAPHIC ROOM AND EQUIPMENT

New York Police Department

TECHNICAL RESEARCH LABORATORY MOBILE UNIT

[PLATE 31]

nologist is generally interested in. The wave lengths of the iron lines are well known; charts of them, together with the lines of the elements which are located close by, are available. By measuring a distance from the known iron line to the unknown line, its wave length may be determined, the charts consulted and its identity ascertained. With experience, the unique pattern of the spectra of the more common elements is recognizable almost immediately by the spectroscopist, and it is not necessary even to make the simple measurements described above unless the number of elements in the specimen under examination is so great that it is advisable to do so for certitude.

There are other methods whereby the identification of the spectral lines of an element can be accomplished, but it is beyond the scope of this book to undertake a complete exposition of spectrography. Rather it is only intended to present a very elementary picture, indicating the general ideas behind spectrographic analysis.

D. Physical Examinations

In the conduct of physical examinations, the number of instruments available and the dexterity and ingenuity of the investigator are the limiting factors which set the framework within which the struggle between technician and problem may take place. A healthful combination of both practical experience and theory will materially assist in deciding upon the correct approach to any case under study. For example, if two copper wires suspected of having originally come from the same roll are under examination, a spectrographic analysis might do; but if their cross-sectional areas, specific resistances, densities and moduli of elasticity were measured and compared, the investigator might feel more satisfied about the results.

The facts of another case in which a physical examination of evidence found at the scene helped to elucidate the circumstances surrounding a homicide and to eliminate the suspicions of a crime having been committed are delineated below:

A man was discovered dead in an incinerator room. Lying beside him were the furnace crank and the inside door handle of the only door in the room. The spindle was broken but was still attached to the outside door knob which was in its proper place. The heavy metal fireproof door was dented on the inside in several places. A spectrographic analysis was made of paint scrapings found on the crank handle and compared and found to be the same as the paint on the door. Stereoscopic pictures were made of the dents and the crank handle, and when these were in juxtaposition it could be observed that the dents could have been made by the handle. In addition, it was possible to make an X-ray examination of the spindle which would reveal any internal flaws that might be present—thus accounting for any ease that might have been experienced in breaking the spindle. These data, together with the autopsy report finding the cause of death to be suffocation, and the lack of marks of violence on the body would indicate that the man died an accidental death when the door failed to open for him. In his attempt to escape he tried to break down the door with the only strong weapon available—the furnace crank—and, being unsuccessful, he was finally overcome by exhaustion and lack of air.

X-Rays (Radiography)—X-ray, or radiographic analysis, is widely known because of its use by physicians and dentists. In police science it is less widely known, but is, nevertheless, a very valuable weapon in the investigation of the internal conditions of finished metal parts (recall door spindle above) or in the case of suspicious packages or bombs. Recently (and fortunately, perhaps) as a result of the demands of World War II, the industrial applications of X-ray analysis from research to routine inspections of finished metal parts have been so great that films designed specifically for the work have become available; special emphasis is placed on giving good definition and speed from the start of the exposure to the developed radiograph (X-ray picture).

X-rays, like visible light rays, are a form of radiant energy and, therefore, affect photographic film. They differ in that the wave lengths of X-rays are very small as compared to visible light rays. This distinguishing characteristic enables X-rays to penetrate or pass through substances which reflect or absorb visible rays. Use is made of this property to examine objects which are otherwise opaque to ordinary light rays. The passage of X-rays through an object and the viewing of internal conditions by means of shadows appearing on a special screen are called fluoroscoping an object. This special screen is usually made of a chemical such as calcium tungstate or similar compounds which have the property of fluorescing or changing the wave length of the X-rays impinging upon them to ordinary visible wave lengths which can be seen by the eye. When the shadow picture spoken of in fluoroscopy is permanently recorded on a photographic plate, it is referred to as a radiograph. Thus a radiograph is made by passing X-rays through an object which has a photographic plate mounted behind the object in suitable holders. The shadows are produced because X-rays do not penetrate all materials with the same ease. The nature of the material and its thickness are the determining factors governing the passage of X-rays through a suspicious package to the viewing screen or photographic plate. Therefore, the lighter portions of the film represent internal regions which are more opaque (say, pieces of metal such as wires or clock works) than the dark portions of the photographic plate which represent the more penetrable regions of the article under examination.

X-rays are produced by high-speed electrons impinging on a metal target—usually tungsten. The electrons are supplied by a heated filament which serves as the cathode and are drawn to the target (anode) by introducing a high potential between the cathode and anode and reducing the pressure in a sealed tube to create a partial vacuum. These factors of electron flow (tube current) and applied potential (voltage) are of great value in the determination of the penetrative power of the X-rays and the exposure to use in making a radiograph. Generally, the greater the tube current (electron flow) the greater the output of X-rays and the shorter the exposure required to make a radiograph; the higher the applied voltage the more penetrating (shorter wave lengths) and more intense are the rays so that again the exposure time is decreased by increasing the voltage. Other factors, such as the distance from the focal point of the rays to the film, use of intensifying screens and type of film, affect the exposure time. The inverse square law obtains in radiography as in visible light. In practice this is used to calculate the exposure required when the focus-film distance is changed (say, increased so as to obtain better definition) and the correct exposure was known for the original distance.

Ultra-Violet Light—It is safe to assume that nothing in police science has been so much written about in recent years as the employment of ultra-violet light. An almost childish belief in the possibilities of this mysterious light has been the result. The ultra-violet light has become a sort of police superstition.

True, this light is indispensable in a police laboratory, no matter how small the place may be. On the other hand, no wonders should be expected from it. Under certain circumstances it may give very valuable service, but in many cases it cannot. Ultra-violet light has been especially overrated in the detecting of forgeries. In the examination of inks, for instance, its use is very restricted. It has the advantage that the examination as a rule is quick and does not alter the object to be examined.

The ultra-violet light is produced by a lamp made of quartz, which, unlike ordinary glass, lets through the ultra-violet rays. Ordinary glass absorbs these rays. The quartz lamp is filled with mercury vapor, which sends out a powerful light rich in the ultra-violet region. If a filter absorbing all other rays is put before the lamp, many substances, when subjected to the pure ultra-violet light, will assume colors other than their natural ones. This phenomenon is called fluorescence. Objects which to the eye have a quite similar color may in the ultra-violet light show different colors, depending on their chemical constitution.[1]

The filter most commonly used consists of a nickel oxid glass that lets through the rays of about 3,650 Angstrom units.[2] It is advisable to work in the dark room, altho the lamps may be equipped with curtains.

1 For further information see Dankworth, *Luminescence Analysis.*
2 The wave length of light is measured in Angstrom units. The Angstrom unit is derived from the following scale: One meter equals one thousand millimeters, one millimeter equals one thousand microns, one micron equals one thousand millimicrons, one millimicron equals ten Angstrom units. One Angstrom unit is therefore equivalent to about one two-hundred-and-fifty-four-millionths of one inch. The unit is named after the Swedish scientist Angstrom. The human eye can only perceive wave lengths of light between 4,000 and 7,500 Angstroms.

The following examinations may be easily made by ultra-violet light:

Questioned documents	Paintings
Mail thefts	Search for stains
Secret inks	Miscellaneous
Forged bills	

Photography—Sometimes it may be necessary to photograph an object while it is fluorescent. The idea that quartz lenses must be used for this purpose is erroneous. The ultra-violet light is reflected from the object as ordinary, visible light, which may be photographed with an ordinary camera. The use of an ordinary lens is to a certain degree necessary, because a small quantity of ultra-violet light is also reflected which may spoil the photographic plate. This unwanted light is absorbed by the glass lens. To absorb all the reflected ultra-violet light a special filter is used. There are now several glass filters on the market for this purpose. A wet filter consisting of a 1% solution of nitrate of ceriammonium may also be used.

The photography must be done in the dark, and the lamp should be put in such a position that the ultra-violet light comes as nearly as possible at a right angle to the object. Rapid pan-chromatic plates are used. The time of exposure is sometimes very long, as much as 20 to 30 minutes at F 6.3. Some of the new intensive ultra-violet arc lamps now on the market, however, shorten the time of exposure considerably.

The German scientist Kogel[3] has obtained some remarkable results by the use of the proper wave lengths of light and very long exposures. For instance, a letter with the envelope missing was examined as to the date of postage. An infinitely small and invisible quantity of dye from the stamp had penetrated the thick envelop into the letter. Exposure at the proper wave length for nearly 24 hours brought out the traces of the stamp.

Microscopy—Microscopic methods play a large rôle in numerous investigations. The personnel of the laboratory must be thoroughly acquainted with elementary microscopic technique.

[3] See Kogel, p. 412.

The microscope may be a great deceiver when used by an inexperienced eye.

We have already mentioned numerous methods in which a knowledge of microscopic technique is indispensable. Every detective ought to have a smattering of knowledge of microscopy. The new, wonderful world which opens for him within the microscope's field of vision will reward the explorer.

Microscopes should be equipped with a set of objectives and oculars capable of enlargements up to 600 diameters; in fact, enlargements from 5 to about 200 times are mostly used in police work.

A good stereoscopic microscope is indispensable. It allows a survey of larger surfaces and gives a three-dimensional view of the objects which may help to form a deciding opinion in many cases.

To the microscopic equipment in the laboratory naturally belong all the miscellaneous small tools, glassware, dyes and chemicals used in microscopic work. To a larger police laboratory also belong a microtome to make cuts, a polarizing microscope, dark-field illuminators and equipment for microscopy in ultraviolet light.[4]

Devices for lighting the object are important. The whole success of a microscopic examination may depend on the light sources. In many cases the ordinary lamp and the arc-light from the photomicrographic apparatus or the microprojector will do. It is, however, advisable to have an especially strong spotlight for certain illuminations.

The present day development of the electron microscope promises to revolutionize the field of microscopy.

E. Photography

Photographic methods of all kinds play a predominant rôle in the work of the police laboratory. A good reproduction

[4] The following books on the subject are recommended: Beck, *The Microscope*, London, 1922; Belling, *The Use of the Microscope*, New York, 1930; Coles, *Critical Microscopy*, London, 1921; Gatenby and Cowdry, *Lee's Microtomists' Vade-Mecum*, Philadelphia, 1928; Else and Garrow, *The Detection of Crime*, London, 1934.

camera with a set of good lenses, a good reproduction light—preferably a white arc-light showing the whole spectrum of sunlight—as well as a complete set of light filters are indispensable for good work.[5]

The modern miniature cameras with fine-grain 35-mm. film may be used to advantage in many cases, saving time and expense.

It is often valuable to make a photographic record of findings in the microscope. Hence, photomicrography also is often used in the police laboratory. A simple photomicrographic apparatus, preferably with arc-light, should belong to the outfit.[6]

In the laboratory there should be a good dark room, equipped with red, light red, green and yellow light, necessary chemicals and trays, an electric agitator for the development of the fine-grain 35-mm. film, a horizontal enlargement apparatus with condenser,[7] a small vertical enlargement apparatus for the 35-mm. film, outfit for tank development, printer, etc.

F. Casting Methods

Like photography, casting methods play a rôle in police science. Both serve the same purpose; namely, to preserve the appearance of a thing in an objective way. Both have been subjected to criticism in the courts. For many years the value of photographs as evidence was attacked by the defending attorneys on the ground that the lens and plate could not reproduce facts in true fashion. Today the fidelity of the photographic picture

5 In the footnote on page 91 are mentioned some elementary textbooks on photography. For the laboratory work the following books published by the Eastman Kodak Co. are especially useful: *The Photography of Colored Objects*, 2d ed., 1932; *Wratten Light Filters*, 2d ed., 1932; *Elementary Photographic Chemistry*; Jones, *Photographic Sensitometry* and *Color Films, Plates and Filters for Commercial Photography*.

6 For the study of photomicrography the following textbooks are mentioned: Hind and Randles, *Handbook of Photomicrography*, New York, 1927; Barnard and Welch, *Practical Photomicrography*, New York, 1925; Eastman Kodak Co., *Photomicrography*, Rochester, N. Y., 1932.

7 The ordinary *vertical* enlargement apparatus *without* condenser will not allow, for instance, the enlargement of a few typewritten letters to desired size, nor will it give pictures sharp enough for criminological purposes.

is uniformly acknowledged when problems of distances and perspectives have no influence in the matter.

Casting methods, however, are in a quite different position, being often criticized even by criminologists. This criticism is based on the fact that in all casting methods a medium is employed which has countless more sources of error than the rays of light, which, assembled through the lens, produce chemical reactions in the photographic plate. It is true that casting methods will not reproduce in faithful fashion under *all* circumstances. All traces should therefore be photographed before the casting is done.

Casting methods have hitherto been chiefly employed for footprints, prints of cloth, prints of teeth, and prints of burglars' tools. Casting methods formerly employed in forensic ballistics have practically disappeared. Raestrups' method of making a cast of the print of the firing-pin in the cartridge shell in order to study the profile of the trace, however, is still sometimes used.

Former casting methods generally employed plaster of Paris for footprints and prints of cloth, and plastelina for tooth prints and prints of burglars' tools. Numerous other materials have been suggested to replace the plaster, but none has any practical value. In the different chapters on tooth prints, footprints and prints of burglars' tools we deal with the employment of plaster. In this chapter we will chiefly discuss the new moulage method.

The Moulage Method—In this method at least two materials are used, namely, one for the negative casts and one for the positive. A third reenforcing material may be used in order to support the brittle cast.

The negative materials are generally semi-elastic substances. They come in small lumps and must be heated before the casting process in enameled ware. They should be brought to a temperature of approximately 100 degrees Centigrade (212 degrees Fahrenheit). If possible, a double boiler should be used, but if necessary it can be heated directly over the flame. In this case it should be stirred gently to avoid burning. On the other hand, the stirring should not be excessive, as the mass will become "dead" and useless. The negative material, even if kept in airtight containers, will eventually lose water and become too thick. When purchased it is of proper consistency, and the addition of water will preserve it in its natural state. At any rate, there is no harm in putting a half or a whole cupful of water to each pound when heating it. Some of the negative materials may be heated at least a hundred times before losing their elasticity and may be used a few hundred times if carefully heated.

As soon as the positive form has been made the negative material should be cut in small pieces and ground in a common meat-grinder. When the negative mass is even and fairly thin, it is spread with a common paint-brush over the surface which is to be reproduced. The spreading is the most difficult part of the operation. The mass begins to congeal rather soon, and when this occurs it does not adhere to the fresh layer. The spreading must therefore proceed rapidly so as to prevent the layers from congealing. At the same time air bubbles must be avoided. The proper application of these substances calls for a great deal of experience.

Traces of Burglars' Tools—In most cases it is not necessary to prepare the surface of the trace except when dealing with wood and porous materials, such as fabric or felt. The trace on wood should be painted with a solution of paraffin and benzol. With the evaporation of the benzol a very fine film of paraffin covers the wood, preventing the negative material from sticking. Porous materials must be soaked with water to prevent the loss of water from the negative material and lessen its elasticity and binding properties. Without this soaking, the material would adhere to the negative mass.

The coat of the negative mass should be at least half an inch thick. Larger casts require reenforcement. This can be made of pieces of soft brass wire inserted into the mass while it is being spread; or pieces of gauze soaked with plaster of Paris can be placed on top of the cast and allowed to dry before the cast is taken off.

The negative cast is carefully lifted from the trace and the positive material should be applied as soon as possible. Long-distance transportation should be avoided. The cast must be kept moist. In dry air it commences to dry after one or two hours. If it is to be kept for some time it should be placed in a container filled with water or surrounded by wet towels.

The positive casting material is generally marketed in large prisms of different colors. It should be melted in an enamel pan directly over the fire. The melting point is between 120 and 150 degrees Centigrade (say, 275 degrees Fahrenheit). Common brushes cannot be used for stirring or spreading: the strong heat would destroy them. A special brush made of so-called "Chinese hair," capable of withstanding high temperatures, should be used.

The positive mass is spread over the negative in a layer not thicker than one-tenth of an inch. It hardens immediately. Before the spreading, if there are air bubbles in the negative cast they should be filled with a special "correction" paste. The second layer of positive material should be reenforced with gauze. This is placed on the first layer and soaked with the aid of a brush. The whole surface must be covered with this soaked gauze. Three or four layers of soaked gauze are applied. This is followed by the final reenforcement.

The reenforcement materials in the market generally have a melting point of over 300 degrees Fahrenheit. They are melted in the same manner as the positive material. Gauze is also used for reenforcement.

The whole casting process should, if possible, be completed at the scene of the crime.

The disadvantage of this method lies in the fact that the substances must be melted and that a certain amount of time is required. However, a trained man should be able to make a cast of a print of a burglar's tool in fifteen to twenty minutes.

The field outfit for making moulages should consist of a thermos bottle containing liquid negative mass, a small enameled pan for heating the positive material, a small lamp, positive material, gauze, and two brushes, one for the negative and the other for the positive mass.

These casts give a microscopic reproduction of all details. This extract reproduction is of the utmost importance, and the time employed in making the cast is well spent. The moulage method is suitable for making casts of traces of burglars' tools and tooth prints. It is less desirable for making casts of footprints, whereas the newly developed methods described in the chapter on footprints will produce quite satisfactory results.

Casts of Heads—The moulage method can also be used to make casts of the heads of living and dead persons. It is recommended that casts of living persons be made to gain practical experience. About two pounds of negative material will suffice to make a cast of an adult's face extending back to the ears. It is also possible to make a cast of the entire head, in separate parts, which are later molded together. On the living person the negative material should not be applied at temperatures higher than about 120 degrees Fahrenheit. A thermometer should be the guide. It is also possible to make a cast of a living person with his eyes open, altho a great deal of experience is necessary. The negative mass is applied so as to surround both eyes. With the aid of artificial eyes a positive cast of the eyes is then molded in the eye-sockets of the negative cast. Usually, however, casts of living persons are made with the eyes closed. The only precaution necessary is to allow the person to breathe freely by leaving an opening for each nostril. The negative mass should be applied quickly with a thick brush, and the layer should be at least one inch thick. Reenforcements are made with plaster-coated gauze, which is placed on the surface of the cast, forming a "basket."

When making casts of the faces of dead bodies the temperature of the negative mass may be higher, altho, especially in cases of "floaters," too much heat may loosen the skin and cause it to adhere to the cast.

The natural appearance of the face and its vivid expression may be better brought out by painting it in natural colors. Any artist with the aid of water colors or oil pigments may easily accomplish this feat. If the face is deformed, positive material or plaster may be used to correct the deformities, altho some artistic talent is required.

Other Casting Materials—Dr. M. Duyster and Dr. O. Tonn, associates at the Toxicological Laboratory of the Netherlands Army in Java, recommend the following negative material:

```
White wax ................. 500
Barium sulfate ............. 500
Balsam of Peru ............. 12
```

This mixture may be prepared in any drugstore; 300 grams of the mixture are added to 250 grams of cocoa butter. The whole is then melted together in a double boiler.

In order to make positive casts of the negative the following mixture is recommended:

```
White wax ................. 500
Paraffin ................... 200
Rosin ...................... 150
```

It is claimed that this positive substance produces very sharp casts which are rich in details, require no corrections, and are not easily broken. They may be painted. Both the negative and the positive substances can be melted and used many times. The two substances have, however, some disadvantages. The negative substance is hard and brittle and cannot be used for casts of objects of irregular form without making the casts in sections. The positive substance is also relatively brittle and has a greasy surface. Because of the facility of obtaining these materials anywhere, they may, however, under certain circumstances be of value.[8]

Making the Commercial Positive Materials Cheaper—Dr. Dionys Schranz, assistant at the Medical Institute in Budapest, Hungary, recommends, for economic reasons, the use of plaster of Paris for the positive cast, and in cases where commercial positive materials are used for the second and following layers he suggests the following: One part used positive material is melted with one part paraffin having a high melting point. While stirring continuously two parts of powdered pitch are added, to be followed by two parts of plaster of Paris. The mixture should be heated in an enameled pan of ample size (as it will froth) and should finally be poured into a container the inside of which has been previously coated with the negative material.

Hardening Casts of Plaster of Paris—Plaster of Paris casts have some drawbacks due to their brittleness and their power of attracting dirt and dust. They are also very difficult to clean.

Plaster of Paris is made of gypsum, which, if moderately heated, loses its water to become plaster of Paris. The latter, when moistened, absorbs the water and solidifies again. The hardness of gypsum—also of hardened plaster of Paris—is equal to 2 according to the hardness scale of Moh.[9] This signifies that the plaster of Paris may be scratched by a fingernail—a serious

---

[8] In recent years moulage methods using a cold process have also been developed.
[9] The hardness of substances is determined by scratching them with certain other objects. The bodies are classified according to their ability to withstand scratching. The hardness scale of Moh is the one most used: 1 and 2, talcum, salt, and plaster of Paris are scratched by the fingernail; 3, calcareous spar has the same hardness as a copper coin; 4, fluorspar has the same hardness as soft iron; 5, apatite has the same hardness as a common windowpane, about 5.5; 6, feldspar has the same hardness as a steel file, about 6.5; 7, quartz, and 8, topaz, scratch glass; 9, corundum, and 10, diamond, cut glass. If a body for instance is scratched by fluorspar but itself scratches calcareous spar, its hardness lies between 3 and 4.

drawback, inasmuch as these casts must be kept for long periods of time and handled repeatedly in the course of the investigation and later when presented as court exhibits.

The porous structure of the plaster of Paris enables dirt and dust to penetrate fairly deeply. The plaster of Paris is relatively soluble in water, and surfaces carrying many details should not be cleaned with water. Cleaning with mechanical agents is also not to be recommended.

Methods of increasing the hardness of plaster of Paris, so as to make it compact and smooth, have been applied for years. This has been accomplished by the addition of such substances as glue, dextrin, agar-agar, tragacanth, borax, sulfate of aluminum, etc. These substances have no influence on its porosity and solubility in water. Beeswax, paraffin, etc., have been tried, but because of their stickiness these substances are not ideal. Special hardening mediums have now been put on the market. These new substances increase the hardness of the plaster of Paris to 2.5 on Moh's scale. The hardening substance is melted and the plaster of Paris object is dipped into it until the hardening has proceeded to the desired depth. If the object is too large to be dipped into the hardening bath, the latter may be penciled or sprayed on the surface. After the object has dried the surface is passed over the flame of a Bunsen burner.

G. Equipment

The choice of equipment must be made in accordance with the size of the department and funds available. For a medium-sized department the following suggestions are given:

One 5 x 7-inch all-round reproduction camera with stand for reproduction and a stable tripod.

A set of white arc-lights for illumination.

A complete set of filters.

A miniature camera using 35-mm. film, with copying attachments and fixed-focus reproduction arrangement.

An enlarger for the 35-mm. camera.

An enlarger with condenser, large enough to hold an 8 x 10 plate. This may be especially useful when enlarging typewritten letters.

Dark-room equipment for developing and printing (contact and enlarging).

A projector for the film to use in court and for educational pictures.

A microscope for all-round work, with a good set of oculars and objectives (oil immersion is unnecessary).

A stereoscopic microscope.

A comparison microscope for the identification of bullets and shells (also the measuring microscope mentioned on page 195). A micrometer ocular and stage micrometer.

A polarizing microscope for use also in metallographic work.

Proper illuminants for microscopic work.

A photomicrographic camera.

A quartz lamp with filter for examinations in ultra-violet light.

A fingerprint outfit, including a device for palm prints.

A fingerprint camera.

A complete range of laboratory apparatus (Bunsen burner, beakers, crucibles, flasks, tripods, pipettes, burettes, graduated glasses, test-tubes).

A complete range of microscopic aiding instruments, such as scalpels, forceps, needles, a microtome, etc.

A small electric motor with emery and polishing wheels.

A complete range of necessary tools, such as vises, files, cutters, etc.

Casting materials (moulage materials, plaster of Paris, etc.).

Balance scales (rough and quantitative).

All chemicals required.

Draftsman's outfit, tape-measures, micrometers, etc.

Motor generator for electricity.

H. Portable Outfit

More or less elaborate portable outfits for the homicide squad will be found in some police departments. They will generally consist of tools, some antiseptic solution, tape-measure, magnifying glass, flashlight and fingerprint outfit.[10]

The outfit carried by detectives in rural districts must naturally be much more elaborate. In a large police department the homicide squad can always fall back on the specialists of the depart-

10 In the homicide squads of the New York City Police Department the following are among the items of equipment carried: 10-inch screw-driver, compass saw, hammer (claw, plain face), half-inch wood chisel, 18-inch steel jimmy, 12-inch shears, 8-inch pliers, electric trouble lamp with wire, flashlight with 3 extra bulbs, steel tape-measure, 6-inch magnifying glass, 2-inch brush, 4-inch glass test-tube, 6-inch test-tube, 8-inch test-tube, mirror in case, rubber gloves, alcohol, 10-inch mill file, taper saw file, slim saw file, cheesecloth, white fingerprint powder, black fingerprint powder, fingerprint ink, fingerprint roller, handle for fingerprint roller, heavy twine, black crayon, white chalk, 100-watt electric bulb.

ment—the laboratory, photograph gallery, etc. In rural districts the detective generally has only himself to rely upon. The following outfit, carried in two different bags for the sake of convenience, one for the photographic outfit and one for the other tools, is suggested for a rural police force:

Photographic Outfit—A good, light 5 x 7-inch camera with two good lenses, one ordinary and one wide angle, film packs, exposure meter, diagram for the depth of focus, yellow light filter, photo-flash, tripod with reversible head, one electric trouble lamp with strong bulb and a resistance coil for use with different currents.

Technical Outfit—Sketch board to adapt on the photographic tripod, compass, tape-measure, flexible steel rule, lead pencils, chalk and crayons, graph paper, small bubble level, fingerprint outfit, footprint outfit (see pages 139-40), four test-tubes in a wood container, magnifying glass, small microscopic outfit, tools (screw-driver, saw, hammer, pliers, cutters, wood chisels, steel jimmy, knives, tweezers, forceps, compass saw, files, and rubber hose), rubber gloves, rubber "policemen" and eye-droppers, antiseptic soap, small first-aid outfit, cheesecloth, twine, rhodokrit (see page 393), leucomalachite reagent, saline solution, filter paper, plastelina, quartz powder with spray.

Portable Outfit for the Laboratory—The portable outfit for the laboratory in a large police department differs according to the taste and tradition of the place. For example, the New York Police Department utilizes a small, compact-sized truck to carry its equipment to the scene.

The outfit carried in the Laboratory Truck of the New York Police Department consists of the following:

Dark room, including X-ray tank solutions, fan, heater, all types of film, photo timer, tank thermometer, film holders, cotton, focusing cloth, X-ray high-speed cassettes, non-screen holders, pliofilm and pliofilm iron, photoflash bulbs, photoflood lights.

Fingerprint camera, Speed Graphic camera, tripod, wide angle lens, synchronizer, photoelectric meter, Leica camera and attachments, three-pan reflector and batteries.

Model D and Model F X-ray units, lead-lined gloves and apron, fluoroscope screen, 110-volt A.C. generator, gasoline-driven, bomb detector and amplifier with extension cord, two flashlights, two 110-volt floodlights with extension cords, two 6-volt floodlights.

Portable ultra-violet lamp.

Electro-magnetic retrieving arm and 6-volt storage battery.

General Kit—Tweezers, forceps, scalpels, spatulas, scissors, needles, filter paper, acetic acid, saline solution, benzidine, known blood samples, fingerprint powders and equipment, lifting tape, test-tubes and rack, pill boxes, square boxes and envelopes for holding samples of evidence.

Plaster-Casting Kit including shellac or sprayer and casting materials such as plaster, Hominit, Celerit, Plastico, paraffin, plastelina, plastic gun and foot-casting form and face-casting form, vacuum cleaner and filters (for collecting dust).

General Supplies—Various size test-tubes, dropper, bottles, litmus paper, medicine droppers, tongue depressors, specimen bottles, tissue-building kit, iodine-fuming kit, rubber gloves, lens tissues, etc.

Complete set of workman's tools, including saws, screw-drivers, hammer, rule-measures, pliers, chisels, files, drills, crowbar, wrenches, etc.

I. Illustrative Cases

In order to portray the laboratory in action and demonstrate the practical application of the procedures described above, a few cases are cited here in which police laboratories have participated. These cases are but a minor indication of the true service which applied science offers those police departments which possess the foresight to use it.

Stains on Clothing Lead to Identification and Conviction of Burglars—Analysis of stains by a police laboratory materially assisted in the conviction of two men for safe burglaries in a large city on the eastern coast in September, 1938. By determining the sources from which the stains came the laboratory was able to place the responsibility for the burglaries squarely on the shoulders of two suspects, who were found in an adjoining building.

Because of lights noted in the building at a time when there are ordinarily no lights burning, police searched the premises, a six-story loft building. On the second floor and on the fourth floor it was found that safes had been ripped open and their contents removed. Evidence that the burglars had been forced to leave suddenly was seen in the fact that their tools were left alongside the safe on the fourth floor. It was the first night of a three-day holiday week-end and the burglars had apparently intended to stay in the building for the three days, opening safes at their leisure, as food and drink sufficient for several days were also found near the safe.

A careful search of the building failed to reveal the perpetrators. However, it was found that a glass-paneled door leading to a fire escape of the adjoining building had been broken. The investigating officers searched this building, and under the cellar stairs they found two men hiding, one of them with a badly cut hand and face. They denied having committed the burglaries and said they were merely seeking shelter for the night in the premises, having no homes.

In order to place the men at the scene of the crime, the investigators summoned the services of laboratory technicians, who immediately responded and made a thorough examination of both buildings.

The clothing of the two suspects was minutely examined. On each of the two men's outer garments, fine white powdery stains were noted. This clothing was removed and a vacuum cleaner equipped with a Söderman-Heuberger filter (see page 248) was employed to remove the white substance.

Both of the burglarized safes had been protected with a white fireproofing material, much of which had necessarily been broken and strewn around by the burglars. Samples of this material also were collected by the technicians.

A trail of blood-drops on the stairs leading from the hiding-place of the suspects to the fire-escape door of the adjoining building was noted. Scrapings of these bloodstains were also removed for analysis.

Bloodstains on the clothing of one of the suspects and the blood scrapings from the stairs were examined by preliminary chemical test (reduced phenolphthalein and benzidine) and biological test (precipitin) and grouped, and all found to be human blood, type B.

A substantial quantity of white substance removed from the suspects' clothing and the fireproofing material of the safe was analyzed and found to contain the following:

	Silicon Dioxid (per cent)	Aluminum Oxid and Iron Oxid (per cent)	Calcium Oxid (per cent)
Concrete from safe	23.50	10.00	17.20
Dust from cuff of trousers of No. 1 man	23.55	9.95	17.25
Dust from trousers leg of No. 1 man..	23.45	10.10	17.15
Dust from trousers leg of No. 2 man..	23.50	10.20	17.00

The two men were tried and found guilty on two counts of burglary and possession of burglars' tools. They were each sentenced to serve a term of seventeen to thirty-four years in State's Prison. In present-day procedure analyses of this type are conducted by spectrographic means.

Conviction for Rape—About nine o'clock on an August night a woman resident of an Eastern city was forced into an automobile, driven to a lot and raped.

At the time of the crime the woman was walking along the street to a mail box in which she intended to drop a letter that she had written to her mother. In this letter she had pasted a one-dollar bill. The perpetrator saw the letter, opened it, and tore out the dollar bill. After placing the bill in his pocket, he returned the letter to her.

When the perpetrator was arrested on suspicion, a one-dollar bill was found in his possession, from the face of which a small portion had been torn. The letter which had been returned to the woman contained a small portion of a one-dollar bill.

At the police laboratory transparencies were made of this bill and of the small portion of the bill. These transparencies were superimposed. The designs matched perfectly and established the fact that the bill found on the defendant was the one that had been torn from the letter.

The defendant was convicted of rape and sentenced to twenty years in State's Prison.

Restoration of Indented Writing—A plainclothesman delivered to the laboratory one pad containing numerous white sheets of paper, the top sheet of which contained indented writing, in connection with the arrest of a bookmaker for violation of the gambling laws. The sheet of paper, containing the name of horse, race, place and amount played, was torn and destroyed by the defendant before being apprehended, thus making it necessary to endeavor to bring out that data on the under page of the pad. Technicians, by means of iodine fumes and photography, were able to bring out the indented writing, which revealed the following:

4P.   C-Note
6 NP. Lady Genie
0-50-50
GKE

The above interpretation shows that the "4P" is the fourth
race at Pimlico; the "C-Note" indicates the name of the horse;
"6 NP" stands for sixth race at Narragansett Park, and the horse's
name "Lady Genie"; "0-50-50" means: 50¢ or $50 for second,
and 50 for third; "GKE" are the initials of the player. A conviction followed.

Spectrographic Analysis Links Thieves to Scene of Burglary—
Some samples of door molding together with a screw-driver were
submitted to the laboratory. The molding had been broken
away from a door in order to gain admittance for the purpose
of burglary. Three suspects were apprehended in a car near
the scene of the crime, and on search of their automobile a
screw-driver with small particles of paint was found. A spectrographic comparison of the paint on the molding and on the
screw-driver was requested to determine if they were the same.

The spectroscopist was subpoenaed to court to testify as to
the result of the analyses, and, when the three defendants were
confronted with this evidence which showed the paints to be
similar, they pleaded guilty and were sentenced.

*Attempted Arson—*A man was taken into custody by members of the Detective Division on a charge of attempted arson,
endeavoring to set fire to an apartment house. In the hallway
of the house were found two burnt matches and a partly burned
cork. In the possession of the prisoner were found a book of
paper matches marked "Publix Cars No. 7900" and a book of
paper matches marked "Diamond Book Matches" containing
eight unburned red-head matches. A laboratory technician after
examination reached the conclusion that one of the burned
matches found in the hallway had been taken and ignited from
the book of "Diamond" matches. The spent match fitted into
the book of "Diamond" matches. This was shown by photomicrographs of the match ends involved. A conviction was
obtained as a result of this testimony.

Conviction for Abortion—A district attorney submitted to a police laboratory a date and appointment book owned by a physician. This was submitted in connection with a campaign to abate criminal abortions.

The assistant district attorney asked the technician at the laboratory to try to determine what writing, if any, had been cut out from a certain page of this book.

The technician processed the page that lay against the page which was under suspicion. A contact picture of the eliminated writing was thereby developed, showing that the name "Richards" had been cut out of the page dated February 1, 19—.

This information led to the successful prosecution and conviction of the doctor, who pleaded guilty to having committed a criminal abortion and was sentenced to an indeterminate term in the penitentiary.

Spectrographic Analysis Used to Trace Source of Spurious Diamonds—A detective requested an examination of twenty-two white stones reputed to be diamonds. These stones were sold for $3,500 to a woman in a "switch" game.

The fact that these stones were readily scratched and powdered in an agate mortar proved them not to be diamonds. However, a spectrographic analysis of the powdered material was made in order to have a permanent record of this glass. This analysis revealed the characteristic impurities of the glass, and this information was essential in tracing these stones to their origin. Also, it served as a ready comparison for similar stones sent to the laboratory.

The analysis was conducted by employing the cathode layer method in order to detect the slightest impurities characteristic of this group of stones.

Homicide—Powder Residue—A defendant involved in the shooting of a young girl stated that the revolver was accidentally discharged about two or three inches away from the deceased while she attempted to wrest the weapon from him.

The dress and an undergarment of the victim were delivered to the laboratory, and it was requested that an effort be made to ascertain the distance between the defendant and the victim at the time the revolver was discharged.

After examination of the powder residue and the two bullet holes in the dress, it was concluded that the muzzle of the revolver was held at a probable distance somewhere between two feet and four feet from the victim at the time of its discharge. A combination of analyses by soft X-rays, spectrographic analyses and the Walker Powder Residue test will be found of value in such cases.

At the trial the laboratory technician testified as to his examination and findings. The defendant was convicted of murder in the second degree and sentenced to thirty years to life in prison.

Etching to Establish Identification of Stolen Automobile—A number of automobiles were reported stolen in a city, and detectives attached to the automobile squad found them very difficult to trace.

After an investigation by members of the Automobile Squad of salvaged and wrecked automobiles, it was ascertained that a number of them were being sold to a Joseph D—.

It was found that the methods used by D— were to purchase salvaged automobiles of recent use from dealers, insurance companies, and individuals in various states from Maine to Florida.

Most of the salvaged cars were badly damaged and in some cases could not be used, but D— would always secure a bill of sale for the complete car so that it would appear legal. These papers were brought to his place of business and kept on hand for future use. Stolen automobiles were brought to him by automobile thieves. D— would then take out the motor of the stolen car and destroy the numbers and transfer the motor numbers of the salvaged cars into the stolen automobile, at the same time destroying all other identification marks on the stolen automobile. He would also transfer certain spare parts from salvaged cars to the stolen automobile, especially those parts which contained numbers. The automobiles would then be sold to unsuspecting buyers.

In May a doctor reported to the local police department the

larceny of a Chevrolet sedan bearing license No. 9K—, motor No. 57—.

In March of the following year detectives attached to the Automobile Squad recovered the doctor's automobile in the possession of a woman. At the time of this recovery the stolen automobile had a changed motor number—No. 62—. The woman had purchased this car from D—. Investigation showed that a car bearing motor No. 62— had been wrecked in New Haven, Connecticut. A check was made of the records of D—. Fifty stolen automobiles were recovered. Technicians of the laboratory, examining one of the automobiles by an etching process, found two numbers of the transmission to reveal changes, the original number being brought out after processing. The purpose of changing the last two numbers on this transmission was to destroy the assembly record of a stolen car. Photographs of these changed numbers and photographs of the automobile were prepared. D— was indicted on twenty-eight counts involving seven stolen cars, and at the trial technicians of the laboratory testified as to their findings and exhibited the photographs.

D— was convicted and sentenced to State's Prison for a period of from five to ten years.

The oxyacetylene torch is found useful in the restoration of numbers changed on the engine.

Incriminating Footprints—On the outskirts of a large metropolitan area a woman school teacher was found unconscious in a ditch, the subject of a recent brutal attack. Examination of the damp earth revealed the outline of a man's foot impression.

A plaster cast was made of the impression. Careful study of the cast disclosed a characteristic mark that would have been made by a worn metal cleat at the back of the heel. A suspect was found whose shoe had precisely the characteristics which were observed in the plaster cast. Confronted with this evidence, the hitherto silent suspect confessed to the crime. A conviction was obtained in court.

Identification of Hit and Run Auto—While crossing the street, a young girl was struck and seriously injured by an automobile which failed to stop. At the scene of the accident were found six fragments of broken headlight lens glass.

The neighborhood for a mile around was thoroughly searched and resulted in the finding of a 1932 Ford sedan, the front left headlight of which was broken. The owner of this car denied knowledge of the accident, despite the fact that fifty-two fragments of lens glass were still found in the shell of the left headlight.

In the police laboratory a complete file of all headlight lenses is maintained. From this file was taken a 1932 Ford lens and a plaster of Paris replica made. On this plaster cast were mounted in such fashion that the prism moldings matched, not only the fifty-two fragments from the suspected vehicle, but also the six fragments found at the scene. These latter fragments fitted perfectly with those found in the vehicle.

When arraigned in court, the defendant pleaded not guilty. However, when the plaster replica with the fragments mounted thereon was presented, he requested permission to change his plea to guilty.

Note: The fragments found at the scene were marked for future identification by the detective who initialed small pieces of paper and pasted them on each fragment. The fragments found on or near the vehicle were similarly marked with a different-colored paper.

Ultra-Violet Light and Chemicals Lead to a Forger—In October, 19—, a man was arrested by a detective for larceny of a Chevrolet sedan, the property of John F— of Ohio, who had reported the theft of his car.

The defendant upon his arrest possessed a license registration certificate corresponding with the license plates on the car. This certificate was brought to the police laboratory. Examination under the ultra-violet light disclosed that obliterations had been made thereon with chemicals. Application of an ammonium hydrosulfide process revealed the name of R— R— on this certificate. Investigation disclosed that R— had lost his registration certificate and license plates sometime before this.

The defendant was indicted for forgery. The detective of the police laboratory testified before the grand jury. A conviction was obtained.

QUESTIONS

1. Discuss the relation that should exist between the detective in the field and the police laboratory.
2. Name three types of chemical examinations which commonly occur in connection with the investigation of crimes.
3. What are some of the advantages of spectrographic over chemical analysis?
4. Describe a hypothetical case in which a spectrographic analysis would be applicable.
5. Mention one application of X-rays in criminology.
6. How is fluorescence in ultra-violet light made useful in the laboratory?
7. What is a stereoscopic microscope? What is photomicrography?
8. What advantages and disadvantages does a cast possess in relation to a photograph?

BIBLIOGRAPHY

Annals of the American Academy, Police and Crime Problem, Philadelphia, 1929.

Anuschat, Pistolen und Revolverschiessen, Berlin, 1928. (Pistol and Revolver Shooting.)

Anuschat, Das Taschenmikroskop und seine Verwendung in der kriminalistischen Praxis, in Arch. f. Krim. Anthrop., 1906. (The Pocket Microscope and Its Use in Criminal Practise.)

Atcherley, Criminal Investigation and Detection, Wakefield, England, 1932.

Ayers and Bird, Missing Men, New York, 1932.

Batley, Single Fingerprints, London, 1930.

Beroud, L'Expertise des faux en écriture par alteration, Lyons, 1923. (The Examination of Documents Forged by Alteration.)

Bertillon, Identification anthropométrique, Melun, 1885. (Anthropometrical Identification.)

Bertillon, Photographie judiciaire, Paris, 1890. (Judicial Photography.)

Best, Crime and Criminal Law in the United States, New York, 1930.

Birnbaum, Kriminalpsychopathologie, Berlin, 1921. (Criminal Psychopathology.)

Bleuler, Lehrbuch der Psychiatrie, Berlin, 1923. (Manual of Psychiatry.)

Bock, Moderne Faustfeuerwaffen, Neudamm, 1923. (Modern Small Firearms.)

Böhmer, Die Blutgruppen als Beweismittel in Kriminal. Monatsh., July and Aug., 1929. (The Blood Groups as Evidence.)

Brill, Fundamental Conceptions of Psychoanalysis, New York, 1932.

Brunswig, Das rauchlose Pulver, Berlin, 1926. (Smokeless Powder.)

Burard, Identification of Firearms and Forensic Ballistics, London, 1934.

Burtt, Legal Psychology, New York, 1931.

Cahalane, The Policeman, New York, 1923.

Carey, Memoirs of Murders, New York, 1932.

Chandler, The Policeman's Manual, New York, 1922.

Chavigny, L'Expertise des plaies par armes à feu, Paris, 1918. (The Examination of Wounds by Firearms.)

Chavigny, Les Traces des vehicules, in Revue Intern. de Criminalistique, v. 1, 1929. (Traces of Vehicles.)

Christiansen, Anvendelse of Kvartspulver ved Skaarsporafstobninger, in Nordisk Kriminalteknisk Tidskrift, No. 4, 1932. (The Use of Quartz Powder in Making Casts of Traces of Tools.)

Clason, Nagra synpunkter pa förfaringssätten vid fosterfördrivning, in Nord. Kriminaltekn. Tidskrift, 1932. (Some Viewpoints on the Technique of Abortion.)

Collins, A Telegraphic Code for Fingerprint Formulæ, London, 1921.

Cuboni, Boll. 1st Sierot, 1928, 7, 1.

Danckworth, Lumineszenz-Analyse im filtrierten, ultravioletten Lichte, Leipzig, 1928. (Luminescence Analysis in Filtered Ultra-violet Light.)

Dauber, Die Gleichformigkeit des psychischen Geschehens und die Zeugenaussagen, Fortschr. d. Psychologie, 1913. (The Similarity of Psychic Happenings and the Testimony.)

David, Photographisches Praktikum, Halle, 1929. (Practical Photography.)

De Biasi, Heredity of Human Blood Groups, in publication.

De Biasi, Studies on Iso-Agglutinins in the Blood of the New-Born, J.A.M.A., 1923, 81, 1776.

De Biasi, Transfusion of Blood, paper read before Assn. of Italian Physicians in A., 1921.

Dennstedt and Voigtlander. Der Nachweis von Schriftfälschungen, Braunschweig, 1906. (The Examination of Forged Documents.)

De Rechter, Des empreintes de pas moulées au plâtre et de leur identification, Société de médecine légale de Belgique, 1924. (Plaster Casts of Footprints and their Identification.)

De Rechter and Mage, in Revue de Droit Pénal, March, 1927.

De Rechter and Tihon, L'Evolution de l'expertise en écritures, Brussels, 1922. (The Evolution of the Examination of Questioned Documents.)

Derome, Expertise en Armes à feu, Montreal, 1929. (The Examination of Firearms.)

Dervieux and Leclercq, Le diagnostic des taches, Paris, 1912. (The Diagnosis of Stains.)

Dost, Die Spurensicherung bei Eisenbahnunfällien und -attentaten, in Kriminal Monatsh., 1933. (The Safeguarding of Clues to Accidents and Assaults on Railroads.)

Dougherty, Criminal as a Human Being, New York, 1924.

Dupré, Le Témoignage: Etude psychologique et médico-légale, in Revue des Deux Mondes, 1910. (Testimony: Psychological and Medico-Legal Study.)

Eames and Daniels, An Introduction to Plant Anatomy, New York, 1925.

Ekstroem, in Adalskomissionens rapport, Stockholm, 1931.

Else and Garrow, The Detection of Crime, London, 1934.

Ferrer, La identificación personal por medio de las impresiones palmares, Madrid, 1917. (Personal Identification through the Medium of the Palmar Prints.)

Ferrer, Manuel de identificación judicial, Madrid, 1921. (Manual of Judicial Identification.)

Fleury and Silvera, Determination de la date d'usage des armes à feu et des munitions, Sao Paolo, 1926. (Determination of the Date of Use of Firearms and Munitions.)

Forgeot, Les empreintes latentes, Lyons, 1891. (Latent Prints.)

Fosdick, European and American Police Systems, New York, 1916 and 1920.

Foyatier, Etude sur les réactions des composés nitrée des poudres, in Ann. de Med. leg. No. 10, 1924. (Study of the Reactions of Nitric Compounds in Powders.)

Frazer, American Pistol Shooting, Marshallton, Del., 1930.

Freud, Tatbestandsdiagnostik u. Psychoanalyse, in Arch. für Krim. Anthrop., 1906. (Diagnosis of Facts in a Criminal Occurrence and Psychoanalysis.)

Fricke, Criminal Investigation, Los Angeles, 1934.

Fuld, Police Administration, New York.

Galton, Fingerprints, London, 1892.

Geissel, Liebermann and others, Kriminalistik im Zahlungsverkehr, Berlin, 1934. (Criminology and Business Methods.)

Goddard, Firearms as Evidence, American Journal of Police Science, Chicago, 1931.

Goddefroy, La police technique et les recherches judiciares, Brussels, 1923. (Police Technique and Judicial Research.)

Goddefroy, Les Empreintes de pattes de chiens comme moyen d'identification, in Revue Intern. de Criminalistique, 1929. (Imprints of the Feet of Dogs as a Medium of Identification.)

Goddefroy, Manuel du portrait parlé, Brussels, 1923. (Manual of the Portrait Parlé.)

Goddefroy, Manuel elementaire de police technique, Brussels, 1922. (Elementary Manual of Police Technique.)

Goddefroy, Sur la fraude possible des plis chargés et assurés portant des cachets à la cire, Brussels, 1923. (Possible Frauds in Insured Envelopes Carrying Wax Seals.)

Gorphe, La critique du témoignage, Paris, 1927. (Criticism of Testimony.)

Graper, American Police Administration, New York, 1921.

Griffon, Mathematical Analysis, New York.

Grop and Höpler, Handbuch fur Untersuchungsrichter, Berlin, 1922. (Manual of Criminal Investigation.)

Gross, Criminal Investigation, Third Edition—Edited by Norman Kendal, C.B.E., London, 1934.

Gross, Criminal Psychology, Boston, 1911.

Gross, Verstehen der Zeugen, in Arch. f. Krim. Anthrop., 1904. (Comprehension of Witnesses.)

Guiral, La valeur de la preuve dans l'expertise des écritures, Lyons, 1927. (The Value of Proof in the Examination of Questioned Documents.)

Gunther, J. D. and C. O., The Identification of Firearms, New York, 1935.

Harbitz, Laerebok i retsmedicin, Oslo, 1926.   (Manual of Legal Medicine.)

Harder-Brunning, Die Kriminalität bei der Post, Berlin, 1924.   (Criminality in the Post-Office.)

Harrison, Police Administration in Boston, Cambridge, 1934.

Heindl, Die Daktyloskopie, Berlin, 1927.

Heindl, System and Praxis der Daktyloskopie.   (System and Practise of Dactyloscopy.)

Hellwig, Einige merkwürdige Fälls von Irrtum über die Identität von Sachen und Personen, in Arch. f. Krim. Anthrop., 1907.   (Some Peculiar Cases of Mistakes in the Identification of Objects and Persons.)

Hellwig, Psychologie und Vernehmungstechnik, Berlin, 1927.   (Psychology and Technique of Interrogation.)

Henderson, Keys to Crookdom, New York, 1924.

Henry, Classification and Uses of Fingerprints, London, 1928.

Hermann, in Archiv für Kriminologie, v. 92, 3-4.

Himmelwright, Pistol and Revolver Shooting, New York, 1928.

Howe, The Modern Gunsmith, New York, 1934.

Inbau, Scientific Evidence in Criminal Cases, in Journ. of Crim. Law and Criminol. Vol. XXIV, No. 6, 1934.

Jeserich, Chemie und Photographie im Dienste der Verbrechensaufklärung, Berlin, 1930.   (Chemistry and Photography in the Service of Criminal Investigation.)

Jörgensen, Distant Identification and One-Finger Registration, New York, 1923.

Jörgensen, Forbrydelsens efterforskning, Copenhagen, 1920.   (Criminal Investigation.)

Kahn, Psychopathic Personalities, New York.

Kaplan and Berger, The Dachis Case, New York, 1930.

Kinberg, Brottslighet och sinnessjukdom, Stockholm, 1908.   (Criminality and Insanity.)

Kippel, Zur Beurteilung von Halschnittwunden, in Arch. f. Kriminologie, B. 79.   (How to Judge Slit Wounds in the Neck.)

Kleinschmidt und Schickerling, Der Verkehrs-Unfall, Berlin, 1930.   (Traffic Accidents.)

Kley-Schneickert, Die Kriminalpolizei, Lybeck, 1924-26.   (The Detective Division.)

Kockel, Die gerichtliche Sektion, in Abderhaldens Handbuch der biologischen Arbeitsmetoden.   (The Legal Autopsy in Abderhalden's Manual of Biological Methods of Work.)

Kockel, Viertelj. f. gerichtl. Med., Bd. XXXVII, 1909, II Suppl.

Krack, Die geruchsphysiologischen und psychologischen Voraussetzungen für die Verwendung des Hundes im Kriminaldienst, in Kriminal. Monatsh., 1929. (The Olfactory and Psychological Prerequisites for the Use of the Dog in Detective Work.)

Kraft-Ebing, Grundzüge der Kriminalpsychologie für Juristen, Stuttgart, 1882. (Elements of Criminal Psychology for Lawyers.)

Kraft, Critical Review of Forensic Ballistics, American Journal of Police Science, Chicago, 1931.

Kratter, Lehrbuch der gerichtlichen Medizin, Stuttgart, 1927. (Manual of Legal Medicine.)

Kuhne, Fingerprint Instructor, New York, 1916.

Lacassagne-Martin, Précis de médicine légale, Paris, 1921. (Manual of Legal Medicine.)

Lambert-Balthazard, Le Poil de l'homme et des animaux, Paris, 1910. (The Hair of Man and of Animals.)

Landsteiner and Levine, J. Exp. Med., 1928, 47, 757.

Larson, Single Fingerprint System, New York, 1924.

Lattes, Die Individualität des Blutes, Berlin, 1925. (The Individuality of Blood.)

Leers, Gerichtsartzliche Untersuchungen, Berlin, 1913. (Manual of Legal Medicine.)

Locard, L'Enquête criminelle, Paris, 1925. (Criminal Investigation.)

Locard, L'Expertise des écritures, in L'Avenir médical, Lyons, 1922. (Examination of Handwriting.)

Locard, Les faux sur découpage, in Revue de Droit Pénal, 1927. (Tracing by Piecing Letters Together.)

Locard, L'Hastoscope, in Revue Internationale de Criminalistique, Aug., 1929. (The Comparison Microscope for Bullets.)

Locard, La police, Paris, 1919.

Locard, La Poroscopie, in Arch. d'Anthr. Crim., Lyons, 1913.

Locard, Manuel de Technique Policière, Paris, 1934. (Manual of Police Technique.)

Locard-Petisne, Instructions pour les recherches technique, Lyons, 1922. (Instructions for Technique Researches.)

Lochte, in Arch. f. Kriminal., Vol. 88.

Lucas, Forensic Chemistry and Scientific Criminal Investigation, London, 1931.

Loock, Chemie und Photographie bei Kriminalforschungen, Düsseldorf. (Chemistry and Photography in Criminal Investigation.)

Madsen, Bidrag til Undersögelsestekniken for Skaarspar i Traevaerk, in Nordisk Kriminalteknisk Tidskrift, No. 12, 1933. (Contributions to the Examination of Traces of Tools in Wood.)

Maliniak, Sculpture in the Living, New York, 1934.

May, The Identification of Knives, Tools and Instruments, a Positive Science, in American Journal of Police Science, v. 1, No. 3, 1930.

May, Scientific Murder Investigation, Seattle, 1933.

Mayer, Die gerichtliche Schriftuntersuchung, Berlin, 1933.   (The Examination of Questioned Documents.)

McKee, The Gun Book, New York, 1918.

Medinger, Contributions au diagnostic de traces minimes de sang, in Revue Intern. de Criminalistique, No. 7, 1931.   (Contributions to the Diagnosis of Small Traces of Blood.)

Metzger, Heess and Haslacher, Atlas of Arms.

Mitchell, The Expert Witness, New York, 1923.

Mitchell-Ward, The Sequence of Strokes in Writing, in The Analyst, London, 1927.

Moriarty, Police Procedure and Administration, London, 1930.

Moylan, Scotland Yard, London, 1934.

Müller, Kriminal Monatsh., No. 1, 1932.

Münsterberg, On the Witness Stand, New York.

National Board of Fire Underwriters, The Crime of Crimes, New York.

National Board of Fire Underwriters, Suggestions for Arson Investigators, New York.

Naudin, L'Enquête criminelle, Paris, 1927.   (Criminal Investigation.)

Nelken, Die Brandstiftung, Berlin, 1925.   (Arson.)

Nelken, Publikum und Verbrechen, Berlin, 1928.   (The Public and Crime.)

Neuburger, Echt oder Fälschung? Leipzig, 1924.   (Authentic or Not Authentic?)

Niceforo-Lindenau, Die Kriminalpolizei und ihre Hilfswissenschaften, Berlin.   (The Detective Division and Its Aiding Sciences.)

Nolte, Psychologie für Polizeibeamte, Berlin, 1928.   (Psychology for Policemen.)

Norsk Braudvern Forening, Handbok i Brandefterforsking, Oslo, 1934.   (Manual of Fire Investigation.)

Osborn, Questioned Documents, New York, 1910, 1929.

Osborn, The Problem of Proof, New York, 1922.

Ottolenghi, Bollettino della scuola di polizia scientifica e dei servizi tecnici annessi, Roma, 1925.   (Bulletin of the School of Police Science and the Annexed Technical Service.)

Paul, Handbuch der kriminalistische Photographie, Berlin, 1900.   (Manual of Criminal Photography.)

Peters Cartridge Co., American Rifleman's Encyclopedia, Cincinnati, 1902.

Philipp, Beobachtungs- und Ermitungs-praxis im Polizei und Detektivdienst, Berlin, 1923.   (Observation and Intelligence Service in Police and Detective Work.)

Phillipp, Kriminalistische Denklehre, Berlin, 1927.   (School of Thought of Criminology.)

Piedelièvre, Les empreintes de vêtements relevées sur les balles de plomb,

Etudes criminologiques, Paris, 1927. (Prints of Wearing Apparel Developed on Lead Bullets.)

Police Journal, Quarterly Review, London.

Pollard, A History of Firearms, New York, 1926.

Polzer, Handbuch für den praktischen Kriminaldienst, Berlin, 1922. (Manual for Practical Detective Service.)

Polzer, Praktischer Leitfaden für kriminalistische Tatbestandsaufnahmen, Berlin, 1921. (Practical Manual for Work at the Scene of the Crime.)

Possehl, Moderne Betrüger, Berlin, 1928. (Modern Swindlers.)

Quirke, Forged, Anonymous and Suspect Documents, London, 1930.

Rehfeldt, Zum Selbsmordsproblem, Berlin, 1929. (The Problem of Suicide.)

Reiss, Manuel de police scientifique, Paris, 1911. (Manual of Police Science.)

Reiss, La photographie judiciaire, Paris, 1903. (Judicial Photography.)

Ribeiro, Policia Scientifica, Rio de Janiero, 1934.

Rüsnaes, Nye Veier i Daktyloskopien, in Nordisk Kriminalteknisk Tidskrift, 1931. (New Methods in Dactyloscopy.)

Schiff, Die Technik der Blutgruppenuntersuchung, Berlin, 1929. (The Technique of Blood Grouping.)

Schneickert, Die Bedeutung der Handschrift in Civil- und Straf-recht, Leipzig, 1906. (The Significance of Handwriting in Civil and Penal Law.)

Schneickert, Der Beweis durch Fingerabdrücke, Berlin, 1923. (The Evidence of Fingerprints.)

Schneickert, Die Verstellung der Handschrift, Jena, 1925. (Disguised Handwriting.)

Schneickert, Kriminalistische Spurensicherung, Berlin, 1925. (The Handling of Clues in Criminology.)

Schneickert, Kriminaltaktik und Kriminaltechnik, Berlin, 1927. (Tactics and Technique in Detective Service.)

Schneickert, Leitfaden der gerichtlichen Schriftvergleichung, Berlin, 1918. (Manual of Examination of Questioned Documents.)

Schneickert, Massensuggestion, in Arch. f. Krim. Anthrop. XVIII, 1905. (Mass Suggestion.)

Schneickert, Verheimlichte Tatbestände und ihre Erforschung, Berlin, 1924. (Secreted Facts and Their Exposition.)

Schneickert und Geissel, Einbruch und Diebstahl und ihre Verhütung, Berlin, 1923. (Burglary and Theft and Their Prevention.)

Shore, Crime and Its Detection, London, 1931.

Sjovall, Om formade märken och vissa säregna skador vid bilolyckor, in Nord. Kriminaltekr. tidskr., 1932. (Markings and Peculiar Injuries in Motor-Car Accidents.)

Smith, Rural Crime Control, New York, 1933.

Smith, The State Police, New York, 1925.

Söderman, Brottets värld, Stockholm, 1927. (The World of Crime.)

Söderman, En ny apparat för uppsamling av damm i förbrytares kläder, in Nordisk Kriminalteknisk Tidskrift, 1931. (New Apparatus to Collect Dust from the Clothes of Criminals.)

Söderman, Ett bidrag till frägan on den kriminaltekniska dammsugningens teknik, in Nordisk Kriminalteknisk Tidskrift, 1931. (Contributions to the Question of the Technique of Criminal Vacuum-Cleaning.)

Söderman, L'Expertise des armes à feu courtes, Lyons, 1928. (The Examination of Small Firearms.)

Söderman, Science and Criminal Investigation, in The Annals of the American Academy of Political and Social Science, Philadelphia, Nov., 1929.

Söderman and Fontell, Handbok i Kriminaltetnik, 1930. (Manual of Police Science.)

Stockis, Le classement monodactylaire, in Revue de Droit Penal, 1914. (Single Fingerprint Classification.)

Stockis, Les empreintes plantaires, in Arch. de medécine légale, Brussels, 1910. (Palm Prints.)

Stockis, Quelques recherches de police scientifique, in Ann. de la societe Med. Leg. de Belgique, 1908. (Some Researches in Police Science.)

Sternack, Ueber die Täuschungen bei der Schätzung von Entfernungen, in Arch. für Krim. Anthrop., 1906. (Errors in Judgment of Distance.)

Strasmann, Lehrbuch der Gerichtlichen Medizin, Stuttgart, 1931. (Manual of Legal Medicine.)

Streicher, Die kriminologische Verwertung der Maschinschrift, Gratz, 1919. (The Criminological Examination of Typewriting.)

Sveen, Det nye monodaktyloskopiske system ved Scotland Yard, in Nordisk Kriminalteknisk Tidskrift, 1931. (The New Single-Fingerprint System of Scotland Yard.)

Tage-Jensen, Undersökelser paa gerningssteder, in Tidskrift for Strafferet, 1923. (Examination of Scenes of Crime.)

Tramm, Hellwig, Rhode, Brandstiftungen und Brandursachen, Kiel, 1933. (Arson and Methods of Arsonists.)

Turkel, Atlas der Bleistiftschrift, Graz, 1927. (Atlas of Lead-Pencil Writing.)

Vogel, Die Personenbeschreibung, Berlin, 1931. (Description of Persons.)

Vollmer and Parker, Crime and the State Police, Berkeley, Cal., 1935.

Vucetich, Dactiloscopia comparada, La Plata, 1904. (Comparative Fingerprints.)

Wachtmeister, Vittnespsykologi, in Sv. Dagbl. 30, 7, 1929. (Witness Psychology.)

Wadsworth, Post-Mortem Examinations, Philadelphia, 1916.

Webster, Legal Medicine and Toxicology, Philadelphia, 1930.

Wedhe and Beffell, Fingerprints Can Be Forged, Chicago, 1924.

Weingart, Kriminaltaktik, Leipzig, 1904. (Tactics in Detective Work.)

Weiss, Publikum und Verbrechen, Berlin, 1928. (The Public and Crime.)

Wentzell, Der Schriftindizienbeweis, Berlin, 1927. (The Evidence Offered by the Examination of Questioned Documents.)

Wilder-Wentworth, Personal Identification, Boston, 1918.

Wood, Chemical and Microscopical Diagnosis, New York.

Woods, Crime Prevention, Princeton, 1918; Dangerous Drugs, New Haven, 1929.

GLOSSARY OF TERMS COMMONLY USED IN CONNECTION WITH FIREARMS

Action—The mechanism of a firearm.

Alloy—Metals mixed by fusing.

Antimony—Used to alloy lead in bullets for hardening the projectile.

Anvil—A small piece of metal, arrowhead in shape, which is placed inside the primer cup and forms the point of resistance as the firing-pin strikes the primer, thereby creating friction which discharges the priming composition.

Ballistics—The science of projectiles.

Battery Cup—The small cup which contains the primer.

Bore—The diameter of the gun barrel; the gage.

Breech—The rear extremity of the rifle.

Bulging—The swelling of a gun barrel.

Bullets—

> Cannelured Bullet: An elongated bullet with grooves around it. These grooves are used for holding the lubricant or for crimping purposes.
>
> Elongated Bullet: Longer than it is wide, the opposite type from the round bullet.
>
> Flat-Point Bullet: One with a flat nose.
>
> Hollow-Point Bullet: One with a hollow point for the purpose of increasing the mushrooming effect upon impact.
>
> Metal-Cased Bullet: One with a jacket of metal which completely encases the nose.
>
> Metal Bullet Point: Bullet having lead bearing and metal tip.
>
> Soft-Point Bullet: A metal-cased bullet with a tip of lead, so that it will mushroom on impact, thereby increasing the striking energy.

Barrel Time—Measured from the fall of the hammer to the muzzle of the gun.

Caliber—A term synonymous with gage (diameter of bore measured in hundredths of an inch).

Chamber—The rear end of a barrel, which receives the shell or cartridge.

Chilled Shot—Refers to hard shot. Hard shot is produced by mixing antimony with the lead.

Choke—The decreased diameter of a shotgun barrel toward the muzzle—for the purpose of regulating the spread or pattern of the shot.

Combustion—Burning of the powder in the barrel.

Cone—The reduction of diameter in a barrel where the chamber joins the bore.

Corrosion—The deterioration on the inside of the barrel caused by the chemical action of the products of combustion after firing; usually due to neglect.

Crimping—A mechanical operation employed in loading metallic cartridges, which consists in turning over slightly or compressing the mouth of the metallic shell or case to hold the bullet securely in its place. Applied also to shot shells.

Drop—As applied to a gun stock, it means downward bend.

Drop Shot—Soft shot.

Energy—The force or power of a charge.

Erosion—The actual wear on the inside of a barrel produced by the flame and gases of the ignited powder.

Extractor—The part of the gun mechanism that withdraws the shell or cartridge from the chamber.

Ejector—Mechanism which throws the fired shell or cartridge from the arm.

Fulminate—One of the ingredients of the priming mixture.

Gallery Load—A light or reduced charge in cartridges for use indoors.

Gage—Diameter of the gun barrel. "12 Ga.," for instance, means that 12 round lead balls of this diameter weigh one pound; lead balls the size of a 10-gage gun weigh ten to the pound; of a 16-gage gun, sixteen to the pound, etc.

Grooves—The cavities inside a rifle barrel, usually spiral, by which a bullet when expanded and forced forward receives a spinning motion, giving to it an accurate flight.

Hangfire—Delayed or slow combustion.

Impact—A blow. The force of a bullet striking an object.

Jacket—A covering for a bullet.

Keyhole—Refers to the shape of the hole made by a bullet that has been traveling off its axis.

Lands—A rifle barrel is bored to a desired size; the inside of the barrel is then called the surface; the grooves are cut into this surface. The raised spiral surfaces left by this operation are the lands.

Leading—The term used to designate the presence of lead on the inside of a barrel.

Leed—The pitch or rate of twist in the rifling of a pistol or rifle barrel.

Machine Rest—An arrangement to which a rifle is affixed, or on which it rests, when tested for accuracy.

Mid-Range—The distance between short range and long range.

Mushrooming—The upsetting or expanding of a bullet on impact.

Muzzle Velocity—The velocity of a bullet at the muzzle.

O'clock—To illustrate, face the target with watch in hand, and with back of watch toward target. A shot in the line of figure XII would be a 12 o'clock shot; one in the line of III, a 3 o'clock shot, etc.

Pattern—Refers to the distribution of the shot charge after leaving the muzzle.

Percentage of Pattern—Number of pellet marks in a thirty-inch circle, over a forty-yard range, divided by number of pellets in the load.

Powder Charge—The amount of powder used in a load.

Powders—The powders used in loading are of three types: black, semi-smokeless and smokeless. Smokeless powders are divided into two types; the first is known as "bulk," meaning that its charge corresponds, or nearly so, in bulk to the charge of black powder; the second is the "dense" type, which means that it is denser and of much less bulk.

Primer—A metallic cup charged with a priming composition. A blow from the hammer or plunger striking the primer ignites the powder charge.

Recoil—The backward movement of a gun in the act of discharge.

Ricochet—Ricochet shot—a glancing shot.

Rim-Fire—A term applied to a cartridge fired by a blow on the rim of the cartridge-head. A rim-fire rifle or pistol is one that fires a rim-fire cartridge.

Semi-Smokeless Powder—See Powders.

Shocking Power—The force delivered by the projectile on impact; the result brought about through combination of striking energy and penetration.

Squib, Squib Load—A defective load. An extremely weak-sounding load.

Striking Energy—The force of the impact measured in foot-pounds.

Take-Down System, or *Take-Down Rifle*—An arm, the barrel of which can readily be taken from the action; employed for securing compactness in carrying the arm.

Trajectory—As applied to a bullet, the curve it describes in its flight.

Trigger Pull—The amount of pressure necessary to release the trigger. Riflemen refer to this as a one-pound pull or two-pound pull, *i.e.*, requiring a pressure of one or two pounds to release the trigger. A hair-trigger pull is a very light pull; other terms are a creeping pull, a dragging pull, a still pull, a hard pull, a smooth pull, a fine pull, etc.

Uncrimped—Ammunition that is not crimped.

Velocity—The speed of a projectile in its flight.

Wad—A yielding substance, usually of felt, placed over the powder of a shot shell for the purpose of controlling the gas blast.

Windage—The allowance made for drift of a bullet.

Wobble—A term applied to the unsteady rotation or spin of a bullet; usually caused by insufficient twist in the rifle barrel.

INDEX

469